GLOBAL ENVIRONMENTAL PROBLEMS

CAUSES, CONSEQUENCES, AND POTENTIAL SOLUTIONS

FIRST EDITION

EDITED BY **Tobias Lanz**
University of South Carolina – Columbia

Bassim Hamadeh, CEO and Publisher
Michael Simpson, Vice President of Acquisitions
Jamie Giganti, Senior Managing Editor
Miguel Macias, Graphic Designer
Zina Craft, Senior Acquisitions Editor
Gem Rabanera, Project Editor
Elizabeth Rowe, Licensing Coordinator
Rachel Singer, Interior Designer

First published in the United States of America in 2016 by Cognella, Inc.

Printed in the United States of America

ISBN: 978-1-63189-060-4 (pbk) / 978-1-63189-061-1 (br)

www.cognella.com 800-200-3908

Contents

Tropical Deforestation

by **TOBIAS LANZ**

CHAPTER ONE

INTRODUCTION

There are 30 types of forests, and scientists classify them in many ways—dryland and moist, montane and lowland, temperate and tropical, and so on.[1] Although biologically and physically different, all share the fact they are being decimated at an alarming rate. But it is the tropical moist forests or tropical rainforests that are suffering one of the most serious cases of deforestation. Tropical rainforests covered about 9.6 million square miles of the Earth's surface prior to the 20th century. Since 1950, about half of this has been lost to human causes.[2] Tropical deforestation is significant for several reasons.

- **Loss of biodiversity:** Tropical rainforests are the world's richest ecosystems (biomes), harboring more plant and animal species than any other. Many are rare or endemic (those found only in a specific niche).
- **Negative impact on regional, even global, climate:** Tropical rainforests play a crucial role in regulating rain levels and distribution, water quality, and temperature variation.
- **Degradation of land and loss of vegetation and other resources for future economic use:** Tropical forests ecosystems provide abundant economic resources, many of which have yet to be discovered.
- **Loss of home and habitat for the majority of the world's remaining hunter–gatherer peoples.**

Understanding tropical deforestation and its consequences first requires an understanding of the significance of the tropical rainforest ecosystem.

TROPICAL RAINFOREST ECOLOGY

Tropical rainforests are found in the equatorial regions of Latin America, Africa, and Asia. They make up about 40 percent of the world's forests, and 6 percent of the Earth's total land area.[3] The largest percentage of tropical rainforest is in Latin America. Rainforests stretch from eastern Mexico into Central America, the Caribbean islands and South America, occupying much of the landmass east of the Andes Mountains (especially the Amazon River basin).

The second largest swath is in Asia, from southern India across Southeast Asia and into the Malay Peninsula, including the major islands of Indonesia and the many smaller islands of the southern Pacific Ocean. The smallest rainforest expanse is in Africa. The main forest area is the Congo River basin, with an adjoining band along the West African coast from Cameroon to Senegal.

The geographic position of tropical rainforest is significant, as the equator is where the sun's rays hit the Earth's surface most directly. This produces tremendous heat, which rises rapidly, condenses, and then produces rain. In contrast, the desert regions of the world—which flank the equator—receive less intense (more indirect) sun. As a result, heat does not rise strongly and rapidly enough to form rain clouds. Instead, high-pressure systems exist that buffer these regions from developing clouds and rain, making them much drier and hotter than rainforests.

Tropical rainforests gain their name from the intense rains that occur there. It is not uncommon to have 100 inches of rain per month with some forests accumulating over 1,000 inches per year. For comparison, the temperate environments of the northeastern United States average about 40 inches of rain per year.

Most scientists define rainforests as those with at least 200 mm (80 inches) of rain per month in ten months of the year. Another defining feature of tropical rainforests is that temperature and moisture remain stable throughout the year, with only small variations between dry and wet seasons. There are temperate rainforests that also receive heavy rains, like those of the Pacific Northwestern United States. But they are seasonal rains, and these forests also have cool or fluctuating climates. The average temperature in tropical rainforests remains constant, and surprisingly moderate—around 80°F.[4]

There are several types of tropical rainforests, defined by moisture and elevation differences. These include montane and lowland rainforests, riverine, swamp, and monsoon forests. There are also deciduous, semi-deciduous, and evergreen rainforests. The "purest" rainforests are the evergreen forests, lowland forests in which rainfall is highest, and moisture and temperature remain constant. They are also the most widespread and ecologically diverse of all the different rainforest types.[5]

Another important distinction is between primary and secondary forest. A forest that has been left undisturbed for decades, even centuries, is a primary forest. It is sometimes known as virgin forest. This is the most mature and thus most biodiverse tropical rainforest. Secondary forest has been disturbed (cut or burned) at some point in its development. Secondary forest can vary in age, with some approaching primary status, and thus having greater diversity than recently disturbed forests.

Water is critical to all tropical rainforest ecosystems.[6] But rainfall is only part of the greater forest water cycle, which regulates temperature, humidity, and rainfall. The cycle begins with rain, which penetrates the soil and is absorbed by tree and plant roots. Trees and plants then release this moisture back into the atmosphere through their leaves—a process known as transpiration. Naturally, this cycle is disrupted by deforestation, leading to changes in climate and weather patterns at regional and global levels.

The abundance of rain and the warm temperatures also produce tremendous biodiversity. Tropical rainforests contain at least five million (and possibly many more) plant and animal species, which represent over half of the world's total. For example, a single hectare of rainforest may harbor 42,000 different species of insect, up to 807 trees of 313 species, and 1,500 species of higher plants.[7] Rainforests are also considered the world's gene pool, with new organisms constantly evolving in them. Destruction of rainforests would lead to a tremendous loss of flora and fauna, and would disturb genetic variation and interrupt evolutionary processes.

The prolific plant life is the most obvious feature of tropical rainforests. The number of trees per acre of rainforest (and their biomass by weight) is greater than any other forest type, reaching 400 tons per acre. This is three to five times the biomass of temperate forests.[8] Rainforest trees are among the world's largest and most spectacular, many reaching heights of 150 feet or more, and include such legendary timber species as teak, mahogany, and ebony. But the vast majority of rainforest plant life comprises smaller species, many of which have yet to be discovered by science.

The lush vegetation also provides home to countless animal species, including mega fauna like elephants, apes, big cats, crocodiles, pythons, and others. But most rainforest animals, like the plants, are small. Birds, reptiles, and amphibians are particularly common. Yet the most common rainforest animals are the invertebrates, especially insect species, which make up the vast majority of all rainforest creatures. And like the smaller plant species, many of these invertebrates are still unknown to science.

What makes rainforest ecology unique is that so many of these plant and animal species are found in specific niches—niches which only the richness of the rainforest ecosystem can provide. There are orchids and bromeliads that grow only on certain trees or at certain heights. Frogs that lay eggs and grow up as tadpoles in the water trapped in the leaves of specific plants. There are monkeys that have never trod on the ground and birds that have never been exposed to sunlight. All are hidden in the secret world of the rainforests.

What is also unique about tropical rainforests is that the majority of plant and animal life lives high in the treetops (the forest canopy). Vines, orchids, bromeliads, ferns, and mosses actually grow in and among the massive rainforest trees—creating tiny forests within forests. The majority of all animal species also live in the canopy. So when rainforests are cut and cleared, most of the forest life is instantly lost.

In contrast to the canopy, the rainforest floor is shady and much sparser with plant and animal life. But because of the heavy decomposition, it is home to tiny organisms that aid this critical process—fungi, insects, and countless microbes. Termites are particularly common, and their massive, often ornate, mounds are spread across the forest floor, helping to break down the mass of rotting wood that accumulates there.

The forest floor is also covered by mats of dense and intertwined roots, which help absorb the rain water and slow and filter any excessive runoff before it enters streams and rivers. The rainforest thus acts as a sponge that controls the quantity and quality of rain runoff. And there are always narrow trails that crisscross the forest floor, where animals and people make their way through the darkness.

Despite the luxuriant plant growth, most rainforest soils are relatively poor. Constant moisture and heat creates an intense life cycle. As such, most biomass is in the form of living plants and animals. Very little is stored in the soil as organic matter. Many are laterites, poor soils that are heavily weathered and laden with iron and aluminum. This gives them a rusty-red appearance, which becomes an obvious feature of clear cut rainforests.

In contrast, considerable biomass is stored in the soil in temperate climates. This is why temperate forests can be cleared and the rich soils farmed for decades, even centuries. But, when rainforests are cut, the result is very different. The nutrient-poor soils are exposed and they erode with constant and heavy rains, making plant regeneration difficult to impossible. The result is a paradox—a desert in the midst of a heavy rainfall ecosystem.

Constant moisture and heat in rainforests also creates a cycle of constant decomposition. And the nitrogen released from this intense decomposition fuels plant growth. This is sometimes referred to as the nitrogen pump, which is the life force of the forest. But when rainforests are destroyed, this pump fails and interrupts the life cycle of all plants and animals tied to this intricate web.[9]

The intense biological activity, constant availability of water, intense heat and light, and the huge biomass of rainforests makes tropical rainforest ecosystems the greatest centers of gas exchange on the planet. Rainforest plants release enormous amounts of oxygen and they absorb equally enormous amounts of carbon dioxide (CO_2), a process that helps cleanse the atmosphere. More importantly this exchange helps sustain forest life and life throughout the planet.

Carbon dioxide exchange is a critical function that has concerned scientists in recent years.[10] Rainforests both store and release CO_2, a delicate balance that deforestation can destroy. Plants naturally remove CO_2 from the atmosphere during photosynthesis, and then reintroduce some of the CO_2 during respiration. Yet most CO_2 is stored in the form of living plant tissue. This storage function is best accomplished by rapidly growing plants. This process is seriously interrupted when tropical forests (and large amounts of living plant tissue) are destroyed.

The result is fewer actively growing trees to absorb and store CO_2 from the atmosphere. In addition, the decay and burning of plant matter also increases the release of CO_2, which results in an overall increase of CO_2 in the Earth's atmosphere. Deforestation thus reverses the rainforest role as a "carbon sink" by releasing more CO_2 into the atmosphere than is absorbed and stored. Many scientists believe this massive increase in CO_2, which is a greenhouse gas, will only hasten climate change. And the connection between tropical deforestation and global climate change has become one of the great environmental concerns in recent years.[11]

RAINFOREST HISTORY

Destruction of rainforest and the relationship between forest loss and climate change is not a new phenomenon. The world's rainforests have expanded and contracted throughout history due to changing climate and other natural factors. However, their current fate is directly related to human activity. Understanding the current state of tropical rainforests thus requires an examination of their history, especially the human impact.

Tropical rainforests are not only the world's richest ecosystem, they are the oldest extant ecosystem, having emerged around 100 million years ago. These ancient rainforests were markedly different from contemporary rainforests in plant and animal species, but their basic physical structure, moisture, and climatic features were similar. And there are still many plants and animal species found in rainforests today that once lived in the ancient forests. They have survived for millions of years because of the rainforest ecosystem's uniform climatic and geological conditions.[12]

The greatest impact on tropical rainforests came with the onset of the Pliocene-Quaternary ice age about 2.5 million years ago.[13] Cooler, drier temperatures dramatically reduced the size and composition of the world's tropical rainforests. Forests became fragmented, and many plant and animal species became isolated and extinct. Change occurred again about 10,000 years ago with the retreat of the last ice age. Rainforests expanded, plant and animal species proliferated, and new species emerged. And most importantly, human beings began to impact the forest.

There is a widespread belief that tropical rainforests (as well as other ecosystems) were pristine—without human interference—until recent centuries. This is mistaken. Even the most remote and seemingly inaccessible rainforests have had some type of human impact for millennia. Historically, this was limited to hunting or the clearing and burning of forests for agriculture.[14]

The original tropical rainforest inhabitants were hunter–gatherers and shifting cultivators. They hunted everything from tiny mammals and birds to elephants and gorillas, and gathered various edible forest foods. These people lived in simple shelters in small mobile communities. As such, their impact on the forest was relatively low. A few hundred thousand hunter–gatherers still survive in the world's rainforests—mainly in the Amazon and Congo River basins—but with dwindling populations (see Case Study 1.1).

Historically, many hunter–gatherer peoples also engaged in some type of simple agriculture, in which areas of forest were cleared and planted, and then abandoned as soils grew poor. Today, small-scale subsistence farmers are still found throughout the world's tropical rainforests, and now represent the majority of rainforest peoples. They still move their cultivation periodically because of the poor rainforest soils, hence the term shifting cultivation.

This farming method is also known as swidden or slash-and-burn agriculture, because farmers slash (cut) and then burn forests. Burning clears the land and provides ash for nutrients. But the land can only be farmed for a few years before soils are exhausted and farmers move on to virgin forest. There is little permanent cultivation in tropical rainforests because of the poor soils.

The overall impact of shifting cultivators on rainforests was low for millennia, as their populations were low. In many cases they even provided benefits to plants and wildlife communities. Burning the forest allowed for the growth of lush new vegetation, which benefited many species, especially large herbivores like elephants. In many parts of Asia and Africa elephants and shifting cultivators formed a symbiotic relationship.

But, as human populations have grown, more forests have been converted to cultivation. What is worse is that the fallow periods (where land is left idle and slowly regenerates) once lasted decades, even centuries. Fallow periods have been dramatically shortened. This has created an intense cycle of destruction, in which rainforests have little chance for regeneration. This is exacerbated by the availability of modern tools and machines. Now large trees, which were once spared, can be easily felled.

The first real assault on the world's tropical rainforests did not begin until after 1500, with the European colonization of the world. Tropical rainforests and their resources were gradually integrated into a global economic system. Tropical timber was one such resource. There was a tremendous demand for tropical wood because of its hardness, density, and beauty. By 1900, most of the world's coastal rainforests—especially those of Brazil and West Africa—had been cut.

Once forests were logged, they were not replanted. Instead, they were converted to plantation agriculture. The production of tropical products like tea, coffee, cocoa, bananas, spices, and rubber has made as decisive an impact on the world's tropical rainforests as logging (see Chapter Eight). As world demand for tropical goods increases, so does pressure on tropical rainforests.

This process accelerated greatly in the 19th century, as industrial demand, urbanization, and population growth required ever-more resources. This trend has increased throughout the 20th century, as continued population growth (especially in the Global South), the spread of markets, and ever-more sophisticated technologies have made almost all the world's remaining tropical rainforests vulnerable to exploitation.

CAUSES OF TROPICAL DEFORESTATION

Deforestation is defined as the partial or complete removal of vegetation from an indigenous forest. Deforestation can be temporary or permanent. Some scholars differentiate between deforestation, which is the complete removal of forest cover, and forest degradation, which is partial destruction. Deforested land is usually converted to agriculture or human settlement.

There are many causes of deforestation, involving direct (underlying) and indirect (proximate) causes. One can also differentiate between agents—actors that directly destroy rainforest (like farmers)—and causes (like poverty) that indirectly facilitate this destruction. Most cases of deforestation involve several agents and causes.

The leading single cause of deforestation today is conversion of land to agriculture—both subsistence and commercial. Logging is another cause of deforestation and its impact is increasing as global economic development and the demand for tropical hardwoods increases.[15] Other factors like road building and mining account for the balance. Yet the causes and agents vary greatly by country and region. They are as follows.[16]

Location

The proximity of rainforests to human habitation is a decisive factor in their survival. Tropical rainforests that are near cities, roads, rails, rivers, and coastlines are most likely to be exploited. As human infrastructure expands, more forests are accessible, increasing the likelihood and intensity of deforestation.

Socioeconomic Factors

Population growth

Human population growth, in general, places pressure on all ecosystems. Population pressures for forest resources can be indirect (timber, minerals, other resources) or direct—land for human habitation and cultivation. The expansion of populations near tropical rainforests places the greatest pressure on these ecosystems.

Economic development

Economic development requires many forest resources—timber, minerals, oil, land for food, cash crops, and other resources. As development, especially industrial development, increases, so do the demands on various rainforest resources. This trend has increased in the age of globalization, in which forest resources now have global markets, and hence, global demand.

Poverty

This is a general problem that exacerbates resource use of all kinds. Poor people have what economists call high time preference value. They value the present over the future because their focus is on daily survival. As a result, they will cut and exploit forest resources intensely with little thought of future conservation.

Institutional Factors

Government rainforest policy

One of the most important factors in determining rainforest survival is whether governments make conservation a priority. Most countries with rainforests are poor or developing economies. As such, these governments view their forests as valuable assets to be exploited. Other institutional actors, namely transnational corporations (TNCs) and international organizations (IOs), can greatly influence government policy—to conserve or exploit. This is especially the case in a globalized world, in which these global actors have increasing influence over public policy.

Logging

The first and most obvious factor leading to rainforest destruction has been the overexploitation of timber. Removal of trees is not the only problem. Other problems are forest destruction by heavy machinery. Some rainforests only contain a few commercially valuable trees per acre. Yet to access and remove these few trees requires the destruction of large areas of surrounding forest. Timber companies also cut roads deep into the forests, which encourages poor farmers and others to enter the forest and exploit it further.

Cattle ranching

After timber has been removed, denuded lands are utilized for commercial cattle ranching. But because of poor soils, vegetation only grows for a few years before the soil is exhausted and ranchers move on, following the same pattern as shifting cultivation. Tropical rainforest ranching is confined to Latin America. High population densities in Asia allow little land for ranching. In Africa, ranching is prevented by the existence of the tsetse fly, which causes sickness and death among cattle.

Plantations

Millions of acres of rainforest have been permanently converted to plantation agriculture. Most plantations grow cash crops, which, like tropical timber, are important sources of revenue for poor countries. Many of these crops, like coffee, tea, cocoa, sugar, and bananas, have become staples of modern urban life worldwide. Others, like palm oil and rubber, are used in industry. Rainforests converted for drug cultivation, namely marijuana and coca plants (cocaine), is an emerging problem (see Case Study 1.2).

Mineral and oil exploitation

Many rainforests sit atop rich deposits of oil, natural gas, and minerals. Vast areas of forest are destroyed in the process of accessing and exploiting these resources. Like timber exploitation, mineral exploitation requires roads, which facilitates more forest exploitation by poor farmers and others.

Resettlement programs

Some countries (namely Brazil and Indonesia) have used rainforest land as a welfare program—a place to resettle landless farmers or urban dwellers. Farmers are given a plot of land to clear and farm. But poor soils force farmers to abandon lands and access new forests after a few years. Many governments pursue resettlement programs to avoid confronting domestic poverty and resource distribution. The rainforest is sacrificed to avoid dealing with these more difficult social problems.

Armed conflict

Armed conflict, initiated by governments or insurgent groups, can lead to deforestation. The most serious destruction of tropical rainforests has been due to bombardment and use of defoliants, which removes tree leaves to reveal enemy troop movements. One of the most devastating cases of defoliant use on tropical forests was by the United States during the Vietnam War.

CONTROLLING TROPICAL DEFORESTATION

Tropical deforestation became a global political issue in the 1980s. It coincided with greater media coverage of environmental problems, greater environmental activism, and the development of the idea of sustainable development through the Bruntland and Rio environmental conferences. Greater awareness has produced some positive results, but deforestation rates remain high and growing in many countries.

Obstacles to halting deforestation include, first, the problem of national sovereignty and country control over resources. Most tropical rainforest countries are poor and their governments use forests for economic purposes. The principle of national sovereignty, which is upheld by the international community of nations, allows a country such rights. It is thus difficult for other nations and global political actors to interfere in such domestic policy decisions.

A second problem is transnational corporations (TNCs), especially timber and agricultural corporations, and their ability to control and access forest resources. Due to their wealth and power, they also have considerable influence over government policy, policy that promotes forest exploitation rather than conservation. A final obstacle is the effective funding, organization, and cooperation of environmental groups, especially in the Global South.

Despite problems, tropical rainforest conservation efforts are growing. At the international level, the creation of the Tropical Forest Action Plan (TFAP) in 1983 was one of the first effort to protect tropical forests. This program, coordinated by the Food and Agricultural Organization and the World Resources Institute, sought to integrate economic development into tropical rainforest conservation. It was essentially an aggregation of national forestry programs that were linked together at the global level, with the involvement of various global actors.

The creation of an international organization (IO)—the International Tropical Timber Organization (ITTO)—also in 1983, was another important international development. The organization, comprised of producer and consumer countries, sought to improve timber harvesting and marketing, as well as reforestation. The ITTO and TFAP have been criticized for focusing too narrowly on timber, at the expense of ecological factors. But their creation did signal that tropical deforestation had become a global problem, requiring a global response involving states, TNCs, IOs, and nongovernmental organizations (NGOs).[17]

The United Nations (UN) has been the leading IO in tropical forest conservation. Its various agencies (the Food and Agricultural Organization, which develops programs to promote better agriculture and forest management; UN Development Program; UN Environmental Program) publish reports and statistics on deforestation and organize conferences like the UN Conference on the Environment and Development that took place in Rio de Janeiro in 1992. More recently, the UN has created the Global Environmental Facility to fund various conservation endeavors.[18]

But it is NGOs that have become, in many ways, the most important part of the tropical rainforest conservation effort. Many are activist groups that put direct pressure on government and industry to improve legislation and conservation efforts. Others focus on practical efforts to improve agriculture and forestry. In developed countries, this has been accomplished by large NGOs like the Rainforest Action Network and Rainforest Alliance (see Case Study 1.3).

In the Global South, organization and activism has been more modest, and usually at the local level. Women and farmers who want to protect forests in order to protect their livelihoods often organize these groups. Indigenous rainforest peoples, especially traditional hunter–gatherer peoples, have become especially active in recent decades. All of these groups are creating more alliances and connections to international conservation and human rights organizations—a positive aspect of globalization.

Consumers in wealthy nations have also become involved in rainforest conservation, by choosing sustainably harvested timber, as well as coffee, tea, cocoa, and other forest products. This has been successful because so many tropical forest goods are now traded worldwide. As a result, the pressure to harvest these commodities sustainably has gained international attention. "Fair trade" and "shade grown" labels are examples of tropical rainforest products that can help small farmers earn income and protect forests.

Despite strides in local and international efforts, policy changes at the national (state) level are still most critical to protecting the world's tropical rainforests. The establishment of protected areas like national parks is a high priority to save large tracts of virgin forest and its biodiversity. The protection of large forest tracts has also involved global actors. The best example is debt-for-nature swaps, in which banks, TNCs, and governments forgive a percentage of debt held by many Global South governments in exchange for forest conservation (see Box 1.1).

However, most observers agree that effective conservation must be coupled with policies that promote better (more sustainable) commercial timber production, and commercial and subsistence agriculture. Improved agriculture and timber production can greatly increase yields per acre, thus reducing deforestation pressures. For example, timber plantations produce far more timber per area than virgin forest. Similarly, more efficient and productive agriculture can increase yields, which reduces poverty, and subsequently, the need to exploit forests.

Most observers also agree that the greatest policy efforts must be on poverty reduction. Poor shifting cultivators, who simply want to survive, destroy most tropical forests. Better agricultural methods and policies is one solution. But poverty alleviation also requires more sweeping social changes, like land reform, urban planning, and political reform. Unfortunately, such social transformations happen slowly.

Perhaps the most important required changes regarding forests and deforestation are conceptual. Tropical rainforests, indeed all ecosystems, must be defined as more than raw materials. Forests play many roles in human social life. As such, forest policies must go beyond simple forest management, to synthesize and integrate forestry with agriculture, industrial development, urbanization, tourism, and religious and cultural practices—in short, all facets of human existence.

Box 1.1 Debt-for-Nature Swaps

Debt-for-nature swaps are one way that poor countries with tropical rainforests can preserve forest and reduce their debt load. It involves purchasing foreign debt at a discounted price, converting the debt into the local currency, and then using those funds to purchase land or fund other conservation activities. It can be a two-way swap, involving only the lender and the indebted country, or a three-way swap, which involves an international organization (IO) or nongovernmental organization (NGO). In the latter case, the IO or NGO usually provides funds to purchase the loan.

The debtor country benefits by reducing its overall debt and loan payments. The lender benefits by receiving payments, which, although lowered, are more consistent. IOs and NGOs are able to develop institutions and policies with a long-term impact. But the greatest benefit is to the forest and its biodiversity.

The Wordwide Fund for Nature (WWF) first developed the debt-for-nature swap idea in 1984. The first case involved the Bolivian government and the IO Conservation International funding a conservation project in the Beni Biosphere Reserve in 1987. Since then, debt-for-nature swaps have been instituted in dozens of countries and over US$1 billion in debt has been relieved. Debt-for-development swaps have also been started, many of which also include environmental provisions.

Critics of debt-for-nature swaps argue that funds often do not reach poor people, and that debt reduction alone does not change government policies and social problems, which are the real causes of deforestation. The swaps are also dependent on global financial conditions. They are more difficult (i.e., expensive) when the cost of credit is high. Also, the overall amount of debt reduced by the swaps is negligible compared to country debt loads.

Despite criticisms, many environmental groups believe they remain a worthwhile endeavor. They are necessary components in broader strategies that seek to address both conservation and economic development.

Source: Pervase A Sheikh. 2010. Debt-for-Nature Initiatives and the Tropical Forest Conservation Act: Status and Implementation. Congressional Research Service Report. March 30.

CASE STUDY 1.1

Forest Peoples—the African Pygmies

The pygmies inhabit Africa's Congo River basin. This region contains over 80 percent of the continent's rainforests, and is the second largest contiguous rainforest bloc in the world after the Amazon River basin. Pygmies have lived in the Congo forests for at least 4,000 years, and their Stone Age ancestors lived there for 40,000 years prior. Their current population is around 500,000 and decreasing.

There are about a dozen pygmy groups scattered about central Africa from eastern Cameroon to Rwanda, with the majority living in the Democratic Republic of the Congo. There are also several "pygmoid" peoples scattered throughout the Congo forest, who are part pygmy but have long intermarried with non-pygmy farming peoples (shifting cultivators) who inhabit the forest edges.

All pygmies share the general feature of short physical stature. Males rarely reach five feet and females are even shorter. There is much debate about why pygmies are diminutive. Some experts believe it is caused by the rainforest environment, in which lack of food (especially protein) and constant shade stunts growth. Others point to genes with low growth hormones.

Pygmies are small in stature and also have small and simple social organizations. They live in groups of a few dozen individuals, with a non-hierarchical political system in which both men and women are participants. Pygmies move their villages periodically according to weather and resource availability. As such, the villages consist of simple structures made of grasses, leaves, branches, and mud.

Traditional pygmy economics centers on hunting and gathering. Women are the principal gatherers, but also do most of the fishing, which is done with traps and snares. Food gathered includes roots, tubers, fruits, nuts, mushrooms, and any small edible animals. Women also gather firewood for cooking, water, and thatch for building huts. They also tend children, who often accompany them on their chores.

Men hunt with long woven nets that are stretched across the forest to trap animals, or by bow and arrow. A few intrepid pygmies are known to hunt elephant by sneaking up to an unsuspecting animal, moving directly underneath its body, and then stabbing it in the heart with a sharp dagger. But the majority of game killed consists of small animals, mainly birds and mammals, especially the forest antelope or duiker. Hunts often last many days—ground-dwelling game is widely dispersed in the forest ecosystem, as food is relatively scarce, most being concentrated high in the canopy.

The rainforest has provided pygmies with food and shelter for millennia, and their forest isolation kept them at a safe distance from larger and more powerful tribes who inhabited the forest fringes and adjacent savannas. In the past, these neighboring tribes often killed pygmies or enslaved them if they encountered pygmies in the forest fringes.

Yet despite its benefits and idyllic appearance, forest life also takes its toll on the pygmies. Diseases, in particular malaria, yellow fever, dysentery, intestinal worms, pneumonia, sleeping sickness, and a host of others, cause disability and death.

But it is deforestation that has taken the greatest toll on pygmies and traditional pygmy life. Forest destruction has reduced resource availability, forcing pygmies into local agricultural economies. Historically, pygmies had symbiotic relations with shifting cultivators, trading meat for crops. But with wild game depleted, pygmies must now work for farmers. In many cases, they are so dependent on farm labor for their survival that they become indentured servants, even slaves. Many pygmy women are forced into prostitution, which has spread AIDS and other diseases among pygmy populations.

The plight of the African pygmy has become a global human rights issue. Abuse, exploitation, and even genocide, especially at the hands of African governments and military insurgents, is one issue. Another is whether pygmies should be allowed to live as hunter–gatherers (with large forests preserved for their benefit) or be peacefully integrated into modern society. The latter option would provide greater economic and social opportunities, but would lead to intermarriage and the dilution, and ultimate extinction, of the pygmy people.

Source: Colin Turnbull. 1987. *The Forest People.* New York: Touchstone Books.

CASE STUDY 1.2

The Drug Trade and Tropical Deforestation

Most people do not link the drug trade with environmental destruction. It is seen as a criminal endeavor with social and psychological consequences. This is because most people do not think about the origin of drugs—especially marijuana, cocaine, and opium. These are plants or plant derivatives that are usually grown in forested areas.

Cannabis (marijuana) and the coca plant (from which cocaine is derived) both grow in tropical rainforests (the opium poppy grows mainly in dryland habitats). As the demand for marijuana and cocaine has grown, so has the planting of coca and cannabis, which has intensified tropical rainforest destruction, especially in Colombia, Peru, and Bolivia.

Of these two tropical rainforest drugs, cocaine is the most destructive to tropical rainforests. It is native to Latin American tropical rainforests and is well suited to tropical conditions. As such, it can be grown anywhere. Coca cultivation has spread dramatically since the early 1960s, with the emergence of a global drug trade. But it is difficult to estimate the total acreage under coca cultivation, given its clandestine nature.

Peru, Bolivia, and Colombia grow the majority of the world's coca. Colombia has been the leading producer for over a decade, but drug enforcement and eradication programs continuously shift production to Peru and Bolivia. The United States and the United Nations, the only entities to provide coca cultivation numbers, estimate that total coca production in these countries was around 150,000 hectares in 2011. This is down from a decade earlier. But critics claim that these numbers are misleading, and that coca cultivation is much higher.

Coca cultivation impacts the environment in several ways. First, rainforests are cleared, destroying biodiversity. Second, clearing is usually done with various biocides (herbicides and pesticides) to control vegetation and insects. Many of these herbicides contain chlorophenoxiacete, a chemical similar to that found in the defoliant Agent Orange. These chemicals naturally seep into the soil, and with heavy rains, run off into streams and rivers.

Once planted, the coca plants require constant weed and insect control, where again biocides are preferred because of their cost and effectiveness. Coca is usually planted on hillsides to ensure proper drainage, which the plants need to thrive. This adds to runoff of topsoil, where nutrients are stored. Growers then resort to heavy doses of chemical fertilizer to compensate for lost nutrients, resulting in more toxic runoff.

Another cause of erosion is the frequency of harvest. Coca plants are harvested four times per year. This frequency is equivalent to defoliation, which causes more soil runoff when it rains. The use of toxins and constant erosion have earned the coca plant the epithet of "the Attila of tropical agriculture." As more land is given to coca cultivation, that destructiveness increases.

But it is the processing of the coca leaf into raw cocaine, or base, that is worst on the tropical forest ecosystem. Alcohol, benzene, sulfuric acid, and kerosene are some of the chemicals required to remove unwanted alkaloids in the leaf to create the raw cocaine. For every 120 pounds of leaf, 30 liters of toxic liquid plus another 25 pounds of toxic solids are used. In the cleansing and pressing process to make paste, another 20 liters of toxic waste is used. One estimate placed the total waste at almost one metric ton per acre of cocaine production.

Ironically, government programs designed to eradicate the drug trade can also create environmental problems. Governments will burn or use pesticides to destroy coca fields. In the 1990s, some drug enforcement personnel even suggested the United States resort to massive applications of defoliants. But President Bill Clinton halted that program, fearing it would be viewed as a form of biological warfare that would have political ramifications, as well as health and environmental ones. As governments have destroyed coca fields in South America, many growers have moved production to Central America, destroying even more virgin tropical rainforests.

To many observers, poverty is the decisive factor in the drug trade. Just as government places poor people in the forest interior in resettlement programs, so criminal gangs place them there to work in the coca fields. The result in both cases is the perpetuation of poverty and tropical rainforest destruction. The failure of genuine economic development in the remote rural corners of the world is an underlying cause of much environmental destruction, which in Latin America is only worsened by the drug trade.

Sources: Washington Office on Latin America (http://www.wola.org); Marc Dourojeanni. 1992. "Environmental Impact of Coca Cultivation and Cocaine Production in the Amazonian Region of Peru." *Bulletin on Narcotics* 44: 37–53.

CASE STUDY 1.3

NGOs and Tropical Rainforest Conservation

Nongovernmental organizations (NGOs) have become some of the most important environmental actors. There are hundreds of environmental NGOs worldwide, of varying size and with a broad range of interests. Because of their size, flexibility, commitment, and expertise, they are often more effective in dealing with environmental problems than governments, businesses, or international organizations.

Two of the most important NGOs that deal with tropical deforestation are Rainforest Alliance and Rainforest Action Network. They were among the first NGOs to address tropical deforestation problems and make them known to the general public.

Rainforest Alliance was founded in 1987 and is headquartered in New York City. It has offices in over 100 countries. The organization's main goals are biodiversity conservation and the promotion of sustainable development. It uses economic incentives to promote sustainable development, focusing in particular on helping small farmers and rural laborers in rainforest areas.

Rainforest Alliance is known for the strict guidelines of its forestry certification program. Certification requires timber operations to conserve biodiversity and support the livelihoods of local peoples and workers. The program began in 1991, and to date it has certified almost 200 million acres of timber land. Rainforest Alliance also helped create the Forest Stewardship Council, which is the world's most rigorous forestry certification organization.

A similar program has been launched to certify the sustainable production of tropical agricultural goods like bananas, coffee, cocoa, flowers, and tea. Some

800,000 farmers worldwide have been certified, the majority of which are small holders. But major growers like Chiquita have also agreed to produce their crops sustainably. Sustainable tourism and environmental education programs, again focusing on rainforest communities, have also been developed.

Products grown in accordance with the Rainforest Alliance standard receive a seal of certification. This, in turn, allows consumers to choose sustainably grown tropical products. As a result, conservation is enhanced, as are the incomes of small producers. Large manufacturers and distributors of tropical goods like Unilever, Nestle, Mars, Kraft, and others have also agreed to purchase these certified products. Thus it is the alliance with producers, and between producers and consumers, that has made Rainforest Alliance a conservation success.

Rainforest Action Network (RAN) has also achieved success, but with a different strategy. The group was founded in 1985 and is based in San Francisco. It has an office in Tokyo and thousands of volunteer scientists, teachers, and concerned citizens worldwide. Its emphasis has been advocacy and grassroots organization, much of it against governments and corporations that destroy tropical rainforests.

RAN achieved international recognition in the 1980s for its successful campaign against the Burger King Corporation. The fast food giant had been using Central American beef for its hamburgers—beef grown on deforested lands. RAN forced Burger King to cancel its contracts and relinquish any beef grown on tropical rainforest lands. This protected forests and made the general public aware of the domestic, corporate, and consumer connections to tropical deforestation.

Recent campaigns have focused on the government of Indonesia for clear cutting forest for plantation agriculture,. Much of this activity is for the production of palm oil. The global agricultural commodity corporation Cargill is involved in these projects, and has also been targeted by RAN to produce more sustainably and to improve working conditions. Food giant General Mills recently announced it will no longer use tropical oils in its products, a move that RAN helped initiate.

One of RAN's most significant victories was in 2012 against the Chevron Oil Corporation. The oil producer had dumped 18 billion gallons of waste in the Amazon River in Ecuador, which destroyed both aquatic and forest life. RAN took the company to court and won, forcing it and the Peruvian government to clean up the toxic waste.

Sources: http://www.rainforest-alliance.org; http://www.ran.org.

ENDNOTES

1. United Nations Environmental Programme World Conservation Monitoring Unit, *Global Ecological Forest Classification and Forest Protected Area Gap Analysis* (Freiburg, Germany: Freiburg University Press, 2009), i.
2. Arnold Newman, *Tropical Rainforest: Our Most Valuable and Endangered Habitat with a Blueprint for its Survival into the Third Millennium* (New York: Checkmark Books, 2002), 10.
3. Ibid., 10.
4. Norman Myers, *The Tropical Source: Tropical Forests and Our Future* (New York: W.W. Norton and Co., 1984), 38.
5. Ibid., 38.
6. For an in-depth analysis of all ecological features and functions of tropical rainforests, see Paul Richards, *The Tropical Rainforest: An Ecological Study*, 2nd ed. (Cambridge: Cambridge University Press, 1996).
7. Newman, *Tropical Rainforest*, 19.
8. Myers, *The Tropical Source*, 25.
9. Richards, *The Tropical Rainforest*, 276–77.
10. Estimates about the CO_2 effect have varied. For an overview, see Alan Grainger, *Controlling Tropical Deforestation* (London: Earthscan, 2009), 165–73.
11. See Union of Concerned Scientists, "Deforestation and Global Warming," http://www.ucsusa.org/global_warming/solutions/stop-deforestation/deforestation-global-warming-carbon-emissions.html; and Ghillian T. Prance, eds., *Tropical Rain Forests and World Atmosphere* (Boulder, CO: Westview, 1986).
12. Catherine Caulfield, *In the Rainforest: Report from a Strange, Beautiful and Imperiled World* (Chicago: University of Chicago Press, 1984), 59.
13. Richards, *The Tropical Rainforest*, 13–18.
14. Michael Williams, *Deforesting the Earth* (Chicago: University of Chicago Press, 2003), 33.
15. The impact of logging is debated. The Worldwide Fund for Nature argues that logging is the primary cause of tropical deforestation. See WWF, "Logging is the Major Cause of Global Deforestation," http://www.rainforestinfo.org.au/good_wood/log_maj.htm.
16. Grainger, *Controlling Tropical Deforestation*, 49–67, 92–102.
17. David Humphreys, *Forest Politics: The Evolution of International Cooperation* (London: Earthscan, 1996), 31–34, 55–60.
18. See http://www.thegef.org/gef/.

RECOMMENDED READINGS/SOURCES

Barber, Edward. 2005. *Explaining Agricultural Land Expansion and Deforestation in Developing Countries.* Green Bay: University of Wisconsin.

Barraclough, Solon L. 2000. *Agricultural Expansion and Tropical Deforestation; Poverty, International Trade and Land Use.* London: Earthscan.

Chazdon, Robin. 2009. "Beyond Deforestation: Restoring Forests and Ecosystem Services on Degraded Lands." *Science* 320 (5882): 1458–1460

Chomitz, Kenneth. 2007. *At Loggerheads? Agricultural Expansion, Poverty Reduction, and Environment in the Tropical Rainforests.* Washington, DC: World Bank.

Douglas, Jim. 2010. *The Future of the World's Forests: Ideas vs. Ideologies.* New York: MIT Press.

Gibson, Clark, Margaret McKean, and Eleanor Ostrom. 2000. *People and Forest Communities, Institutions, and Governance.* Cambridge, MA: MIT Press.

Grainger, Alan. 2009. *Deforestation, Controlling the Tropical Rainforest.* London: Earthscan.

Humphreys, David. 1996. *Forest Politics: The Evolution of International Cooperation.* New York: Routledge.

Humphreys, David. 2006. *Logjam: Deforestation and the Crisis of Global Governance.* London: Earthscan.

Jepma, Catrinus. 1995. *Tropical Deforestation: A Socio-Economic Approach.* London: Earthscan.

Meyfroidt, Patrick, and Eric F. Lambin. 2011. "Global Forest Transition: Prospects for an End to Deforestation." *Annual Review of Environment and Resources* 36: 343–71.

Myers, Norman. 1984. *The Primary Source: Tropical Forests and Our Future.* New York: W.W. Norton and Co.

Richards, Paul W. 1996. *The Tropical Rainforest: An Ecological Study*, 2nd ed. Cambridge: Cambridge University Press.

Rudel, Thomas K. 2005. *Tropical Forests: Regional Paths of Destruction and Regeneration in the Late Twentieth Century.* New York: Columbia University Press.

Streck, Charlotte, Robert O'Sullivan, Toby Janson-Smith, and Richard Tarasofky, eds. 2008. *Climate Change and Forests: Emerging Policy and Market Opportunities.* London: Chatham House.

Williams, Michael. 2003. *Deforesting the Earth: From Prehistory to Global Crisis.* Chicago: University of Chicago Press.

Wildlife Depletion

by **TOBIAS LANZ**

CHAPTER TWO

INTRODUCTION

Animal extinction evokes more emotion and interest than almost any other environmental issue. People are fascinated by the appearance and behavior of wild animals, especially mega fauna like big cats, wolves, bears, elephants, and rhinos. And because wild animal behavior is often similar to that of domestic animals, even humans, there is a certain sympathy for these creatures and their plight. As such, the loss of wildlife through human agency carries a heavy emotional and ethical cost.

It also carries a heavy ecological one. The loss of wild animals undermines the proper functioning of ecosystems. Without their presence, the fragile relationships between carnivores and prey, plants and animals, is undermined. This can also have negative impacts on human society. Mega fauna in particular are considered "keystone species," the presence of which signals a complete and healthy biome. Today, many of the world's ecosystems are devoid of wildlife, especially keystone species, meaning many of the world's ecosystems are unhealthy.

THE HISTORY OF WILDLIFE AND PEOPLE

Peoples around the world killed wild animals and were killed by them for millennia. People killed animals for food, fur, and other body parts. Animals were also killed because they threatened human life, crops, and livestock. It was a struggle for survival. And the outcomes between people and animals were relatively equal. However, this began to change as human populations grew and spread over the world in the last 100,000 years. After that time, hunting began to cause extinctions of many large animals.

The relationship between people and wildlife changed even more dramatically about 10,000 years ago with the emergence of agrarian civilizations. The rise of agrarian civilization was marked by a revolution (the Neolithic revolution) in food production and animal domestication. This, in turn, allowed for vastly increased human populations and more complex institutions, weapons, and tools. As a result, large areas of wildlife habitat could be converted to farmland and, with better weapons, the systematic killing of animals was now possible.

This occurred in every agrarian society around the world, especially in the larger civilizations—the so-called cradles of civilization—and it continued for thousands of years. One of the first examples of mass extermination of wild animals was in ancient Egypt. By the time of the Old Kingdom (2950–2350 BC), animals such as elephants, rhinoceroses, and giraffes had already disappeared from the Nile River valley.[1]

And as social hierarchies and technologies became more complex, so did methods of killing. Hunting is a good example. Sport or big game hunting became a pastime for the ruling classes—the aristocracy. The focus was almost always mega fauna. They were shot as trophies, signs of the hunter's prowess and social status. The aristocrat was at the apex of the human kingdom, so he naturally killed his animal equivalent—those at the apex of the animal kingdom.

Nowhere was the aristocratic hunt as spectacular as in ancient India. Both Mogul (Muslim) and Hindu rulers organized massive safaris (shikar) that comprised scores of hunters who utilized thousands of beaters, servants, and retainers, and hundreds of elephants and horses. They went into the field for months at a time and covered hundreds of square miles. The number of animals killed was staggering. The Mogul emperor Jahangir (1569–1627) shot over 17,000 mammals—tigers, lions, bears, foxes, otters, hyenas, antelope, deer, and mountain goats and sheep—by the time he was 50. He also bagged over 13,000 birds.[2]

Yet these same Moguls and maharajas also established large hunting preserves—as did other aristocrats around the world. Although their motivation for doing so was selfish, it had an unintended consequence for modern conservation. Many of these very same royal hunting preserves are now national parks and wildlife sanctuaries. If the aristocrats had not set them and their wildlife populations aside centuries ago, many of these areas would not have been preserved.

But the trend to exploit wild animals remained greater than the trend to conserve. And with European exploration and colonization of the world after 1500, exploitation increased dramatically. Superior transportation allowed greater access to animals, and superior weapons made killing more efficient. But it was the creation of global markets and global demand that initiated the exploitation of wildlife at an unprecedented scale.

The rate of exploitation increased even further in the 18th century, with the beginnings of the Industrial Revolution. Animals and animal parts were now integrated into vast global production and consumption systems. By the 19th century, the scale of killing was becoming unsustainable. It was slaughter. Seals, whales, and otters were killed for their oil and skins, birds for plumage, and fish and a host of other animals for food. Big game hunters killed elephants, rhinos, big cats, bears, deer, sheep, buffalo, and antelope for trophies.

The American bison almost became extinct. Some 40 to 60 million bison once roamed the North American plains. Around 1830, the slaughter began. Bison were killed for their fur, leather, and bones (for fertilizer). But many were simply killed for "sport," their carcasses left to rot on the plains. By 1880 there were about 800 bison left in the wild. The American government finally intervened to save this remainder. The population has grown to a few thousand since then, but most are confined to sanctuaries.

Other animals were less fortunate. Two American birds—the passenger pigeon and the Carolina parakeet—became extinct in the early 20th century. Australia lost several marsupial species, including its largest predator—the Tasmanian tiger (see Case Study 2.1). In Africa, the last zebra-like Quagga died in 1883.[3] These events, and the growing scientific and journalistic accounts of them, finally prompted conservation measures by various governments.

The modern-day conservation movement began in the latter decades of the 19th century. The protection of animal species was paralleled by the creation of protected areas. Yellowstone National Park was established by the United States government in 1872. This marked the beginning of the national park system that now has 59 parks covering 84 million square miles of territory.[4] The British established similar schemes in various colonies, especially Africa, which now has some of the largest national parks in the world.

The conservation movement also gained public awareness, as witnessed by the creation of zoological gardens and societies. Captivity exposed the general public to wild animals and familiarized them. These institutions also pioneered conservation funding and research. Today, many endangered species owe their survival to zoos.

Breeding programs, in particular, have sustained their populations. And there are some wild animal species that survive only in zoos.

The conservation movement also led to the creation of numerous non-governmental organizations (NGOs). The Sierra Club was the first in America, founded in 1892. Other significant conservation NGOs are the Audubon Society, Friends of the Earth, the Wilderness Society, and Greenpeace. The largest international NGO, which is devoted exclusively to wildlife protection, is the World Wildlife Fund (WWF). It was created in 1963—by former big game hunters.

The development and coordination of conservation policies and programs between governments, business corporations, and NGOs increased after World War II. Much of this was facilitated by the creation of International Organizations (IOs). The world's oldest and foremost conservation IO is the International Union for the Conservation of Nature (IUCN), organized in 1948. It coordinates policies between various international actors, and funds research and conservation projects.

Two of its most significant contributions to wildlife conservation are the categorization of the world's protected areas according to ecological criteria, and the creation of the IUCN Red List of Threatened Species, which provides the conservation status of the world's plants and animals (see Box 2.1). The IUCN also helped promote the Convention for the International Trade in Endangered Species (CITES) in 1973. This treaty identifies and protects endangered species that are especially vulnerable to economic exploitation and global trade.

Another important IO involved in wildlife conservation is the United Nations. The main UN conservation body is the UN Environment Programme (UNEP), created in 1972. It produces reports and has helped negotiate international treaties and conventions to preserve habitats to protect wildlife. It has worked closely with the WWF and the IUCN.[5]

Wildlife conservation has become a political issue and social goal the world over. This is especially true in the wealthy industrialized nations. However, the greatest challenges to conservation are now in the developing nations of the Global South. This is where the world's biodiversity is concentrated. This also where the world's human populations are increasing rapidly. The demand for land, coupled with hunting for food and poaching, now threatens many wildlife populations in these countries. The struggle for survival between people and wild animals has not ended.

Conservationists have enacted new programs—even new conservation philosophies—in response to these challenges. The emergence of the participatory or populist conservation models is one such change. The focus is away from government or I.O. directed conservation to a model that includes local communities. Its emphasis

Box 2.1 The International Union for the Conservation of Nature

The International Union for the Conservation of Nature (IUCN) is the oldest and largest global conservation organization. Founded in 1948, it coordinates government, IO, NGO, and corporate conservation activity worldwide. It is based in Gland, Switzerland.

Two important IUCN conservation activities include the creation of the Red List for endangered species and the Protected Area categories.

The IUCN Red List of Threatened Species provides the conservation status of the world's plant and animal species. It provides seven categories for relative risk of extinction:

1. Extinct: no known species living
2. Extinct in the wild: species known to exist only in captivity
3. Critically endangered: high risk of extinction in the wild
4. Endangered: moderate risk of extinction in the wild
5. Vulnerable: low risk of extinction in the wild
6. Near threatened: lower risk of extinction in the wild
7. Least Concern: no present risk of extinction in the wild

The IUCN Protected Area (PA) categories are used to classify habitat to best conserve biodiversity. These are widely accepted and used by governments and IOs. The categories range from Ia, strictest human use, to VI, moderate (sustainable) human use and access.

Ia. Strict Nature Preserve

Ib. Wilderness Area

II. National Park

III. National Monument/Feature

IV. Habitat/Species Management Area

VI. Protected Landscape/Seascape

VII. PA with Sustainable Resource Use

Source: http://www.iucn.org/.

is on 1) including local people in decision making; 2) using local (indigenous) knowledge—rather than just scientific expertise—in policy making; 3) developing new economic activities and resource use zones around protected areas and 4) encouraging ecotourism to increase local revenues.[6]

Such programs are not without problems. But many conservation professionals feel that excluding local communities, especial in the Global South with its growing human populations, will only worsen the prospects for effective wildlife conservation.

ENDANGERED MEGA FAUNA

Since 1600, over 80 mammals, 100 birds and 300 smaller animals have vanished from the Earth.[7] The number of invertebrates lost is even greater—most of these are in the world's rainforests, with their high and concentrated biodiversity (see Chapter One). Yet it is the mega fauna and their fate that garners the most attention from scientists, policymakers, and the general public.

Mega fauna fascinate people more than any other animals because of their size, their intelligence, a long shared history with human populations, and their social habits, which are similar to those of people. But their size and often aggressive behavior also puts them in conflict with people, a conflict that has been around for millennia, but has tilted decisively in favor of people in the last two centuries. Today, many mega fauna are endangered, and some are on the verge of extinction.

The best known mega fauna and their conservation status are discussed below.

Bears

There are eight bear species in the world.

1. The American black bear (*Ursus americanus*): Historic range is forests of North America.
2. The brown/grizzly bear (*Ursus arctos*): Historic range is forests and plains of North America, Eurasia, central Europe, and North Africa.
3. The polar bear (*Ursus maritimus*): Historic range is the polar ice pack of the Arctic Circle.
4. The sloth bear (*Melursus ursinus*): Historic range is forests of southern Asia.

5. The Asiatic black bear (*Ursus thibetanus*): Historic range is forests of the northern tier of southern Asia, northeastern China, eastern Russia, Taiwan, Korea, and Japan.
6. The sun bear (*Helarctos malayanus*): Historic range is forests of Southeast Asia, southern China, and Sumatra.
7. The spectacled bear (*Tremarctos ornatus*): Historic range is forests and grasslands of the Andes Mountains of South America.
8. The panda bear (*Ailuropoda melanoleuca*): Historic range is forests of central China.

The IUCN classifies the panda bear as endangered, and all other bears as vulnerable. Only the American black bear and the brown bear are classified as least concern.

Bears are large animals, with some, like the polar bear, reaching eight feet in height and weighing over 1,500 pounds. Most bears are omnivorous (eating a range of foods), except the polar bear, which is purely carnivorous. Bears are generally peaceful and solitary, but can become aggressive and kill people when provoked or surprised. Females with young are the most aggressive.

This aggressive behavior, plus the bears' habit of eating crops and livestock, has led to their persecution by people throughout history. Bears are also killed for their meat and body parts (gall bladders, feet, et cetera), which are dried and used for traditional medicines in Asia. But the loss of habitat is the main reason for the demise of bear populations worldwide.

One of the most dramatic declines in bear populations in recent centuries was that of the North American grizzly bear (a type of brown bear). It was once common throughout the western United States, and was so abundant in California that it became the state symbol and is displayed on the state flag. But ranchers and game hunters hunted the grizzly to the brink of extinction in the 19th century. Today fewer than 1,000 survive in the continental United States—only in the far western states of Montana, Wyoming, Idaho, Utah, and Washington. The last grizzly bear in California was shot in 1922.[8]

The world's most celebrated bear is the Chinese panda bear. Scientists once believed it was more closely related to raccoons. But in appearance and habits, it is certainly bear-like. And in the popular mind, it is a bear. It is also the most endangered of all the bear species, with fewer than 2,000 individuals surviving in the remote bamboo forests of central China.[9] Its endangered status and distinct black and white coloration is what led to its selection as the official logo of the WWF.

Rhinoceroses

There are five rhinoceros species living in Africa and Asia.

1. The white rhinoceros (*Ceratotherium simum*): Historic range is savannahs of western, eastern, and southern Africa.
2. The black rhinoceros (*Diceros bicornis*): Historic range is savannahs of western, eastern, and southern Africa.
3. The Indian rhinoceros (*Rhinoceros unicornis*): Historic range is forests and wetlands of the northern tier of southern Asia.
4. The Javan rhinoceros (*Rhinoceros sondaicus*): Historic range is forests and wetlands of Southeast Asia to southern China, the Malay Peninsula, Java, and Sumatra.
5. The Sumatran rhinoceros (*Dicerorhinus sumatrensis*): Historic range is forests and wetlands of Southeast Asia, the Malay peninsula, Sumatra, and Borneo.

The IUCN classifies the white rhino as near threatened, the Indian rhino as vulnerable, and the other three as critically endangered, with some subspecies already extinct.[10] All the rhino species have suffered from habitat loss and hunting, especially illegal poaching for their body parts (namely the horn), which is used in traditional Asian medicines and as ornamentation in the Arabian peninsula.

The white and black rhinos of Africa are the two most well-known species. The names have nothing to do with their color, as both are gray. The popular theory is that the name "white" is derived from the Dutch word "wijd," which means wide, and refers to the animal's broad upper lip. The other African rhino was simply named "black" to differentiate it from the white rhino. This etymology is still debated.

The white rhino became one of the world's most endangered species in the 1980s—its total wild population having dropped to a few dozen animals. This was entirely due to uncontrolled poaching. The white rhino is the second largest land animal after the elephants, so it naturally has a large and sought after horn. However, strict conservation policies enacted by the South African government has controlled poaching in that country, allowing the white rhinoceros population to increase substantially. Currently there are **15,000–20,000** white rhinos found in the wild, almost all in southern Africa.[11]

The protection of the white rhinoceros made poaching gangs shift their attention to the black rhino. The animal's solitary habits and its aggressive behavior (it readily charges people) made it an easy target. As a result, black rhino populations have plummeted. Today there are about 5,000 animals remaining in small populations in southern and eastern Africa. Some subspecies are already extinct.[12]

Asian rhinoceroses have not fared much better. The Indian rhinoceros is a large animal, the second largest rhino after the white rhino. Like its big African cousins, it has suffered from severe poaching pressures. Unlike the African species, it has also been subject to greater habitat loss, as it lives on a continent with greater human populations. Today about 3,000 Indian rhinos survive in India, Nepal, and Bhutan.[13]

The two least known of the world's rhinos are also the most endangered. Poaching and habitat loss have contributed to their plight. The Javan rhino may be the world's most endangered large mammal, with only 40 animals surviving in Ujung Kulon National Park, Indonesia. The Sumatran rhino lives only in Sumatra, and its population is a few hundred.[14]

Elephants

There are two elephant species in the world—the Asian elephant (*Elephas maximus*) and the African elephant (*Loxodonta africana*). The native range of the former is the forested regions of the Middle East, through southern and Southeast Asia, and into southern China. The latter is found in the savannahs of Africa, with a subspecies, the African forest elephant, living in that continent's rainforests.[15] The IUCN classifies the African elephant as vulnerable and the Asian Elephant as endangered.[16] The main threats to elephants are habitat loss and poaching for ivory.

The Asian elephant has a long history with people. It is more easily trained than its African cousin. As such, it has been used as a beast of burden and in warfare for centuries. It is also the common circus elephant, and is more common in zoos. The Asian elephant is smaller than its African cousin, with a rounder head and higher shoulder. The female has no tusks and some males are also born without tusks. Many scientists fear that future populations may become entirely tuskless as poachers eliminate tusked males. The current wild population of Asian elephants is between 40,000 and 50,000 animals confined to southern and Southeast Asia.[17]

The African elephant is far more common, with about 450,000 to 650,000 found in the wild.[18] But most are concentrated in eastern and southern Africa. It has been almost wiped out in west Africa, and populations are small and fragmented in central Africa. This is due to greater human populations in these regions and resulting habitat loss, as well as poaching pressures. The degree of threats to elephants in different African countries has created conflicts over conservation policy.[19]

Countries with many elephants, mainly those of southern Africa, favor culling herds and selling ivory legally on the international market. But scientists fear that poachers could access legal markets and sell illegal ivory, thus increasing overall threats to elephants. Thus ivory sales have remained strictly controlled since the international ivory ban of 1990. Despite the ban, the poaching of elephants for ivory has become one of the most pressing wildlife problems in the world, and has resulted in dramatic population declines of the animal in Africa and Asia in recent decades (see Case Study 2.2).

Big Cats

The cat family (*Felidae*), like the canids, are widespread and adaptable animals, with some three dozen species worldwide.[20] And many of these cats, from small to large, are becoming rare and endangered. But it is the plight of the big cats, genus *Panthera*, which is best known to the general public.

1. The tiger (*Panthera tigris*): Historic range is forests from the Caspian Sea through southern and Southeast Asia, including Java and Bali, China, Korea, and far eastern Russia.
2. The lion (*Panthera leo*): Historic range is savannah and scrub forests of the Middle East, Africa, and South Asia.
3. The leopard (*Panthera pardus*): Historic range is savannah, scrub, and moist forests of Africa, the Middle East, and Asia.
4. The jaguar (*Panthera onca*): Historic range is the scrub and moist forests of the southern and southeastern United States, Mexico, Central America, and South America.
5. The snow leopard (*Panthera uncia*): Historic range is the mountains of Eurasia, from central Russia, central Asia through northern India, Tibet, and western China.

The leopard and jaguar are listed by the IUCN as near threatened. The lion is listed as vulnerable, and the tiger and clouded leopard as endangered. Some big cat subspecies are already extinct, and others are critically endangered.[21]

The leopard is the most widespread of the big cats. It is absent in its former range only in areas with high human population densities and intense agricultural development. Because of its relatively small size (less than 200 pounds) and adaptability, it can thrive even close to human habitation, and in degraded habitats. Most leopards are found in Africa, but significant populations exist throughout Asia.

The African lion, like the leopard, is relatively common in many parts of its former range, especially eastern and southern Africa. It is the Asiatic lion that is critically endangered. This animal once ranged throughout the Middle East, North Africa, southern Asia, and even southern Europe. The lion was actually the historical symbol of India, not the tiger. Today, a few hundred Asian lions survive in protected areas of western India.[22]

The snow leopard is not a subspecies of the common leopard, but a distinct cat species adapted to snow and ice. It is found above the tree line of Eurasia's highest mountain ranges, including the Himalayas. It is a solitary animal, rarely seen by humans, and is well adapted to the rocky, icy terrain where it feeds on ungulates, birds, and mammals. Its main threats are hunting for its fur, and retaliation for killing livestock. Remote and difficult terrain has allowed several thousand snow leopards to survive in the wild.[23]

The jaguar is the only big cat found in the New World. (The mountain lion or cougar is a large cat, but genetically and physiologically it is not classified with the *Panthera*.) It is also the third largest cat after the tiger and lion, with males reaching 350 pounds. Although listed as near threatened, it is absent from many parts of its former range. The Amazon basin is its real stronghold, with over 10,000 living there.[24] Hunting and habitat loss are its main threats.

The tiger is the most imperiled of all the big cats. There are eight subspecies, of which three are already extinct, and several are critically endangered. These subspecies range in size from the 300-pound Sumatran tiger to the 800-pound Amur (Siberian) tiger, which is the biggest cat on Earth. Tigers have suffered from habitat loss throughout their range. In recent decades, poaching for their bone, which is ground up and used in traditional Asian medicines, has decimated them (see Case Study 2.3). Total world tiger populations are around 5,000.[25]

Another cat, which is not a big cat, but is well known and endangered, is the cheetah (*Acinonyx jubatus*). Historically, it ranged throughout the savannahs and scrub forests of Africa and central and southern Asia. Habitat loss and trophy hunting have taken their toll. The African cheetah survives mainly in protected areas in east and southern Africa. It is classified as vulnerable, with over 10,000 surviving in the wild.[26]

The Asian cheetah is far less fortunate. It is critically endangered, with only a few dozen animals surviving in Iran and Pakistan. Historically, it ranged throughout the

Middle East and India. Population pressures, in particular, have led to its demise. All cheetahs are also threatened by naturally low genetic diversity, making them vulnerable to inbreeding, which worsens their survival odds.

Dogs and Wolves

There are three dozen dog species (*Canidae*) worldwide. They are one of the most adaptable and widespread of all mammal species. Yet, there are a number of canids that are endangered, with one species—the Falkland Island wolf (*Dusicyon australis*)—having gone extinct in 1876.[27] The largest canids are the wolves and the African hunting dog. The gray wolf is listed as least concern, the African hunting dog as endangered, and the red wolf as critically endangered.[28]

The gray or timber wolf (*Canis lupus*) is the wolf of legend—and for good reason. It is the largest canid, sometimes weighing over 100 pounds. It travels in packs of a dozen or more, and can kill animals as large as a moose or musk ox, as well as people. Wolves have been persecuted for millennia because they threaten people and their livestock.

Historically, the gray wolf ranged throughout North America, Eurasia, the Middle East, North Africa, southern Asia, China, and Japan. It was the most widely distributed mammal on Earth after *Homo sapiens*. Today, it has been eliminated from much of its former range, save Canada, Alaska, and Eurasia. Small populations are still found in the Middle East and South Asia. Although the IUCN classifies the wolf as least concern, it is still threatened locally and regionally throughout the world.[29]

The red wolf (*Canis rufus*), native only to the southeastern United States, is less fortunate. It is an animal of dense forests and wetlands, habitats that have diminished greatly in the last century. And although this wolf feeds on small game, even fish and crustaceans, it has a reputation as a livestock killer, and has been duly persecuted. But the worst threat to the red wolf is interbreeding with the coyote. The number of "pure" red wolves is only a few dozen, and they are confined to protected areas in the southeastern United States.

The African wild dog (*Lycaon pictis*) is that continent's main canid predator, and is native to its savannahs. Like the gray wolf, it travels in packs and can kill formidable prey, including people. The dog's habit of eating livestock and its large hunting range has brought it into conflict with human beings. Pressures on hunting dog populations have increased with increases in African human populations. The African hunting dog is listed as endangered; it still numbers in the low thousands, but mainly in protected areas.[30]

Great Apes

The great apes are the largest primates. Because they share so many habits and physical features with human beings, they are also the most popular of all the animal species. There are six species of great apes.

1. The western gorilla (*Gorilla gorilla*): Historic range is tropical forests of western and central Africa.
2. The eastern gorilla (*Gorilla graueri*): Historic range is tropical forests of eastern Africa.
3. The Bornean orangutan (*Pongo pygmaeus*): Historic range is tropical forests of Borneo.
4. The Sumatran orangutan (*Pongo abelii*): Historic range is tropical forests Sumatra.
5. The chimpanzee (*Pan troglodytes*): Historic range is tropical forests and savannahs of western and central Africa.
6. The bonobo (*Pan paniscus*): Historic range is tropical forests of central Africa.

The eastern gorilla, Bornean orangutan, chimpanzee, and bonobo are listed by the IUCN as endangered. The western gorilla and Sumatran orangutan are critically endangered.[31]

The gorilla is the greatest of the great apes. Its size (six feet tall and over 600 pounds), strength, and pure black coloration make it an impressive and frightening creature. The gorilla was only discovered by Western science in the mid 19th century. But it quickly became a legend, especially after its depiction as a wild and dangerous creature in *King Kong*. The monster image has been associated with the animal ever since.

In truth, the gorilla is a shy herbivore that avoids people whenever possible. The main threats to the animal are poaching, as its meat is a local delicacy in Africa. Recently, the Ebola virus has taken a heavy toll. The loss of tropical rainforest habitat also reduces the gorilla's survival odds. Both western and eastern gorillas populations are declining. Total population is in the low thousands.

One eastern gorilla subspecies—the mountain gorilla—is perhaps the most famous primate, due to the groundbreaking research by primatologist Dian Fossey. It lives in the highland forests of Rwanda and Uganda, where a few hundred survive. Its natural scarcity, in combination with poaching pressure and habitat loss, make its existence precarious. This situation has worsened in recent decades due to political instability in the region, which has intensified poaching.

The orangutans are the second largest of the apes, with male adults reaching five feet in height and weighing over 250 pounds. And, like the gorilla, it is a peaceful creature. Scientists recently divided the orangutan into two distinct species—the Bornean and Sumatran. Tropical deforestation has been a particular threat to all orangutans, as they are the most arboreal of the great apes. Over 50,000 orangutans survive in the wild—but only 10 percent are Sumatran orangutans.[32]

Chimpanzees have also been recently divided into two species—the chimpanzee and the bonobo. The latter was once called the pygmy chimpanzee because of its smaller size and milder disposition. It is confined to the tropical forests of the Congo basin. The common chimpanzee is the closest relative to human beings and is better known by the general public, as it is commonly kept in captivity, trained, and studied by science. Its intelligence and communication skills are the most developed in the animal world. Several hundred thousand still exist in the wild, but they are threatened everywhere by habitat loss and poaching.

CASE STUDY 2.1

The Extinction of the Tasmanian Tiger

The Tasmanian tiger has become a symbol for modern animal extinction. Its demise is somewhat of a mystery, with many disputes existing over the causes, as well as whether the animal still survives somewhere.

The animal itself is also an enigma—both in appearance and habits. The Tasmanian tiger or Tasmanian wolf, as it is sometimes called, is neither cat nor dog, but a carnivorous marsupial. Its scientific name is thylacine (*Thylacinus cynocephalus*), meaning "dog-headed pouched one" in Greek. Indeed it looks like a mongrel with a largish head, short, rounded ears, and a short, dense, yellow-brown coat. The term "tiger" stuck because of the dark brown stripes that straddle the animal's back and tail.

The thylacine is the apex predator in the land of marsupials, averaging four feet plus tail in length, and weighing up to 60 pounds (historically, nine-foot specimens have been reported). Thylacines can kill animals as large as kangaroos, but usually feed on smaller game. They once ranged across the temperate parts of New Guinea, Australia, and Tasmania—but have not been seen anywhere for over 80 years.

Climate change seems a possible reason for extinction. The Australian continent became hotter some 5,000 years ago. Thylacine habitat was reduced and, according to fossil evidence, their numbers plummeted. But the Australian climate had changed considerably prior without impacting populations, and suitable thylacine habitat exists in Australia even today—but without thylacines. Other factors were at work—namely, human beings.

The thylacine's first relationship with people was with Australian Aborigines, hunter–gatherers that have lived on the continent for 20,000, maybe 50,000 years. Many Aborigine songs, stories, rituals, and cave paintings were about thylacines.

Cave paintings give a potential clue about their extinction, as they show thylacines being hunted. So, were they hunted to extinction? Probably not in a land as large as Australia. Hunting most likely pushed thylacines into more remote areas.

A more compelling reason for extinction is competition with dogs and dingoes, which were brought to Australia by humans some 4,000 years ago. The nature of canid–thylacine conflict is unknown. Large dogs could easily kill thylacines, but conflict was probably indirect. It may simply have been a case of the survival of the fittest. The canids are far more fecund, agile, and adaptable, and could simply have driven the thylacine to extinction.

The mystery of thylacine extinction in Australia raises even more questions about its extinction in Tasmania—the animal's last known refuge. The factors present in Australia were not present, at least not to the same degree, in Tasmania. The island had abundant thylacine habitat, the Aborigine population was very low, and, most importantly, dogs and dingoes never lived there. Yet, when Europeans arrived in the 17th century, thylacines were already scarce.

Abel Tasman—the island's namesake and first European explore—arrived on the island in 1642, and saw footprints of "wild beasts having claws like a tiger." But no tigers were seen. Sporadic reports of striped tigers, wolves, hyenas, and hyena possums circulated for decades among the settlers and explorers who began arriving in the late 17th century.

The first recorded sighting was in 1805, after people had settled the island's interior. Forests were soon cleared for farming, especially sheep herding. But sheep quickly became easy prey for thylacines, and sheep farmers claimed high losses, so they retaliated. Large land-owning companies created a new occupation—the "tiger man." His sole purpose was to kill tigers. And he did.

Tiger killing accelerated after the government created a bounty system in 1888. European demand for tiger skins to make waistcoats for men also hastened this trend. By 1910, 2,000 bounties had been claimed. And then the killing suddenly stopped. From 1910 to 1912, no bounty was claimed, and only a few were claimed in subsequent years. The thylacine simply disappeared.

It was not the only Tasmanian mammal to do so. Tiger cats also vanished. This coincidence points to some other factor, namely disease—distemper or pleuropneumonia. This complicates the story of thylacine extinction further. While people reduced thylacine populations to a dangerous level, it was disease that pushed a naturally rare creature over the demographic threshold so that it could no longer reproduce to sustain population levels.

By 1920 thylacines were extremely rare. In 1929, the Tasmanian government gave the animal partial protection by stopping hunting. The last wild thylacine was seen the following year. It was summarily shot by Wilf Batty, who had seen the animal stalking around his farm for weeks. The last living thylacine died in a Tasmanian zoo in 1936, the same year it finally became a totally protected species.

Since that day, there have been hundreds of reported thylacine sightings, but there is no any hard evidence to support their existence. The Tasmanian tiger is either very elusive, or, as most experts fear, it is indeed extinct.

Source: Guiler, Eric. 1985. *Thylacine: The Tragedy of the Tasmanian Tiger*. New York: Oxford University Press.

CASE STUDY 2.2

The African Elephant Poaching Crisis

People have killed elephants for their valuable ivory for thousands of years. It has been used for jewelry, carvings, and other ornamentation. There is an extensive international market in ivory dating back centuries. Arab traders sent huge caravans into the African interior, transported the ivory to the coasts, and then shipped it throughout the Middle East and Asia. The world ivory trade increased after European colonialism, with much of the ivory sent to Europe and North America, where it was made into billiard balls and piano keys.

Elephant populations were substantial enough in the past to withstand this demand. But in the late 20th century, growing human populations, shrinking habitat, and increased demand for ivory has placed tremendous pressure on African and Asian elephant populations. The 1980s saw a dramatic rise in illegal ivory poaching, leading to elephant population declines in Africa. This first ivory crisis led to a global awareness and stricter controls over the ivory trade, especially in Europe and North America, where it was largely banned. Elephant populations rebounded—until recently. Populations have again plummeted in the 2000s due to strong Asian demand.

The illegal trade in African ivory increased threefold from 1998 to 2007. In 2011 alone, 17,000 African elephants were killed, a number that has increased in subsequent years. Most animals killed are from western and central Africa, areas with already low elephant populations (most African elephants live in southern and east Africa, with Tanzania, Botswana, and Zimbabwe accounting for half of all African elephants). As a result of poaching, the elephant may disappear from half of Africa.

There are a number of factors that contribute to this slaughter. First is the number of Asian ivory traders and buyers who work in Africa (mainly Chinese). They hire local poachers, often poor people. The ivory is then handled by international criminal gangs, who smuggle it by land, air, or sea. Most is hidden on container ships that depart from East Africa and then make their way to China, Thailand, and Malaysia. Political instability and armed conflict intensifies poaching, as militias sell ivory, as well as meat and hides, to purchase weapons.

Some poachers are small, one-man operations. Others are large organizations, employing dozens of trackers, hunters, and vehicles, even airplanes and helicopters, to pursue their quarry. Poachers are successful even in stable African countries, where they can often bribe officials to access elephant herds, even those protected by national parks. Sadly, game wardens are often involved in poaching, as are higher-ranking conservation officials.

IOs and NGOs—the United Nations Environment Programme, the International Union for the Conservation of Nature, and the Worldwide Fund for Nature, in particular—have been on the forefront of combating the current poaching crisis. Increased monitoring of elephant populations and tracking of smugglers and smuggling routes have been implemented. Conservation efforts in individual countries have also been strengthened. But this is always difficult in unstable political environments. Finally, pressure is being placed on ivory-importing countries, especially China and Thailand, to curtail the ivory trade and halt all illegal ivory sales.

It must be noted that ivory can be legally sold on international markets, but these sales are strictly regulated. This legal ivory is from the elephant-rich countries of southern Africa. It must also be noted that the same poaching rings and criminal syndicates involved in the ivory trade also smuggle rhino horn. And the rhino population, which is much smaller than the elephant, has also plummeted in recent years. The demand for rhino horn is also from Asia—but is used for medicinal purposes.

Source: UNEP, CITES, IUCN, TRAFFIC. 2013. *Elephants in the Dust: The African Elephant Crisis.* (New York: UNEP).

CASE STUDY 2.3

Plight of the Indian Tiger

India has over half of the world's tigers, but that population is now gravely threatened. Poaching is now the greatest threat to the great cat, surpassing even habitat. Some 2,000 tigers have been killed since the early 1990s to supply body parts, mainly bone, for traditional Asian medicines. Tiger bone is used to treat a host of ills, including rheumatism, stomach ailments, and impotence.

The greatest demand for tiger parts is from China; the greatest supply is in India. The cat is caught in this violent economic intersection. As the supply of tigers decreases, price goes up. As demand for tigers increases, prices to go up further. Tiger bone is now in such short supply and great demand that its value per ounce has surpassed that of many precious metals.

Tiger poaching is nothing new. The poor have always broken laws to kill problem tigers. So have the rich, to get that trophy at any cost. But in the past these events were isolated and localized. Modern poaching is different in degree and kind. It has evolved into a distinctly modern form of tiger hunting, in which money and technology are the driving forces. As a result, tigers are no longer killed out of defense or survival, or even as trophies, but as commodities harvested, traded, processed, and sold on global markets.

In the past, the number of tigers was so great and the demand relatively low enough that tigers were never seriously threatened. China had tens of thousands of cats as late as the 1960s. But the Chinese leader Mao Zedong ended that. He killed off the county's tiger population in a few short decades as part of his "Great Leap Forward," a program designed to rapidly modernize the "backward" countryside by clearing anything that stood in the way of progress—peasant villages, forests, swamps, and vermin-like tigers. It was a tremendous success.

China transformed its countryside, modernized its economy, and reduced its entire tiger population to fewer than 50 animals.

Mao's ambitious project killed thousands of tigers, creating stockpiles of bone and other tiger parts, which supplied traditional medical practitioners for decades. The stockpiles finally ran out in the 1990s, and new supplies were needed. They were found in India and Southeast Asia. The demand for these tigers is now being fueled by a richer, more populous and powerful China. They want tigers and their demands are being met.

Local crime syndicates, as aggressive and cunning as any multi-national business, organize the actual killing and transportation of tigers. They utilize modern communications and mass transportation networks, and kill with state-of-the-art weapons, traps, and poisons.

Their lucrative incentives can corrupt villagers and government officials alike, presenting grave dilemmas for the Indian government. Can an already corrupt and inefficient government bureaucracy be kept from being seduced by dynamic and powerful poaching networks? And how can policies and programs convince poor, rural people that they should protect the tiger rather than kill it? What kinds of policies are most effective in stopping poaching?

Many believe the Indian government must invest more in personnel and technology. Train staff and buy better equipment—jeeps, telecommunications, and weapons. Most Indian forest guards are armed with simple walking sticks, while their criminal counterparts often have AK-47s. Others argue that it is the villagers who must be won over first. Invest in economic development; provide alternatives to poaching, as well as other types of forest exploitation. Create incentives to protect rather than poach. Create alternative economies.

Both are important ways of stopping poaching. But it is not enough. To many observers, poaching is at root a political problem, a question of will and leadership.

First, there is the problem of political priorities. The Indian government can build a nuclear arsenal, a transcontinental rail system, a globally competitive high technology industry, and massive hydroelectric dams (that have flooded thousands of acres of wilderness), but they cannot protect their tigers. Conservation interferes with the drive for economic development. The desire to become an "advanced industrial democracy" takes precedence over any environmental concern. Conservation does not create jobs, does not add to gross national product and income, and it cannot be taxed. Ecology gets in the way of economics.

There is also ineptitude and corruption. The two feed off each other, creating incentives to commit crimes—a market to be exploited. Some of the worst problems are at the judicial level, where powerful crime syndicates can readily bribe lawyers and judges. And then there is the labyrinth of Indian laws and procedures that slows the legal process to a virtual standstill, thwarting even honest efforts at prosecution. There are currently hundreds of wildlife cases pending in New Delhi, and some take a decade before coming to court. Others never do. The defendants skip bail, move, or die. The overall conviction rate for wildlife crimes remains below five percent.

Source: Tobias J. Lanz. 2009. *The Life and Fate of the Indian Tiger.* Westport, CT: Praeger.

ENDNOTES

1. Clive Ponting, *A New Green History of the World* (New York: Penguin, 2007), 135.
2. Divyabhanusinh, *The End of a Trail: The Cheetah in India* (New Delhi: Oxford University Press, 1999), 170.
3. Don E. Wilson and DeeAnn M. Reeder, *Mammal Species of the World: A Taxonomic and Geographic Reference*, 3rd ed., vol. 1 (Baltimore, MD: Johns Hopkins University Press, 2005), 632.
4. National Park Service, *Summary of Acreage* (Washington, DC: Land Resources Division), https://irma.nps.gov/Stats/Reports/National.
5. United Nations Environment Programme, *International Partners*, https://www.unep.org/regionalseas/Partners/international/default.asp.
6. For a good overview of community involvement in conservation see K. B. Ghimire and M. P. Pimbert. *Social Change and Conservation* (New York: Routledge, 2009).
7. Convention on Biological Diversity, *Chapter 1 Status and Trends of Global Biodiversity: Trends in Species Diversity* (Montreal, Quebec, Canada, 2001), https://www.cbd.int/gbol/chap-01–02.shtml.
8. Bernd Brunner, *Bears: A Brief History* (New Haven, CT: Yale University, 2007), 154.
9. Z. Lü, D. Wang, and D. L. Garshelis (IUCN SSC Bear Specialist Group), *Ailuropoda melanoleuca* (The IUCN Red List of Threatened Species, version 2014.3, 2008), http://www.iucnredlist.org/details/712/0..
10. Wilson and Reeder, *Mammal Species of the World*, 634–36.
11. R. Emslie, *Ceratotherium simum* (The IUCN Red List of Threatened Species, version 2014.3, 2012), http://www.iucnredlist.org/details/4185/0.
12. R. Emslie, *Diceros bicornis* (The IUCN Red List of Threatened Species, version 2014.3, 2012), http://www.iucnredlist.org/details/6557/0.
13. B. K. Talukdar, R. Emslie, S. S. Bist, A. Choudhury, S. Ellis, B. S. Bonal, M. C. Malakar, B. N. Talukdar, and M. Barua, *Rhinoceros unicornis* (The IUCN Red List of Threatened Species. version 2014.3, 2008), http://www.iucnredlist.org/details/19496/0.
14. N. J. van Strien, B. Manullang, Sectionov, W. Isnan, M. K. M. Khan, E. Sumardja, S. Ellis, K. H. Han, Boeadi, J. Payne, and E. Bradley Martin, *Dicerorhinus sumatrensis* (The IUCN Red List of Threatened Species, version 2014.3, 2008), http://www.iucnredlist.org/details/6553/0.
15. Wilson and Reeder. *Mammal Species of the World*, 90–91.
16. Ibid.
17. A. Choudhury, D. K. Lahiri Choudhury, A. Desai, J. W. Duckworth, P. S. Easa, A. J. T. Johnsingh, P. Fernando, S. Hedges, M. Gunawardena, F. Kurt, U. Karanth, A. Lister, V. Menon, H. Riddle, A. Rübel, and E. Wikramanayake (IUCN SSC Asian Elephant Specialist Group), *Elephas maximus* (The IUCN Red List of Threatened Species, version 2014.3, 2008), http://www.iucnredlist.org/details/7140/0.

18. J. Blanc, *Loxodonta africana* (The IUCN Red List of Threatened Species, version 2014.3, 2008), http://www.iucnredlist.org/details/12392/0.
19. Ibid.
20. Wilson and Reeder, *Mammal Species of the World*, 532.
21. Ibid., 546–548.
22. H. Bauer, K. Nowell, and C. Packer, *Panthera leo* (The IUCN Red List of Threatened Species, version 2014.3, 2012), http://www.iucnredlist.org/details/15951/0.
23. R. Jackson, D. Mallon, T. McCarthy, R. A. Chundaway, and B. Habib, *Panthera uncia* (The IUCN Red List of Threatened Species, version 2014.3, 2008), http://www.iucnredlist.org/details/22732/0.
24. A. Caso, C. Lopez-Gonzalez, E. Payan, E. Eizirik, T. de Oliveira, R. Leite-Pitman, M. Kelly, and C. Valderrama, *Panthera onca* (The IUCN Red List of Threatened Species, version 2014.3, 2008), http://www.iucnredlist.org/details/15953/0.
25. R. S. Chundawat, B. Habib, U. Karanth, K. Kawanishi, J. Ahmad Khan, T. Lynam, D. Miquelle, P. Nyhus, S. Sunarto, R. Tilson, and Sonam Wang, *Panthera tigris* (The IUCN Red List of Threatened Species, version 2014.3, 2011), http://www.iucnredlist.org/details/15955/0.
26. S. Durant, L. Marker, N. Purchase, F. Belbachir, L. Hunter, C. Packer, C. Breitenmoser-Wursten, E. Sogbohossou, and H. Bauer, *Acinonyx jubatus* (The IUCN Red List of Threatened Species, version 2014.3, 2008), http://www.iucnredlist.org/details/219/0.
27. Wilson and Reeder, *Mammal Species of the World*, 579.
28. Ibid., 575, 581.
29. Ibid.
30. R. Woodroffe and C. Sillero-Zubiri, *Lycaon pictus* (The IUCN Red List of Threatened Species, version 2014.3, 2012), http://www.iucnredlist.org/details/12436/0.
31. Wilson and Reeder, *Mammal Species of the World*, 182–184.
32. I. Singleton, S. A. Wich, and M. Griffiths, *Pongo abelii* (The IUCN Red List of Threatened Species, version 2014.3, 2008), http://www.iucnredlist.org/details/39780/0.

RECOMMENDED READINGS/SOURCES

Craigies, Ian D., Jonathan E. M. Bailie, Andrew Balmford, Chris Carbone, Ben Collen, Rhys E. Green, and Jon M. Hutton. 2010. "Large Mammal Population Declines in Africa's Protected Areas." *Biological Conservation* 143 (9): 2221–28.

Crosby, Alfred. 1993. *Ecological Imperialism: The Biological Expansion of Europe.* Cambridge: Cambridge University Press.

Ellis, Richard. 2005. *Tiger Bone & Rhino Horn: The Destruction of Wildlife for Traditional Chinese Medicine*. Washington, DC: Island Press.

International Union for the Conservation of Nature. *IUCN Red List of Threatened Species*. http://www.iucnredlist.org/.

Isenberg, Andrew. 2001. *The Destruction of the Bison: An Environmental History, 1750–1920.* Cambridge: Cambridge University Press.

Johannesen, Anne B., and Anders Skonhoft. 2005. "Tourism, Poaching and Wildlife Conservation: What Can Integrated Conservation and Development Projects Accomplish." *Journal of Resource and Energy Economics* 27 (3): 208–26.

Krausman, Paul R. 2013. *Wildlife Management and Conservation: Contemporary Principles and Practices.* Baltimore, MD: Johns Hopkins University Press.

Lanz, Tobias. 2009. *The Life and Fate of the Indian Tiger.* Westport, CT: Praeger.

Mackenzie, John. 1997. *The Empire of Nature: Hunting, Conservation and British Imperialism.* Manchester: Manchester University Press.

Mills, J. Scott. 2006. *Conservation of Wildlife Populations: Demography, Genetics, and Management.* Hoboken, NJ: Wiley-Blackwell.

Reeve, Rosalind. 2002. *Policing International Trade in Endangered Species: The CITES Treaty and Compliance*. London: Earthscan.

Richards, John F. 2014. *The World Hunt: An Environmental History of the Commodification of Animals*. Berkeley: University of California Press.

Wilson, Don E., and DeeAnn M. Reeder. 2005. *Mammal Species of the World: A Taxonomic and Geographic Reference*, vols 1 and 2. Baltimore, MD: Johns Hopkins University Press.

Wishart, David J. 1979. *The Fur Trade of the American West, 1807–1840*. Lincoln: University of Nebraska Press.

Woodroffe, Rosie, and Simon Thirgood. 2009. *People and Wildlife, Conflict or Coexistence (Conservation Biology).* Cambridge: Cambridge University Press.

Desertification/ Dryland Deforestation

by MANALI BARUAH

CHAPTER THREE

INTRODUCTION

Desertification is the accrued result of ill-adapted land use and the effects of a harsh climate in drylands.[1] The process is caused by a combination of natural and man-made factors that change over time, vary by location, and interact with each other in a complex manner. These causes include direct factors, such as unsustainable land use practices and climate-related processes (e.g., droughts), and indirect factors, such as population pressure, socioeconomic and policy factors, and international trade. The consequences of desertification are manifold: aggravated economic conditions, an increase in poverty, migration, disease, political instability, and conflict. Countries around the world recognize land degradation as a critical environmental issue; in fact, over 70 percent of them declare that land degradation and drought are national security issues.[2]

Drylands cover more than one-third of the world's land surface. These are arid, semi-arid, and arid subhumid areas,[3] which generally excludes hyper-arid areas or deserts, such as the world's driest places—the Atacama desert in Chile and the Namib desert in southwest Africa. Drylands are generally characterized by low, infrequent precipitation, lack of water, soils containing low organic matter, and huge differences between day- and nighttime temperatures. Plants and animals in dryland areas are usually adapted to extreme climatic variables. They may be heat resistant or have the ability to survive in low moisture conditions. Despite being drylands, these areas support most human activities and are home to diverse habitats and biological forms. In fact, drylands support 50 percent of the world's livestock and account for nearly half of all farmland. Most of the planet's 2 billion dryland residents live in developing countries, usually living below the poverty line without access to basic necessities such as fresh water and sanitation.

One of the persistent challenges of dryland environment is water scarcity. Although rainfall may occur in many dryland environments, rainfall is scant, irregular, and unpredictable, with water evaporating at much higher rates compared to the rate of precipitation. Human settlements in these areas, therefore, are found concentrated mainly around sources of water such as rivers, springs, wells, reservoirs, and oases.

The word desertification has a Latin origin: "*fication*, means the action of doing (or creating) which originates from *fieri*, the passive form of the verb *facere*, meaning to do, while desert is derived from both the adjective *desertus*, meaning uninhabited, and the noun *desertum*, a desert area."[4] The United Nations Convention to Combat Desertification (UNCCD), an international agreement to combat desertification, eventually emerged in 1994 from the 1992 Rio Summit (Box 3.1). The UNCCD defines desertification as "the degradation of land in arid, semi-arid and dry sub-humid areas. It is caused primarily by human activities and climatic variations."[5]

Desertification does not refer to the expansion of existing deserts. It occurs because dryland ecosystems, which cover over one-third of the world's land area, are extremely vulnerable to exploitation and inappropriate land use. Other factors include climatic variations and extreme climatic events, such as floods or droughts, which can accelerate the process of desertification. Poverty, political instability, over-dependence on dryland agriculture, deforestation, over-grazing, and poor irrigation practices can all weaken the productivity of crop land. Desertification directly affects over 250 million people, and about 1 billion people in over one hundred countries are at risk. Populations at risk from desertification are some of the world's poorest, most marginalized and politically weak. Take, for example, the Republic of Yemen, a politically volatile and poverty ridden country in the Arabian Peninsula, where over 90 percent of land is at threat of desertification.[6]

DRIVERS OF DESERTIFICATION

Desertification is not a linear process. A number of drivers, both human-related and climatic, interact in complex ways, leading to land degradation in the drylands. Here are some of the major drivers of desertification.

Box 3.1 The United Nations Convention to Combat Desertification (UNCCD)

The 1992 Rio Earth Summit recognized desertification, along with climate change and the loss of biodiversity, as the greatest challenges to sustainable development. The UNCCD is the only legally binding international agreement linking environment and development to sustainable land management. The UNCCD focuses primarily on the drylands, where some of the world's poorest populations live in extremely vulnerable ecosystems. In the 10-year strategy of the UNCCD (2008–2018) that was adopted in 2007, parties to the Convention further specified their goals: *"to forge a global partnership to reverse and prevent desertification/land degradation and to mitigate the effects of drought in affected areas in order to support poverty reduction and environmental sustainability."*

The 195 parties of the UNCCD work together to fulfill a common mission, which is to improve the living conditions of world's dryland residents by maintaining and restoring land and soil productivity, and by mitigating the effects of drought. As the issues of land degradation, climate change, and biodiversity conservation are intimately connected, the UNCCD collaborates closely with the other two Rio Conventions—the Convention on Biological Diversity and the United Nations Framework Convention on Climate Change—collectively, these three Conventions seek to meet these complex assemblages of environmental problems and find solutions for sustainable use of natural resources.

However, UNCCD is also one of the most underfunded of the international conventions, because many developed nations do not view desertification as a critical environmental issue. In 2011, the Global Environment Facility, an international institution that serves as a financial mechanism to help countries implement the Rio Conventions, spent just $369 million on UNCCD projects. This amount is only about 10 percent of the money allocated towards biodiversity. Many rich countries have also found a way to get around land shortages and expand agricultural production by buying up land in sub-Saharan Africa. A World Bank report states that during 2009, some 45 million hectares of land in developing

Continued...

countries were under negotiation for allocation, of which 70 percent was in Africa. (Source: http://siteresources.worldbank.org/DEC/Resources/Rising-Global-Interest-in-Farmland.pdf).

Source: World Bank, Rising Global Interest in Farmland: Can it Yield Sustainable and Equitable Benefits, Washington DC: World Bank, 2010. http://siteresources.worldbank.org/DEC/Resources/Rising-Global-Interest-in-Farmland.pdf

Climatic Variations

The natural recurring drought processes, which may be caused by global climatic changes that are difficult to evaluate, may lead to land degradation. There is historical evidence that indicates that natural climatic patterns produce cycles of drought, followed by periods of relatively higher rainfall.

Precipitation is often irregular, scanty, and unpredictable in dryland regions. This deficiency in precipitation over a prolonged period results in droughts, with adverse impacts on vegetation, animals, and people. During droughts, there is soil water deficit and ground water reserves are reduced, which creates difficult conditions for vegetation growth. Consequently severe hydrological imbalances endanger natural production systems and intensify soil loss and degradation.

Human Activities

In dryland regions, where agriculture and pastoralism[7] are the main economic activities, human activities compound the problem of land degradation, mainly through over-cultivation without adequate fallow periods The intense land use strips soil of nutrients and organic matter; overgrazing, which removes the vegetation cover make soil vulnerable to erosion; deforestation, which destroys the vegetation cover that binds the soil to the land; and poor irrigation techniques, which increase soil salinity and degrade agricultural lands.

Figure 3.1. Prolonged grazing leads to land degradation in the drylands.

Many extractive industries, such as mining, also trigger land degradation by lowering water tables, disturbing soil structure, and accelerating soil erosion. Other drivers of soil degradation include lack of knowledge, agriculture-dependent economies, poor crop productivity, unsustainable tourism practices, pre-existing socioeconomic challenges, and unstable political environments and conflicts.

WHAT DOES LAND DEGRADATION INVOLVE?

Soil Salinization

Soil salinization involves the buildup of salt in soil over time. This is often linked to irrigated lands or overuse of chemical fertilizers in poorly drained soils. While irrigation could improve food production, poor irrigation techniques lead to soil salinization. For example, salinization is reducing the world's irrigated area by 1–2 percent every year, hitting the arid and semiarid regions the hardest.[8] Often after irrigation, the water added to soil is used by crops or evaporates, leaving behind salt deposits in the soil. Salty groundwater may also contribute to salinization. Mineral salts in ground water can be transported to the surface by capillary action, and high evaporation in drylands results in an accumulation of salt at the surface. This makes soil unsuitable for most crops and vegetation. In areas outside of drylands, with sufficient precipitation, salts are often leached out of the soil by drainage water, but this natural desalinization does not occur in dryland areas.

Deforestation

Pastoralism is a dominant economic activity in drylands. Frequent intensive or prolonged grazing periods affect vegetation cover, because there is not enough time for vegetation to regenerate between grazing periods.

Along with grazing, tree clearing for fuelwood exposes bare soil to erosion in drylands. In fact, standing vegetation has several positive impacts on soil conditions. Vegetation, with the help of roots, maintains soil structure, helps water infiltration, and retains moisture, resulting in productive soil. Leaves and other decaying vegetation matter add organic components, thereby enriching soil. So, deforestation has a very direct consequence on soil degradation.

Environmental Degradation

Overall, land degradation has far-reaching implications for the state of the environment. Land is one of the most important natural resources. Populations living in drylands are often poor, living in a harsh environments and struggling to make ends meet. The decline in soil fertility further reduces agricultural productivity and the prospect of additional income. Desertification may also cause sedimentation in rivers and lakes, downstream flooding, poor water quality due to increased sediment load, and the blockage of reservoirs and navigation channels due to the deposition of silt. Land degradation can also trigger dust storms and air pollution, reduced visibility, unsafe communication, risks to health, aggravate respiratory diseases, and mental stress. Land degradation therefore not only affects agricultural productivity and income generation, but can generate a cycle of environmental degradation, poverty,

Box 3.2 The Shrinking of the Aral Sea

The shrinking of the Aral Sea, which is in fact a lake, is one of the worst cases of environmental degradation. Central Asia's Aral Sea, was once the fourth-largest lake in the world. Decades-old water diversions for irrigation during the Soviet era, and a more recent drought, have rendered the lake completely dry (image on right). The Aral Sea was fed by two important rivers of Central Asia: the Amu Darya and the Syr Darya. In the 1960s, Soviet engineers built an enormous irrigation network, including 20,000 miles of canals, 45 dams, and more than 80 reservoirs, to irrigate the cotton and wheat fields in Kazakhstan and Uzbekistan. Decades later, the inefficient and faulty irrigation system reduced the once-flourishing drainage system, teeming with aquatic resources, to a few desiccated lakes with high levels of salinity.

In the early 2000s, dam and restoration activities began in Kazakhstan, with the aim of improving the health of the Syr Darya River and increasing the flow into the North Aral Sea. Since then, there have been some positive changes that include increase in water level and reduced salinity.

In the early 2000, dam and restoration activities began in Kazakhstan with the aim of improving the health of the Syr Darya River and increasing the flow into the North Aral Sea. Due to these activities, some positive changes have been observed, including an increase in water level and reduced salinity.

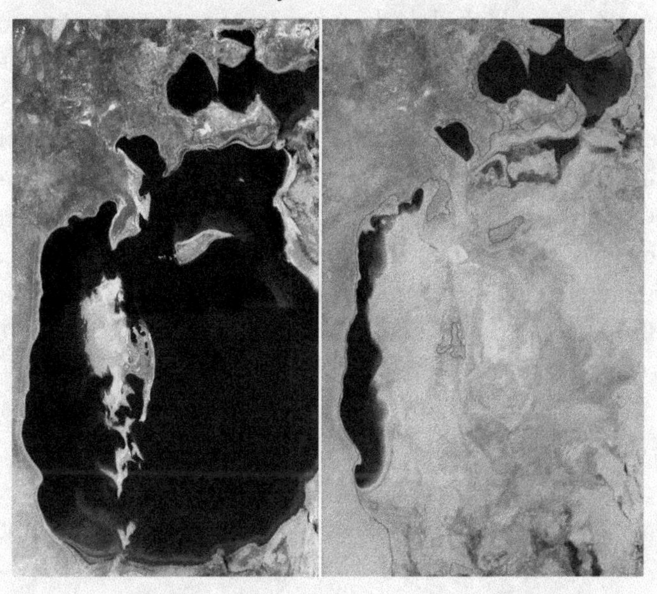

Figure 3.2. A comparison of the Aral Sea in 1989 (left) and 2014 (right). NASA, https://commons.wikimedia.org/wiki/File:AralSea1989_2014.jpg. Copyright in the Public Domain.

migration, and conflict, often jeopardizing the stability of affected countries and regions.

DESERTIFICATION AND OTHER ENVIRONMENTAL ISSUES

Climate Change

Climate change and desertification are intricately linked. In fact, desertification is intensified by climate change, and vice versa. For the past two centuries, greenhouse gas concentrations in the atmosphere have been increasing at an alarming rate, mostly as a result of human activities, driven by rapid and widespread industrialization. Desertification contributes to greenhouse gas emissions through loss of vegetation, thereby reducing carbon sinks. Land use change and degradation is responsible for about 20 percent of carbon emissions globally.[9] Carbon sequestration is the process by which CO_2 is removed from the atmosphere and stored in sinks, such as oceans, soils, vegetation, or geologic formations. On land, soils contain approximately 75 percent of the carbon pool which is three times more than the amount stored in living plants and animals. Whenever soil is depleted, soil carbon sequestration is stopped. On the other hand, land restoration and enhancing soil quality allows soil to sequester carbon and prevent emission. Afforestation in drylands generates carbon sinks for greenhouse gases.

According to the UNCCD, there is evidence that droughts have led to migration and conflict in the past, in countries such as India, Bangladesh, Mauritania, Senegal, Morocco, and Eritrea. In many degraded agricultural areas, challenges posed by climate change aggravate pre-existing socioeconomic and climatic challenges, compelling people that depend on farming, pastoralism, and other natural resources into forced migration.

Water Scarcity

Water scarcity refers to the condition where there is not enough water to meet the demands of all the sectors of a region, such as industry, environment, and transport. As population increases, water problems will become even more acute. According to the United Nations, around 1.2 billion people, or almost one-fifth of the world's population, live in areas of physical water scarcity. In the future, an additional

500 million people are likely to experience the same. According to the UNCCD, by the year 2020, almost two-thirds of the world's population may be exposed to increased water stress as a consequence of desertification, land degradation, and drought may expose.[10] Increased water scarcity could lead to annual grain losses equivalent to 30 percent of the current world consumption.[11] Water scarcity and poor water quality threaten public health, food and energy production, and regional economies. In the drylands, practically all sources of water are over utilized. Repeated use without recharge often contaminates water reserves, thereby spreading numerous diseases.

The water cycle is also directly affected by land degradation in the drylands. Prolonged periods of low rainfall means drought and no groundwater recharge; as a result, plants and animals die, and humans struggle to survive. Higher than average precipitation in degraded lands can cause flash floods, significant loss of soil, and, when land dries to form a hard crust from high evaporation rates, very little water infiltration to recharge ground water reserves.

It has been argued that sustainable land management can increase water productivity by up to 100 percent. Water use efficiency in multiple-cropping systems is often 18 to 99 percent higher than in single-crop systems. Water harvesting is another sustainable and cheap option to improve water security and address water scarcity. For example, a typical sand dam road crossing can enhance rural infrastructure and yield 50,000 liters of water per day.[12] Conservation agriculture can reduce water runoff by 40 to 69 percent. This decreases herbicide, nitrate and soluble phosphate contamination of surface waters (by 70%, 85%, and 65%, respectively).[13]

Environmental Migration

Desertification can be a push factor, forcing people to move out from the affected regions. As land becomes degraded and productivity goes down, economic development becomes a challenge, and people are often compelled to move internally from rural to urban areas, from drier parts of a country to more productive frontiers, or to immigrate to neighboring countries. Estimates show that some 135 million people may be displaced by 2045 as a result of desertification.[14] Migration often causes social and political tensions and conflicts. It also puts stress on the environment, infrastructure, and other critical resources. Because of how it affects migration, desertification is a global challenge, in the same way as climate change or biodiversity loss. It is estimated that 50 million people are at risk of displacement in the next ten years if desertification is not checked.[15]

Biodiversity

Drylands support a wide diversity of plant and animal species that have undergone incredible adaptation to the harsh conditions of dryland environment. Recurring and sustained periods of drought that leads to desertification is a key threat to dryland species and impedes the range of ecosystem services they provide. Animal and bird droppings help fertilize the soil and help plants to germinate. Animal movement tills the soil, increasing vegetation productivity. Animals also consume vegetation and help reduce fire loads and fires. People living in dryland depend on biodiversity for basic subsistence, and for recreational and spiritual purposes. Many livelihoods in drylands, including pastoralism, agriculture, and tourism, are dependent on biodiversity. In sub-Saharan Africa, nature-based tourism is the mainstay of many communities, such as the semi-nomadic Masai people of southern Kenya and northern Tanzania. For generations, these traditional communities have adapted their pastoral and agricultural practices to be in tune with the indigenous biodiversity. They have domesticated indigenous plants and animals that are more suitable for the harsh conditions than imported varieties.

The mutually reinforcing forces of desertification and climate change exacerbate biodiversity loss. As a result of land degradation, indigenous species of dryland environments that are dependent on vegetation have to migrate to other areas to find sufficient resources, or risk extinction. Loss of highly adapted dryland biodiversity is significant threat to global species biodiversity. This also increases food insecurity and impedes basic subsistence activities of the world's poorest populations. Desertification significantly reduces the natural resource capital available to dryland communities, making them extremely vulnerable and aggravating their already impoverished situation.

Forests

Over the last ten years, approximately 5.2 million hectares of forest has been destroyed each year.[16] Dry forests cover 18 percent of the land in arid zones, and approximately 81 percent of tropical and subtropical dry forests are located in Africa, Latin America, and Asia.[17] Dryland forests are especially vulnerable to degradation because there is not enough water in the root zone, and dryland resources such as land and soil, along with forests, are over-exploited. Forests and tree cover combat land degradation and desertification by stabilizing soils, reducing water and wind erosion, and maintaining nutrient cycling in soils. Therefore, the degradation of forest ecosystems in drylands results in a loss of biomass and biodiversity, water resources, and carbon storage capacity. However, this can be avoided through soil conservation, proper irrigation techniques, silvopastoral practices, afforestation, and switching to alternative energy sources.

Energy

The use of firewood and charcoal is one of the principal causes of desertification. In many tropical arid areas, wood is the principal source of domestic energy for cooking and lighting both in rural and urban populations. Many countries in Africa depend heavily on wood for household energy needs, with fuelwood often constituting more than half of primary energy consumption.[18] Due to the physical water scarcity in the drylands, regeneration of vegetation is very slow. According to the Food and Agriculture Organization, woodfuel consumption in Africa reached 623 million cubic meters in 1994—the highest per capita woodfuel consumption of any continent.

However, land management practices such as rotational grazing, increasing grazing range, and increasing fallow periods have outstanding regenerating effects on drylands forest. Energy crops such as the Jatropha plant can offer an alternative to wood and non-renewable energy sources, if managed responsibly. This plant species does not compete with food crops on cultivated land, and helps stabilize soils. In drylands, therefore, a mixed cropping approach, with a combination of food and non-food crops, could significantly reduce competition between food and energy security. The approach could also help diversify income-generating opportunities, and prevent soil degradation. A number of Jatropha projects have been piloted in developing countries such as India and Mali. Other environment friendly, low-carbon alternatives to address the energy security include uptake of fuel efficient technologies, biomass, geo-thermal, wind, and solar energy. Government and donors can invest in electric power supply infrastructure, promote clean energy sources, and support increasing technical and institutional capacity in addition to technology transfer.

Food Security

Dryland ecosystems are spread over more than 30 percent of the world's land area. These ecosystems are vulnerable to overexploitation and degradation and are likely to make around a billion people, food insecure.[19] Poor farmers in the dryland areas of the developing world are the most vulnerable to food insecurity. Their vulnerability is compounded by the lack of access to productive agricultural land and lack of knowledge, infrastructure, access to financial services or money to use sustainable farming techniques. There are a number of factors characteristic of dryland regions that exacerbates food insecurity. These drivers of food insecurity include poor soils, water scarcity, low agriculture yields, population growth, poverty, malnutrition, and a gender gap in accessing critical resources and capital. Between March 2007 and March 2008, global food prices increased by an average of 43 percent. Increasing food prices caused protests in many countries, as both the poor and the working classes could no longer afford the food they needed, or were compelled to spend a majority of their earnings on food. The beginning of the year 2011, world food prices were only 3 percent below their 2008 peak. Other factors that affect productivity and threaten food security include the weather, disease and pests, farming methods, lack of investment, external markets, conflict, migration, and governance issues. In 2008, more than 60 food riots occurred worldwide in 30 different countries, 10 of which resulted in multiple deaths.[20] If desertification is not prevented and reversed, it may lead to malnutrition, starvation, and ultimately, famine. Sustainable land management is key to food security.

Gender

Pastoralism and agricultural activities are the mainstay of many rural communities in dryland regions. However, in many such communities, men and women experience differences in ownership of critical resources, such as land and access to important assets. For example, in a number of agricultural communities in the Sahel, men own the land and produce cash crops while prevailing gender norms dictates that women confine themselves to the production of subsistence foods, in small parcels of land allotted to them by the male members of their family. In Uganda, although 97 percent of women have access to land only 7 percent actually own land.[21] In many such patriarchal societies, women's access to resources is mediated by their relationships with men.

Female-headed households are comparatively at a greater disadvantage, which makes them more vulnerable to the environmental and economic crises caused by desertification. They suffer from the effects of male migration, since the men leave for the cities in search of jobs to support their families. This gender gap in accessing productive resources and credit also endangers food security.

HOW DO WE DEAL WITH DESERTIFICATION?

Combating desertification requires both management and policy approaches that are closely tied with sustainable resource use and the involvement of local communities. Rehabilitation of degraded land, as with many other environmental challenges, is difficult and costly. The cost of land restoration ranges from €33 to €227 [$50 to $345] per hectare.[22] So, promoting alternative livelihoods and sustainable long-term conservation strategies when desertification is in the initial stages is far less costly, and can help stop the damage in the long run. However, even in the worst scenarios of land degradation, the land can be rehabilitated and restored—but the success of land rehabilitation depends on the availability of funds, human resources, technology, and infrastructure. Some simple measures include planting trees, growing selected species of crops and other vegetation beneficial to the local environment, and capacity-building and awareness-raising at various levels. We will look at some of these measures now.

Land Management and Land Restoration

Land degradation is not permanent. Land can be restored with improved crop techniques, such as enriching it with organic matter, and selecting different crop varieties. Water has to be used judiciously, with the aim of maximizing production with minimum input. Modern drip irrigation is one such example where the best crops are raised using the least amount of water. Proper irrigation management and adequate drainage are crucial for the prevention of salinization. These techniques also help improvement of soils saturated with salts. Implementing proper irrigation involves removing any surplus water, monitoring the changes in groundwater level and soil salinity in the affected areas, draining, and irrigating. Planting trees also helps since roots will prevent the soil from leaching away. To replenish degraded soils, necessary steps to restore fertility should be taken. Intensive agriculture without adequate time for natural soil regeneration is one of the main reasons for soil degradation. Natural compost and fertilizers should be used to re-establish soil fertility. Rainwater harvesting, adopting newer drought resistant crop varieties, agro-forestry, and efficient energy are also critical for sustainable land management and minimizing drought risk.

Erosion control is crucial for restoring the productivity of damaged soil, thereby combating desertification. Some simple mechanical measures, such as fences made from local plant species, hedges, or barriers made from other materials, help counter the effects of wind on dry soil by acting as a barrier and preventing displacement of loose soil particles. Other measures include afforestation activities, planting vegetation that helps fix soil, discontinuing unsustainable irrigation techniques, and regulating grazing of livestock.

In order to address the challenge of overgrazing, local farmers and pastoralists have to be sensitized to the necessity of rotating pastures to allow them time to recover, and to reducing herd numbers. It can be challenge in certain communities where livestock numbers signify social status and wealth. A potential solution could be to diversify livelihoods and offer them new economic opportunities that are different from their traditional income-generating activities. This could help reduce pastoral pressure and the land degradation that results from it.

Afforestation

Afforestation has proven to be very effective in reversing desertification. Tree planting supports soil, as when a plant grows, it roots into the sandy dryland soil and helps circulate nutrients and moisture that replenishes the soil. Trees play several key roles: they fix soil and prevent erosion by water and wind; many plant species such as legumes enhance soil fertility by fixing nitrogen, recycling organic matter, and carbon sequestration; they can also act as a barrier to wind and sand blasts, and thereby protect young crops. For example, the young agroforestry parklands of southern Niger sequester 4 to 5 tons of carbon per hectare.[23] Vegetation also facilitates water penetration in the soil during rain, and contributes to maintaining humidity for long periods. Trees are extensively used for firewood, fodder and construction materials in dryland areas.

Diversity Livelihoods and Production

Desertification can be avoided by gradually decreasing the dependency on traditional income-generating activities typical to drylands. Greenhouse agriculture and tourism-related activities can provide alternative livelihoods, and thus help lessen the pressure on local land and natural resource use.

Another way to avoid desertification is to grow different varieties of crop and diversify animal production. Mixed farming and rotational crop production can sustain different plants and animals over long duration of time, since the nutritional needs of different species vary. Mixed farming is also insurance, especially during natural disasters or drought, because certain species are better adapted to counter drought than others. Stress on drylands ecosystems can also be reduced by creating economic opportunities in urban centers and areas outside drylands.

Alternative Green Energy

A large number of populations in dryland areas use wood as their major source of energy. This dependency on fuelwood and non-sustainable use of forest exacerbates desertification through deforestation, and also increases the greenhouse effect by releasing carbon dioxide. Identifying and using alternative renewable energy sources, such as solar and wind energy, are therefore important in preventing desertification.

Increase Population Resilience

According to the Millennium Ecosystem Assessment (2005), populations in drylands live under the worst economic conditions.[24] The impacts of desertification are mostly felt at the local level—by households, individuals, and communities. Drylands have the lowest gross domestic product per capita, and the highest infant mortality rates. Although land degradation and drought, affect both the rich and poor, the poor are hardest hit, because their ability to deal with, and recover from, these extreme events depends on their access to critical assets such as land, and their ability to mobilize resources. For example, when drought strikes, rich individuals, groups, or communities can invest their assets elsewhere to meet short-term needs, whereas that is not an option for the poor.

In order to reduce risk from desertification, populations living in drylands have to be made more resilient by increasing the availability of alternative livelihoods and non-farm jobs. Preventing land degradation is essential to strengthening population resilience, but it is not the only approach available. Sustainable land management, drought-risk management, and biodiversity conservation have to come to the forefront of the design, implementation, and monitoring of desertification prevention and adaptation action in the affected areas. Insurance schemes for smallholder agriculture can give farmers greater security. Ethiopia and Kenya are piloting such schemes, which offer them insurance against crop failure. Awareness generation, sharing knowledge and research about desertification and ways to prevent it are also crucial for making meaningful changes. Building resilience will also involve institutional strengthening at the local level, empowerment and capacity development, and focusing on vulnerable sections of the population, such as the poor and women.

Box 3.3 Combating Desertification

Re-greening in Niger

Biophysical variables, such as Normalized Difference Vegetation Index (NDVI) derived from satellite images, help in detecting and monitoring long-term land cover changes. Vegetation indices such as NDVI quantify photosynthetic activity. Researchers can often compare current NDVI data with available long-term averages to find out whether the vegetation productivity in a given region is typical, or whether the plant growth is significantly more or less productive. Lower-than-average NDVI values for a particular region could indicate drought or unusually cold temperatures.

In the late 1970s, farmers throughout Sahel, started planting trees in their fields. During the initial stages of the afforestation initiative, farmers began

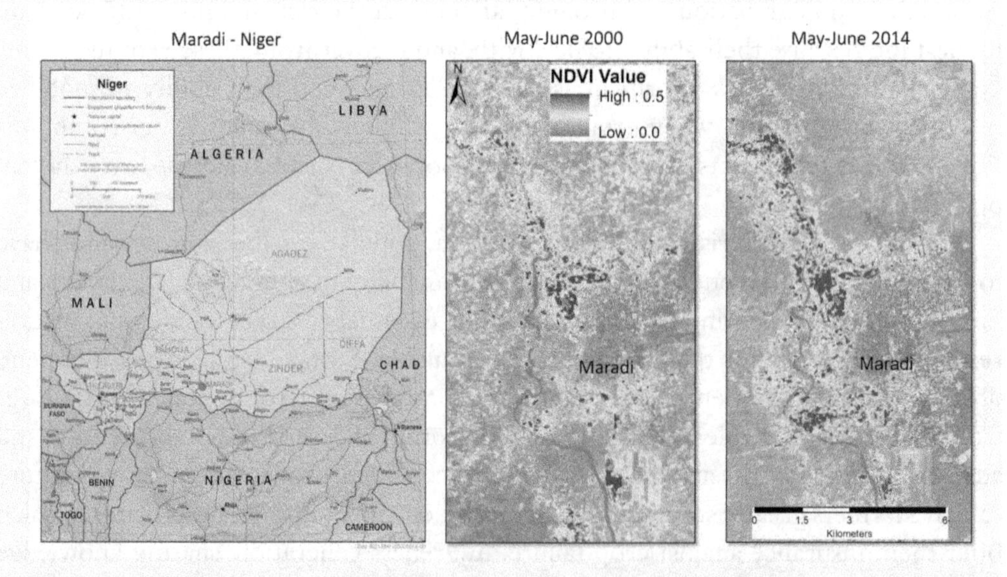

Figure 3.3. A comparison of the impact of afforestation and land restoration in Maradi, Niger. (left) Location of Maradi, Niger in Africa from CIA map library; (center) 32-day Normalized Difference Vegetation Index (NDVI) composite from Landsat 7 data, 2000; (right) 32-day NDVI composite from Landsat 8 data, 2014.

Source: Landsat

protecting the trees in their fields by encouraging and managing spontaneous natural regeneration. This technique is also known as farmer-managed natural regeneration (FMNR), and is especially applicable to dryland tropics. FMNR involves systematic regeneration and management of trees and shrubs from tree stumps, roots, and seeds. Trees are often integrated into crop land and grazing pastures, which helps land restoration and increases soil fertility. Over 5 million hectares of degraded land in the Sahel have been restored through FMNR. This has resulted in an additional half a million tons of grain production each year, and enough fodder to support many more livestock and has improved the food security of about 2.5 million people

The UNCCD states that in the Maradi region of Niger, one village reintroduced 35 different tree and shrub species that had disappeared in the 1970s. During the 2005 famine in the area, the reforested villages fared better because they could sell firewood and fodder. And when the rains in Niger arrived late and stopped early in the 2007 season, the farmers in the Maradi and Zinder regions with trees in their fields had a better harvest than those with fewer trees.

Source: (CGIAR, 2013).

Coordination and Global Partnership

Coordination and global partnership are required to deal with desertification. Addressing desertification is critical and essential for meeting the millennium development goals successfully.[25] Combating desertification results in multiple local and global benefits, and helps achieve the goals of other major environmental conventions on biodiversity loss and global climate change. Therefore, coordinated efforts and joint implementation of approaches to conserve biodiversity and mitigate climate change can lead to increased efficacy and positive long-term impacts benefiting people living in the drylands. Goals of these major conventions can be embedded within national strategies to reduce poverty, and in national action programs to combat desertification.

Box 3.4 The Drylands Development Centre

The Drylands Development Centre (DDC) is an international policy center, headquartered in Nairobi, Kenya, that is part of the United Nations Development Program (UNDP). Its overall focus is to promote sustainable and socially inclusive development in the world's dryland ecosystems. Specific functions of the DDC are as follows:

- global policy advocacy on drylands development
- research and policy analysis
- policy advice and technical assistance to drylands governments and populations
- facilitating partnerships with drylands communities
- building the knowledge base, sharing experiences, and facilitating learning on drylands development issues

The DDC began in 1973 and was initially called the United Nations Sudano–Sahelian Office (UNSO). Its initial focus was the African Sahel. The UNSO focus became global after the UN Convention to Combat Desertification (UNCCD) was adopted in 1994. The convention was the first legally binding agreement negotiated in direct response to Agenda 21—the action plan adopted at the 1992 Earth Summit (The UN Conference on Environment and Development). Thereafter, UNSO helped facilitate programs in many countries throughout the world in accordance with the UNCCD.

The UNDP established the Drylands Development Centre in 2002. It incorporated the UNSO and broadened its scope. The center launched the (Integrated Drylands Development Programme) IDDP that same year, which promotes dryland management policies in Africa, the Middle East, and Asia. The main goals of these policies are as follows:

- To integrate dryland development issues into national development policy

- To reduce vulnerability and increase resilience of drylands to environmental and economic obstacles
- To improve the general management of dryland ecosystem resources

Source: http://www.undp.org.

CONCLUSION

Desertification is caused by land degradation in drylands. Drivers of land degradation are both anthropogenic and climatic. The climatic factors include droughts and projected reduction in freshwater availability due to global warming. Desertification triggers soil infertility, poor water and air quality, and disturbs ecosystem integrity. It adversely effects human health, and overall social and economic well-being. The societal impacts of desertification are related to migration and economic refugees, leading to conflict and political instability. There is also a great degree of spatial and temporal variation in the magnitude and impacts of desertification.

Desertification can be avoided by the integration of land and water management. In order to be effective, these initiatives should include local communities in the implementation of sustainable land and water management policies. On the human side, desertification can also be avoided primarily by introducing alternative livelihoods that have less of an impact on dryland resources, and by creating economic opportunities in urban centers and areas outside drylands.

Desertification is linked with other social and environmental issues, such as food security, climate change, and loss of biodiversity. Therefore, approaches to combat desertification should be synergistically implemented with efforts to mitigate biodiversity loss and human-induced global climate change. While land degradation is detrimental to the growth and development of all countries, it is the world's rural poor that suffer most. Addressing desertification is key to reducing global poverty—the issue of land degradation cannot be resolved in isolation, and therefore requires concerted efforts and commitment from rich and poor nations alike. After all, it is not far-fetched to state that land degradation concerns energy, environment, poverty, resources, and geopolitical stability.

ENDNOTES

1. There are different definitions of drylands. The United Nations Environment Programme bases its definition on the aridity index—areas with an aridity index value of less than 0.65, meaning annual precipitation is less than about two-thirds of potential evapotranspiration.
2. Environmental Justice Foundation, *The Gathering Storm. Climate Change, Security and Conflict* (London: EJF, 2014), 8.
3. Areas, other than polar and sub-polar regions, in which the ratio of annual precipitation to potential evapotranspiration falls within the range from 0.05 to 0.65.
4. Monique M. Mainguet, Desertification in Environmental Geology, (Netherlands: Springer, 1999):125–29. Online ISBN 978-1-4020-4494-6
5. United Nations, *Agenda 21: Programme of Action from Rio* (New York: United Nations, 1993), Chapter 12.
6. Source: https://desertification.wordpress.com/2008/06/20/yemen-97-of-lands-suffer-desertification-google-yemen-times/
7. People who derive more than 50 percent of their income from livestock and livestock products (as distinct from agro pastoralists, who derive less than 50 percent of their incomes from livestock and livestock products, and most of the remaining income from cultivation).
8. Food and Agriculture Organization, 2002, Source: http://www.fao.org/worldfoodsummit/english/newsroom/focus/focus1.htm
9. UNEP-WCMC, *Carbon in Drylands: Desertification, Climate Change and Carbon Finance*, 2008:5 Source: http://www.unep.org/pdf/carbon-drylands-technical-note.pdf
10. United Nations Convention to Combat Desertification (UNCCD). Source: http://www.unccd.int/en/programmes/Thematic-Priorities/Food-Sec/Pages/Internal-factors.aspx
11. The Water Resources Group, Background, Impact and the Way Forward, Briefing report prepared for the World Economic Forum Annual Meeting 2012 in Davos-Klosters, Switzerland:1–87 Source: http://www3.weforum.org/docs/WEF/WRG_Background_Impact_and_Way_Forward.pdf
12. Ian Neal, *10 Reasons to Harvest Water from Road Crossings Across Seasonal Rivers* (http://www.rain4food.net/10-reasons-to-harvest-water-from-road-crossings-across-seasonal-rivers/).
13. Ceris Jones, et al., "Conservation Agriculture in Europe: An Approach to Sustainable Crop Production by Protecting Soil and Water?" (SOWAP, 2006):1–56 Url: http://ec.europa.eu/environment/life/project/Projects/index.cfm?fuseaction=home.showFile&rep=file&fil=SOWAP_ConservationBooklet.pdf
14. Global Humanitarian Forum, *Human Impact Report—Climate Change* (Geneva: Global Humanitarian Forum, 2009), Source: http://www.ghf-ge.org/human-impact-report.pdf.

15. Desertification: Experts Prescribe Global Policy Overhaul to Avoid Looming Mass Migrations, United Nations University, 2007 Source: http://archive.unu.edu/media/archives/2007/files/mre29-A-07.pdf
16. Food and Agriculture Organization, *State of the World's Forests* (Rome: Food and Agriculture Organization, 2012), 9–27.
17. Millennium Ecosystem Assessment report Ecosystems and Human Well-Being: Desertification Synthesis. Source: http://www.millenniumassessment.org/documents/document.355.aspx.pdf
18. Desertification: a visual synthesis, Source: http://www.unccd.int/Lists/SiteDocumentLibrary/Publications/Desertification-EN.pdf
19. FAO. 2011. The state of the world's land and water resources for food and agriculture (SOLAW)—Managing systems at risk. Food and Agriculture Organization of the United Nations, Rome and Earthscan, London. Source: http://www.fao.org/docrep/017/i1688e/i1688e.pdf
20. Lagi Marco, Karla Z. Bertrand, and Yaneer Bar-Yam, *The Food Crises and Political Instability in North Africa and the Middle East*, 4, 2011 Source: http://necsi.edu/research/social/foodcrises.html.
21. Mukasa, C., Tibazalika, A., Mango, A. and Muloki, H.N. 2012 Gender and forestry in Uganda: Policy, legal and institutional frameworks. Working Paper 89. CIFOR, Bogor, Indonesia: 1–54. Source: http://www.cifor.org/publications/pdf_files/WPapers/WP89CIFOR.pdf.
22. World Resources Institute, *A World of Opportunity* (http://www.wri.org/sites/default/files/world_of_opportunity_brochure_2011-09.pdf, 2011), 1.
23. United Nations Convention to Combat Desertification, Source: http://www.unccd.int/en/programmes/Thematic-Priorities/Food-Sec/Pages/FS-SLM.aspx
24. Millennium Ecosystem Assessment report Ecosystems and Human Well-Being: Desertification Synthesis. Source: http://www.millenniumassessment.org/documents/document.355.aspx.pdf
25. The eight millennium development goals are: 1. eradicate extreme poverty and hunger; 2. achieve universal primary education; 3. promote gender equality and empower women; 4. reduce child mortality; 5. improve maternal health; 6. combat HIV/AIDS, malaria, and other disease; 7. ensure environmental sustainability; 8. develop a global partnership for development. Source: http://www.un.org/millenniumgoals/.

RECOMMENDED READINGS/SOURCES

Arnalds, Ólafur, and Steve Archer. 2002. *Rangeland Desertification*. New York: Springer.

CGIAR Research Program on Climate Change, Agriculture and Food Security (CCAFS) and the Technical Centre for Agricultural and Rural Cooperation (CTA). 2013. *Climate-Smart Agriculture. Success Stories from Farming Communities Around the World*. Wageningen, the Netherlands: CTA Publishing.

Griffith, Brian. 2001. *The Gardens of Their Dreams: Desertification and Culture in World History*. London: Zed.

Imeson, Anton. 2011. *Desertification, Land Degradation and Sustainability*. Hoboken, NJ: Wiley-Blackwell.

Low, Pak Sum, ed. 2013. "Economic and Social Impacts of Desertification, Land Degradation and Drought." White Paper I. UNCCD 2nd Scientific Conference, Bonn Germany, prepared with the contributions of an international group of scientists.

Mainguet, Monique. 2012. *Desertification: Natural Background and Human Mismanagement*. New York: Springer.

Millennium Ecosystem Assessment. 2005. *Ecosystems and Human Well-Being: Desertification Synthesis*. Washington, DC: World Resources Institute.

Overseas Development Institute. 2012. *The 2011/2012 European Report on Development, Confronting Scarcity: Managing Water, Energy and Land for Inclusive and Sustainable Growth*. London: Overseas Development Institute, European Centre for Development Policy Management, German Development Institute/Deutsches Institut für Entwicklungspolitik.

Reynolds, James F., D. Mark Stafford Smith, Eric F. Lambin, B. L. Turner II, Michael Mortimore, Simon P. J. Batterbury, Thomas E. Downing, Hadi Dowlatabadi, Roberto J. Fernández, Jeffrey E. Herrick, Elisabeth Huber-Sannwald, Hong Jiang, Rik Leemans, Tim Lynam, Fernando T. Maestre, Miguel Ayarza, and Brian Walker. 2007. "Global Desertification: Building a Science for Dryland Development." *Science* 316 (5826): 847–51.

Schlesinger, William H., James F. Reynolds, Gary L. Cunningham, Laura F. Huenneke, Wesley M. Jarrell, Ross A. Virginia, and Walter G. Whitford. 1990. "Biological Feedbacks in Global Desertification." *Science* 247 (4946): 1043–48.

Secretariat of the Convention on Biological Diversity, Global Mechanism of the United Nations Convention to Combat Desertification and OSLO Consortium. 2013. *Valuing the Biodiversity of Dry and Sub-Humid Lands. Technical Series No. 71*. Montreal, Quebec, Canada: Secretariat of the Convention on Biological Diversity.

World Resources Institute, the United Nations Development Programme, United Nations Environment Programme, and World Bank. 2008. SIM International Project Staff "Turning Back the Desert: How Farmers Have Transformed Niger's Landscapes and Livelihoods." In *World Resources 2008: Roots of Resilience—Growing the Wealth of the Poor*. Washington DC: World Resources Institute.

World Bank Food Price Watch. February 2011. http://www.worldbank.org/foodcrisis/food_price_watch_report_feb2011.html.

Marine Fisheries Depletion

by **WILF SWARTZ** and **LAURENNE SCHILLER**

CHAPTER FOUR

EXPANSION BEYOND IMAGINATION

Are fisheries exhaustible? In the inaugural address to the International Fisheries Exhibition in 1883, famed English naturalist Thomas Huxley posed this question. Suggesting that, due to the immense size of many marine fish populations, total mortality for these fish could not be impacted by the contribution of fishing, Huxley concluded:

> I believe, then, that the cod fishery, the herring fishery, the pilchard fishery, the mackerel fishery, and probably all the great sea fisheries, are inexhaustible; that is to say, that nothing we do seriously affects the number of the fish.

Just over a century later—on July 2, 1992—the Canadian government announced a moratorium that closed the commercial fishery for the northern stock of Atlantic cod. The fishery operated on one of the richest fish stocks in the world, which boasted catches of over 800,000 metric tons in the early 1960s, but had been diminished to 1 percent of its previous level. Twenty years on, it is evident that this collapse was far more severe than initially believed; both the Grand Banks ecosystem and the society depending on it have been dramatically transformed by the loss of these fish.[1]

To his credit, Huxley did condition his aforementioned conclusion on "in relation to our present modes of fishing." Perhaps, if fishing methods and technologies had remained static, his prediction would not have been far from the truth. However, in terms of both scale and efficiency of operation, fisheries are significantly different today than they were in Huxley's time.

A critical factor in the development of the world's fisheries has been the rapid pace of technological advancement. Vessel and gear enhancements have enabled fishermen to fish not only with more precision and efficiency, but to fish farther from shore. One of the fastest times of technological acceleration occurred after World War II, when many wartime innovations became available: diesel engines, acoustic fish finders, radar, synthetic netting, and improved refrigeration were all readily available to large commercial fisheries.[2] These enhancements quickly turned fishing into a more industrial and intensive practice, with vessels over 100 meters long operating at sea for months at a time, and factory ships capable of processing (i.e., filleting, canning, freezing) much of the catch before even returning to port.

Today, fishing vessels continue to spend long stretches at sea and incorporate new technologies, such as precise satellite navigation and positioning. Fishing is now truly a global operation, with fleets operating far from shore and capturing fish in all the world's oceans, including areas that were previously impossible to fish. Huxley never supposed that remote places, such as the sea floor, the high seas, and Antarctica (which in his time were essentially natural reserves for exploited species to reproduce and live without interference) would one day be exploited with the same intensity as many coastal regions. And, as many near-shore fisheries are catching fewer and smaller fish, the last remaining frontiers in the world's oceans continue to be exposed to unprecedented and unrelenting levels of exploitation.[3]

FISHERIES 101: ECOLOGY OF FISHING

Since fish are living resources, all fish stocks are renewable. That is, they have the capacity to replenish their population size naturally, or push back against fishing pressure (unlike minerals extracted through mining). In theory, all fish stocks can be exploited (within limits) on a continuing basis without being permanently depleted.

When a previously unexploited population is first fished, the population size is reduced below the carrying capacity of its habitat.[4] This initial reduction in the size of the fish population eases some of the internal competition for resources and, as such, increases the overall survival of the remaining population, allowing for greater survival of the new generation of fish. While some of this new production must be allowed to survive and reproduce to maintain the population (i.e., recruitment into the stock of juveniles surviving to adulthood), the remaining fish—or surplus production—is

Box 4.1 Climate Change Impact on Global Fisheries

Climate change affects ocean properties. The heat content of the ocean (and its temperature) have been increasing over the past century, causing shifts in physical features of the world's oceans—from circulation patterns (i.e., strengthening the stratification between warm surface layers and cooler deep-sea waters) to reducing sea-ice coverage in the polar regions. Increased ocean temperature is also changing ocean chemistry, with evidence indicating an expansion of oxygen minimum zones and rising ocean acidity. These changes all affect marine fishes and fisheries.

For most marine fishes, their physiological performance (e.g., respiration, osmoregulation) is strongly dependent on temperature and oxygen content. As such, the distribution of a given species is constrained within a certain geographical range of water temperatures.[1] Consequently, as the oceans warm up, these fish have to shift their distribution in order to maintain themselves in habitats with their preferred temperature. We see this in the seasonal migration patterns of some species that track the temperature gradient along the coast, or move to deeper waters during the summer seasons. A recent series of studies has found that, as a result of ocean warming, many fish species are shifting their distribution, mainly to higher latitudes and deeper waters.[2] Naturally, these shifts are apparent in the compositions of the global fisheries catch (i.e., warmer-water species increasingly becoming prominent in temperate waters).[3] Moreover, it is expected that these shifts will continue, leading to strong species turnover,[4] redistribution of catch potential,[5] and decreases in the maximum body size of fish.[6] Specifically, tropical regions are predicted to see high rates of local extinction and decreases in catch potential. Given that many coastal communities in the tropics are highly dependent on fishery resources for food and livelihood, these regions are likely to be those that are most vulnerable to the impacts of climate change. Unfortunately, these places are often marginalized and lack the economic capacity to adapt. How to mitigate the negative impacts of climate change to the fisheries in these regions, and improve their adaptive capacity, will

Continued...

be important global questions that must be addressed, not only in the context of the climate change agenda, but in the context of global food security and human rights.

Endnotes

1. Daniel Pauly, *Gasping Fish and Panting Squids: Oxygen, Temperature and the Growth of Water-Breathing Animals*, vol. 22 (Oldendorf/Luhe, Germany: International Ecology Institute, 2010).
2. William W. L. Cheung, Vicky W. Y. Lam, Jorge L. Sarmiento, Kelly Kearney, Reg Watson, Dirk Zeller, and Daniel Pauly, "Large-Scale Redistribution of Maximum Fisheries Catch Potential in the Global Ocean Under Climate Change," *Global Change Biology* 16, no. 1 (2009): 24–35. doi:10.1111/j.1365–2486.2009.01995.x.
3. William W. L. Cheung, Reg Watson, and Daniel Pauly, "Signature of Ocean Warming in Global Fisheries Catch," *Nature* 497, no. 7449 (2013): 365–68. doi:10.1038/nature12156.
4. William W. L. Cheung, Vicky W. Y. Lam, Jorge L. Sarmiento, Kelly Kearney, Reg Watson, and Daniel Pauly, "Projecting Global Marine Biodiversity Impacts Under Climate Change Scenarios," *Fish and Fisheries* 10, no. 3 (2009): 235–51. doi:10.1111/j.1467–2979.2008.00315.x.
5. William W.L. Cheung, Vicky W.Y. Lam, Jorge L. Sarmiento, Kelly Kearney, Reg Watson, Dirk Zeller and Daniel Pauly, "Large-Scale Redistribution of Maximum Fisheries Catch Potential in the Global Ocean Under Climate Change." *Global Change Biology* 16 (2010): 24–35.
6. William W.L. Cheung, Reg Watson, and Daniel Pauly, "Signature of Ocean Warming in Global Fisheries Catch." *Nature* 497, no. 7449 (2013): 365–368.

available to be captured by the fishery. When a fishery is catching within this surplus of fish, the population can sufficiently replenish itself and the catch can be maintained indefinitely (so long as the environmental conditions also remain constant).[5] Under these conditions, the fishery is operating in a sustainable manner.

Thus, overfishing occurs when the amount of fish extracted from a population exceeds its surplus production. In most cases, overfishing is a consequence of; 1. the adult spawning population becoming so small that it only produces a limited number of recruits; 2. the depletion of larger individuals, which forces the fishery to target smaller, younger individuals (often before they have had the chance to spawn); and 3. degradation of fish habitat through the use of destructive gears (e.g., bottom trawls), which damage nursery grounds and thus the carrying capacity of the habitat.[6] At its onset, fishing on a previously unexploited stock can yield exceptionally high catch as the fishery "mines out" the standing stock that has accumulated over time and, subsequently, the stock's productivity increases with reduced population density. (This was the case in the northern cod fisheries during the 1960s.) However, the tipping point between fishing at the maximum sustainable yield (i.e., where density-dependent stock productivity is highest) and overfishing can be very acute. As has been seen repeatedly over the last fifty years, the negative consequences of overshooting this point and not responding with an immediate reduction in fishing effort can be severe and long-term. As such, management of fisheries, based on reliable estimates of population size and status, and the application of the precautionary principle when determining the target population size, are critical.

It has been said that counting fish is akin counting trees, except you can't see them, and they move. As such, reliable estimates of population status and size are hard to come by. And, in the absence of robust scientific surveys (which usually come with hefty price tags), the assessment of fisheries and fish stocks must rely on information derived from the fisheries themselves. The problem is that there are multiple possible explanations for certain observed trends. For example, if the catch from a given stock is declining, this may be because we are fishing less (i.e., spending less time fishing or deploying fewer boats on the water), or because there are fewer fish available (i.e., the underlying fish population has been depleted). While, in general, the more abundant fish are, the less effort is needed to catch them, and, as such, measuring catch per unit of effort exerted can be used to infer the state of fish populations, over-reliance on such statistics alone can have catastrophic consequences.[7]

In the case of the collapse of the northern cod off Newfoundland, the misinterpretation of the fisheries-related statistics, particularly on the catch-per-unit-effort is often cited as the key contributor.[8] The assessment of the cod fisheries at the time failed to understand the complex behavioral patterns of both fish and fishermen. It is now believed that when the cod stock was undergoing depletion, these fish reduced their distribution range, thus maintaining their relative stock density, while fishermen were skilled in modifying their fleet distribution in order to locate these pockets of high fish density. Consequently, the trend observed in the catch and effort statistics was that of a stable fishery, rather than one approaching collapse. In general, assessment errors such as the one in the northern cod fisheries can contribute to overfishing through optimistic forecasting, build-up of overcapacity, and delays in management response.[9]

Of course, no fish is an island. Animals prey on one another in order to obtain the energy necessary for growth, survival, movement, and reproduction. Large fish such as tunas and sharks prey upon small fish like mackerel, which eat even smaller fish such as herrings and anchovies. These smaller fish, in turn, feed on plankton—a variety of microscopic animals (zooplankton) and plants (phytoplankton). Phytoplankton obtain energy from sunlight to produce more phytoplankton, which is similar to how plants proliferate in terrestrial systems. Thus, ocean ecosystems are composed of various communities of fish and other organisms that are interconnected through complex marine food webs. Consequently, when fishermen capture fish from the oceans, they slightly alter not only the population of the fish that they target, but the entire marine ecosystem within which that species survives. When too many fish are extracted, there can be dramatic changes to the composition and dynamics of the surrounding ecosystem.

One way in which a fishery's impact on the ecosystem manifests itself is through a phenomenon described as "fishing down the marine food web."[10] When the complex web of trophic (i.e., predator–prey) interactions in a marine ecosystem are gradually eroded away, as fisheries exploit and deplete large, highly profitable species at the top of the food chain, species lower in the chain are released from the pressures of predation. When stocks of large species become so depleted that it is no longer economical to fish them, fisheries begin to target these smaller species, subsequently depleting them as well (Figure 4.1). This transition has been documented in fishery catches

Figure 4.1. Fishing down the marine food web (from Pauly et al. 1998). Copyright © Hans Hillewaert (CC BY-SA 4.0) at https://commons.wikimedia.org/wiki/File:Fishing_down_the_food_web.jpg.

from many parts of the world,[11] and has been found to be more extensive than had been previously thought—particularly when the geographical expansion of fishing fleets is taken into account.[12]

THE NUMBERS: GLOBAL TRENDS

Global marine fisheries production has grown considerably in the last 60 years, with the official landings increasing from less than 20 million tons in the 1950s, to over 80 million tons.[13] Nevertheless, the global trend in the past decade or so has been generally stable, with slight decreases. The marine fisheries production is highly concentrated to small groups of coastal countries, with 18 nations accounting for more than 75 percent of global catch. Asian countries make up 11 of these 18 countries, and their share in the global production is likely to continue to grow with human population increases.

In total, the ten most productive fish stocks account for about 24 percent of world's marine catch. These stocks are either fully fished and, therefore, have no potential for further increase in production, or overfished, and require substantial investment into rebuilding of the stock. In fact, nearly 30 percent of the world's fish stocks are deemed overfished, while 60 percent are fully exploited.[14] Meanwhile, the proportion of underutilized stocks has declined from 40 percent in the 1970s, to less than 10 percent in 2011. Thus, the current mode of fishing has been described as a "sequential" overexploitation that maintains the high level of the production (i.e., catch) through geographical expansion[15] and the introduction of species previously thought to be unmarketable, some via renaming (e.g., Patagonian toothfish *Dissostichus eleginoides* as Chilean sea bass), others via mislabeling.[16]

Apart from reported, landed catch, there is generally a proportion of fish in each haul that is discarded. These fish are often juveniles of the targeted species, or non-targeted species that live in the same habitat and were caught as a result of the unselective nature of the fishing gear used. These fish generally have little or no market value and are thrown overboard. The volume of discards is rarely adequately captured in catch statistics.[17] Moreover, official statistics tend to be biased toward large, commercial fisheries, and often fail to adequately capture the amount of fish caught in subsistence and recreational fishing sectors. Illegal fishing is also an increasingly common component of the total catch of some species (namely tuna), with estimates ranging between 11 and 26 million tons.[18] However, independent of whether a fish is caught and kept, or thrown back to sea, and if the operation was legal or not, the fish is still dead, and this information needs to be considered when assessing the health and fishing potential of a population.[19] As mentioned earlier, stock assessments are heavily reliant on fisheries-related statistics. When a certain amount is excluded, there can be large errors in the outputs of these assessments (which can lead to over estimating a stock's productivity or abundance, and thus lead to over fishing).

While the global catch (both reported and unreported) appears have peaked in the 1990s, fishing effort (measured in vessel number, fleet capacity, fishing days, et cetera) continues to intensify. Of the estimated 3.2 million vessels considered to be operating in marine waters, about 30 percent still lack an engine. The degree of motorization in marine fishing fleets varies greatly across regions: non-motorized vessels account for less than 5 percent in Europe, but over 60 percent in Africa.[20] While there is no standardized definition for "industrial" fishing vessels, it is estimated that about 2 percent of the world's motorized fishing vessels belongs to the vessel class of 24 meters and larger (or 100 gross registered tonnage). The average nominal fishing effort is estimated to have increased by over 50 percent from the 1950s to 2010,[21] and when corrected for increases in efficiency (i.e., technological advances), the intensity of fishing effort is believed to have grown ten-fold during this period. It is predicted that the global fishing capacity will continue to grow, though any additional increases in fishing effort are not likely to yield higher catches. Rather, they will lead to continued decline in catch-per-unit-effort.

In terms of economics, the reported catch of global fisheries is estimated to be worth around US$80 billion annually.[22] Overall, approximately 260 million people around the world are engaged in fishing, processing, and product distribution, which is equivalent to 203 million full-time employees in this sector. Of these, about 10 percent would be considered small-scale fishermen.[23] The total economic contribution of marine fisheries, when considering their impact on secondary economic activities from boat building and retailing, is estimated to be about three times the value of the landings at first sale—between US$225 and $235 billion per year.[24]

FIXING THE ECONOMICS OF FISHERIES

As is evident from the preceding section, the current state of marine fisheries can be summarized as "too many boats chasing too few fish"—in other words, overfishing of marine fish populations and overcapacity of the world's fishing fleets. It has been suggested that overfishing that has occurred in the past century has diminished the production potential in many of the world's important fish stocks, therein contributing to substantial loss of potential revenues today.[25] As such, a substantial rebuilding of global fish stocks through reduction in fishing capacity is required.[26] Yet current fishing trends all point to the continuation and intensification of the global fisheries crisis. As is often the case, the root cause of this pattern appears to be economics, more specifically the presence of "perverse incentives" to overexploit under the current structure of marine fisheries.[27]

When taking into account the economic dynamics of fisheries, it is important to keep in mind two unique differences between fisheries and other types of food production systems, such as agriculture. First, fishing involves the exploitation of a wild resource (stock), unlike farming, where the output is directly linked to input investment and maintenance. The famous expression "you reap what you sow" holds true to farms much more so than fisheries. As such, ownership of marine resources is less defined, and thus has always suffered from the classic issues presented in Hardin's "tragedy of the commons."[28] In the absence of appropriate management measures and enforcement, the optimal strategy for an individual, rational, fisherman is to fish now with little consideration for long-term stock status or the sustainability of the fishing industry as a whole. Second, fisheries operate under what economists refer as a "backward-bending" supply curve. In general, industrial outputs increase with increased inputs—the more factories you have, the more products you'll generate. However, in fisheries, because production is derived from natural productivity of the fish stock, increasing input (i.e., number of boats) does not necessarily result in more catch being landed. In fact, more effort often leads to rapid depletion of the production base (fish) and reduction in the total output (catch). Thus policies such as subsidies that encourage greater effort may in reality be harmful to both the ecosystem and the industry.

Are Rights-Based Fisheries the Solution?

A recent approach used to address the open access nature of marine fisheries, and to mitigate the tragedy of the common outcomes, is rights-based fisheries. In this system, each fisherman (or vessel) is allocated an annual catch quota, or "fishing right," as permitted by the management body. These rights to catch—when effectively enforced—eliminate the "race to fish," since a fisherman's final catch is determined by their share of the quota, not by the intensity of their fishing effort. Under such programs, other positive outcomes include extended fishing season, higher quality of catch, reduction in production glut (and lower price), and improvements to fishing safety, as fishermen can choose to avoid operating under unfavorable weather conditions, with their share of catch guaranteed. Lastly, long-term ownership of this share of the total catch will provide incentives for fishermen to act with the long-term status of the stock in mind, leading to greater engagement and compliance with management policies.[29]

Many proponents of such rights-based fisheries further argue that by enabling owners of fishing rights to trade their share of the total catch, the fishery can utilize the market to distribute these rights to those who are most efficient at capturing fish, and allow the stock to be exploited in an economically optimal manner.[30] Moreover, these supporters suppose that for fisheries suffering from overcapacity, the rights-based approach will effectively reduce the capacity to the optimal level by driving many fishermen to sell their quota and exit the fishery.[31] In fact, rights-based management is becoming increasingly prevalent around the world, with approximately 250 fisheries (~10% of the global marine catch) currently managed under this system.[32] These numbers are likely to increase in the near future, as both the European Union and Japan are discussing the effectiveness of Individual Transferable Quota (ITQ) systems for their marine resources.[33]

Yet rights-based management also presents a number of difficulties. As already noted, the effectiveness of these programs depends on strict monitoring and enforcement. Quota-based systems are also susceptible to the practice of high-grading, where small-sized fish are discarded in order to fill one's quota with high-value fish. Thus, strict discarding regulations must be in place for fisheries managed under this system. Another important and often neglected aspect of the rights-based system is that of social equity. Under the tradable fishing-rights systems, any increase in the value of the fishing quotas due to improvements in the fishery, be it from effective management or simply the result of favorable environmental conditions (i.e., pure luck), is captured by the quota holders. In principle, however, such value (or economic rent, to use more technical term) should be returned to the rightful owners of the resource (i.e., society). Many objections are raised, since some people view this as an inappropriate give away of public resources to a few private owners.[34] Concentration of quota ownership (particularly when quotas are bought up by non-active fishermen), and the subsequent leasing of fishing quotas that transfer profits from fishermen to speculative investors, are other examples of the social issues surrounding rights-based fisheries.

Getting Subsidies Right

In fisheries, subsidies are provided for reasons such as stimulating industry development (with food security considerations), supporting regional and rural communities (in some cases, with national defense or strategic motivations), and improving the economic conditions of fishers up to an acceptable minimum. Globally, it is estimated that fisheries subsidies are worth US$25–30 billion annually,[35] or equivalent to one-third of the landed value of the world's capture fisheries catch (US$100 billion annually).[36]

Yet, the negative effect of fishing subsidies can readily be predicted. Since subsidies lower the cost of fishing, or increase revenues, such programs will lead to higher effort levels and greater depletion of fish stocks. Even if the effort is regulated and depletion prevented, subsidized fisheries will likely result in the expansion of fishing capacity (in terms of engine size and adaptation of new technologies) and shortening of fishing season, all of which can be considered economic waste.[37] In fact, the negative effects of fisheries subsidies have been recognized by the international communities. The World Trade Organization, which has rules in place to mitigate the market-distorting effects of subsidies among its members, has been actively engaged in the negotiation for improvements in its subsidies rules in order to address the production-distorting effects (i.e., reduction in stock productivity resulting from overexploitation by subsidized fishing fleets) of fishing subsidies. Yet, the diversity of domestic political considerations involved with subsidy programs has so far prevented any major breakthroughs, and the negotiation continues ten years on.[38]

To substantiate his belief in the indefinite availability of the world's fish stocks, Huxley further suggested that "any tendency to over-fishing will meet with its natural check in the diminution of the supply ... long before anything like permanent exhaustion has occurred." In other words, that commercial extinction of fisheries will prevent the biological extinction of the exploited fish stock. Once again, he could not have predicted the scale to which the current global fishing industry is subsidized.

FISHING IN THE GLOBAL WORLD

Seafood is one of the most highly traded food commodities in the world.[39] In today's world, it is virtually impossible for an industry to operate in complete isolation from the global economy. As noted above, global marine fisheries operate across all oceans, including deep-sea regions and the vast high seas, that constitute waters beyond the sovereign waters of every coastal country and island (i.e., the 200–nautical mile exclusive economic zone [EEZ]). Markets for fisheries products are also undergoing expansion, with the growing middle-class in developing countries (particularly in

Asia) and their appetite for high-valued seafood. The emerging demand for fishmeal and oils for the aquaculture sector is poised to enable another major destination for marine fish as well.

Fishing in Multinational Waters

Unlike (most) humans, fish do not respect international boundaries and borders. In particular, highly migratory species such as tuna, sharks, and billfishes (i.e., swordfish, sailfish) spend different parts of their lives in both national (EEZs) and international (the high seas) waters. As can be imagined, their dynamic travels make these species nearly impossible to manage on a domestic basis. Thus, international management bodies called regional fisheries management organizations (RFMOs) are responsible for the supervision and regulation of the fisheries that catch these highly migratory species. Similar to domestic management groups, RFMOs are responsible for setting and allocating catch quotas, conducting regular stock assessments, and monitoring and enforcing the actions of their member fishing countries. However, managing fleets on the high seas is significantly more challenging than it is in coastal waters.

Many countries that fish for tuna travel thousands of kilometers and spend months at sea, sometimes with only limited observer coverage. Since these vessels need to maximize the value of their catch, distant water tuna fleets often have high discard rates, since they keep only the biggest fish and most valuable species (i.e., there is lots of high grading at sea). Little quota enforcement is available, since much of the catch is landed back at the home country's ports and—since the high seas is technically international waters—there are no legal requirements for fishing within this part of the ocean. As such, RFMOs are largely criticized for lacking teeth and being unable to enforce quotas and penalize fleets that fail to abide by rules and regulations.[40] In addition, human rights issues—including slavery and illegal immigration—are among the many concerns facing the tuna fleets of the high seas.

Within an EEZ, fishing activity is managed domestically; generally, only fishermen from a given country are permitted to access the resources within its EEZ. If a foreign country wishes to fish within another country's EEZ, the two countries must establish an access agreement, which details the activities permitted (i.e., which species can be caught and what gears can be used), the location of such activities, and any monetary compensation provided by the foreign country for this access. Host countries are generally coastal developing countries, many of which have local populations that are heavily dependent on artisanal and small-scale commercial fishing activities for both food and livelihood. Conversely, foreign fishing fleets are generally from wealthier, more powerful developed countries (many of which have depleted their own coastal stocks and are seeking new regions in which to fish). Worldwide studies of fishing agreements have found that the fees received by host countries are low compared to the value of what is extracted by the foreign fishing fleets.[41] As such, these access arrangements have been widely criticized and some of the recent arrangements have begun to explicitly address these concerns (see Box 4.2).

International Trade of Seafood and its Implications on Marine Resources

Several factors have contributed to the growth of the seafood trade since the 1960s. In particular, improved storage and preservation technology, and low costs of international transportation over the past 50 years have greatly expanded the capacity of the global seafood trade network. Additionally, despite outputs from capture fisheries leveling off (and even declining in some regions), the expansion of aquaculture has endowed an even greater supply of seafood to land in markets around the world. The adoption of 200-mile exclusive economic zones (EEZ) also gave strong incentives for trade, as countries with distant water fleets (e.g., Japan) were excluded from the coastal waters of other nations. This resulted in increased reliance on imports to meet domestic demand.[42]

Broadly speaking, increased trade is beneficial for exporters, who can access foreign markets that provide a higher price for their product. At the same time, it is also beneficial for consumers (and processors) in the importing country, as imports allow for a larger and more stable supply of seafood at more competitive prices. For local consumers in exporting regions, increased exports often lead to higher prices, which in some cases may present a food security challenge. Increased imports can also be negative for domestic fishermen in the importer's market, since imports tend to put downward pressure on demand, and thus the price of their product. With trade, prices become insensitive to local overexploitation of the resource, encouraging further intense exploitation in the absence of sufficient regulations and management.[43]

A high level of trade in seafood products suggests that trade policy as a means of promoting marine conservation can have significant economic implications. The proposal to list Atlantic bluefin tuna (*Thunnus thynnus*) under the Convention of International Trade in Endangered Species of Wild Fauna and Flora (CITES) in 2010 highlighted the possibility of applying trade-based measures to seafood products.[44] At the same time, concerns over food safety and traceability in the seafood trade are on

Box 4.2 Artisanal Fishing in the Global World

Some of the fishing techniques still employed today are thousands of years old. While there are many different suggestions as to what constitutes "artisanal" fishing, typically this type of fishing involves the use of traditional gears that catch small quantities of fish at once (e.g., handlines, traps, cast nets, spears). Artisanal fishing lacks substantial technological assistance, and a fisherman's success is largely based on his or her own skill and traditional knowledge of the proper technique to target a specific fish.

What artisanal fishermen lack in technology they make up for in sheer quantity. The world today is home to about 12 million artisanal fishermen (the majority of whom are found in developing coastal countries). Artisanal fisheries are so pervasive that they catch roughly the same amount of fish as the industrial commercial fleets (~30 million tons annually). However, unlike many industrial fishing methods, artisanal gears are highly selective, and discarding unwanted catch is rare. In addition, artisanal fisheries are often a family affair, with both men and women having equal involvement in harvesting and processing the catch.

In addition to concerns about food security from the ever-rising global human population, and the environmental impacts of climate change, many artisanal fisheries are under increasing stress from industrial fishing practices. Particularly in the Pacific Island countries and territories (PICTs), where industrial distant-water vessels fish extensively for tuna, artisanal fisheries are suffering the effects of depleted stocks and irresponsible industrial fishing methods. Since 1990, the catch within the Exclusive Economic Zones of the PICTs has increased by 150 percent, and the bycatch of industrial longline and purse seine vessels includes species of commercial importance to the local artisanal fisheries (e.g., mahi mahi, wahoo, rainbow runner).[1] Although distant-water fleets pay for access to these waters, the amount of money put back into the local island economy is a fraction (~5%) of the value of the catch (US$3 billion in 2011) taken by these fleets.

Endnote

1. Secretariat of the Pacific Community, *Balancing the Needs. Industrial Versus Artisanal Tuna Fisheries*, Policy Brief, June 30 (Noumea, New Caledonia, 2013).

the rise—particularly in the wake of recent scandals over the mislabeling of some fish products.[45] Exporters are therefore increasingly required to meet various standards, such as Hazard Analysis and Critical Control Point (HACCP), ISO certifications, or other national standards set by importing countries. These regulations can act as additional barriers to trade, and countries are often accused of implementing high safety and traceability standards as disguised measures for protectionism.[46] Given that the competition for seafood in the international market is expected to intensify in the future, it is likely that disputes over trade regulations will also continue to proliferate.

CONCLUSION

Fish are the last remaining source of wild protein that is consumed globally, and fishing is the last form of large-scale commercial hunting that exists in the world today. However, as this chapter has demonstrated, the pursuit of productivity is not necessarily desirable for long-term sustainability; rapid technological developments have allowed fisheries to become too efficient, and many fish stocks are suffering. In addition, since we are dealing with dynamic natural ecosystems, management and policy measures have complex foundations and often result in unintended impacts and consequences. Thus, while the precautionary principle should be applied when exploiting a natural system, it even more critical for the long-term productivity and sustainability of fisheries. For coastal communities, fisheries are often one of the only local sources of economic activity. As industrial fisheries operations intensify, and the climate continues to alter the marine realm, these communities will be increasingly vulnerable in terms of both food security and livelihood. Any discourse in the international area must take these challenges into account.

As is evident with our own daily lives, perceptions change over time, often without our knowledge or awareness. In understanding global trends in fisheries—or for any environmental issue for that matter—it is crucial to keep in mind the danger of "shifting baselines syndrome," or the notion that our current idea of what is considered normal is vastly different than what others considered normal in the past.[47] For example, the amount of fish, their individual size, and the diversity of species that constituted a good catch a few generations ago are all dramatically different than they are today.[48] However, with few people still alive to remember the times of old, we lack insight into how good (or bad) today's catch really is. As is the case with any type of environmental degradation, when a reference point from a previous generation is lost, an artificial view of the state of the ecosystem is created (i.e., a new baseline is established). As the environment becomes increasingly degraded, ever lower baselines are created, while the records of past abundance and pristine ecosystems disappear or are dismissed as myth.

ENDNOTES

1. William E. Schrank and Roy Noel, "The Newfoundland Fishery and Economy Twenty Years After the Northern Cod Moratorium," *Marine Resource Economics* 28, no. 4 (2013): 397–413. doi:10.5950/0738–1360–28.4.397.
2. Daniel Pauly, "The *Sea Around Us* Project: Documenting and Communicating Global Fisheries Impacts on Marine Ecosystems," *AMBIO: A Journal of the Human Environment* 36, no. 4 (2007): 290–95. doi:10.1579/0044–7447(2007)36%5B290:TSAUPD%5D2.0.CO;2.
3. Wilf Swartz, Enric Sala, Sean Tracey, Reg Watson, and Daniel Pauly, "The Spatial Expansion and Ecological Footprint of Fisheries (1950 to Present)," *PloS One* 5, no. 12 (2010). Public Library of Science: e15143. doi:10.1371/journal.pone.0015143.
4. The maximum amount of fish that a given habitat (e.g., coral reef, seamount, region of open water) can support, based on factors such as food availability, number of predators, living space, and suitable spawning locations.
5. See Box One for example of how changes in environmental conditions can drive fisheries to a new state.
6. Daniel Pauly, "From Growth to Malthusian Overfishing: Stages of Fisheries Resources Misuse," *Traditional Marine Resources Management and Knowledge Information Bulletin*, no. 3 (1994): 7–14.
7. George A. Rose and David W. Kulka, "Hyperaggregation of Fish and Fisheries: How Catch-Per-Unit-Effort Increased As the Northern Cod (*Gadus Morhua*) Declined," *Canadian Journal of Fisheries and Aquaculture Science* 56, no. 1 (1999): 118–27.
8. Carl J. Walters and Jean-Jacques Maguire, "Lessons for Stock Assessment From the Northern Cod Collapse," *Reviews in Fish Biology and Fisheries* 6 (1996): 125–37; Rose and Kulka, "Hyperaggregation of Fish and Fisheries."
9. Walters and Maguire, "Lessons for Stock Assessment From the Northern Cod Collapse."
10. Daniel Pauly, "Rationale for Reconstructing Catch Time Series," *EC Fisheries Cooperation Bulletin* 11, no. 2 (1998): 4–7.
11. Examples can be found at http://www.fishingdown.org/.
12. Kristin Kleisner, H. Mansour, and Daniel Pauly, "Region-Based MTI: Resolving Geographic Expansion in the Marine Trophic Index," *Marine Ecology Progress Series* 512, October (2014): 185–99. doi:10.3354/meps10949.

13. Food and Agriculture Organization of the United Nations (FAO), *The State of World Fisheries and Aquaculture 2014*. Rome: FAO.
14. Ibid.
15. Wilf Swartz, Enric Sala, Sean Tracey, Reg Watson, and Daniel Pauky, "The Spatial Expansion and Ecological Footprint of Fisheries"; F. Berkes, T. P. Hughes, R. S. Steneck, J. A. Wilson, D. R. Bellwood, B. Crona, C. Folke, L.H. Gunderson, H.M. Leslie, J. Norberg, M. Nystrom, P. Olsson, H. Osterblom, M. Scheffer and B. Worm, "Globalization, Roving Bandits, and Marine Resources," *Science* 311, no. 5767 (2015): 1557–58.
16. Jennifer L. Jacquet and Daniel Pauly, "Trade Secrets: Renaming and Mislabeling of Seafood," *Marine Policy* 32, no. 3 (2008): 309–18. doi:10.1016/j.marpol.2007.06.007.
17. Dirk Zeller and Daniel Pauly, "Good News, Bad News: Global Fisheries Discards Are Declining, but So Are Total Catches," *Fish and Fisheries* 6 (2005): 156–59.
18. David J. Agnew, John Pearce, Ganapathiraju Pramod, Tom Peatman, John R. Beddington, and Tony J. Pitcher, "Estimating the Worldwide Extent of Illegal Fishing," *PloS One* 4, no. 2 (2009): 1–8. doi:10.1371/journal.pone.0004570.t001.
19. Daniel Pauly, "Rationale for Reconstructing Catch Time Series."
20. FAO, *The State of World Fisheries and Aquaculture 2014*.
21. J. A. Anticamara, Reg Watson, A. Gelchu, and Daniel Pauly, "Global Fishing Effort (1950–2010): Trends, Gaps, and Implications," *Fisheries Research* 107, nos. 1–3 (2011): 131–36. doi:10.1016/j.fishres.2010.10.016.
22. Wilf Swartz, U. Rashid Sumaila, and Reg Watson, "Global Ex-Vessel Fish Price Database Revisited: A New Approach for Estimating 'Missing' Prices," *Environmental and Resource Economics* 56, no. 4 (2013): 467–80. doi:10.1007/s10640–012–9611–1.
23. Lydia C. L. Teh and U. Rashid Sumaila, "Contribution of Marine Fisheries to Worldwide Employment," *Fish and Fisheries* 14, no. 1 (2013): 77–88. doi:10.1111/j.1467–2979.2011.00450.x.
24. Andrew J. Dyck and U Rashid Sumaila, "Economic Impact of Ocean Fish Populations in the Global Fishery," *Journal of Bioeconomics* 12, no. 3 (2010): 227–43. doi:10.1007/s10818–010–9088–3.
25. U. Thara Srinivasan, William W. L. Cheung, Reg Watson, and U. Rashid Sumaila, "Food Security Implications of Global Marine Catch Losses Due to Overfishing," *Journal of Bioeconomics* 12, no. 3 (2010): 183–200. doi:10.1007/s10818–010–9090–9.
26. U. Rashid Sumaila, William W. L. Cheung, Andrew Dyck, Kamal Gueye, Ling Huang, Vicky Lam, Daniel Pauly, et al., "Benefits of Rebuilding Global Marine Fisheries Outweigh Costs," *PloS One* 7, no. 7 (2012): e40542. doi:10.1371/journal.pone.0040542.; Daniel Pauly, Villy Christensen, Sylvie Guenette, Tony J. Pitcher, U. Rashid Sumaila, Carl J. Walters, Reg Watson, and Dirk Zeller, "Towards Sustainability in World Fisheries," *Nature* 418 (2002): 689–95.

27. Gordon Munro and U. Rashid Sumaila, "The Impact of Subsidies upon Fisheries Management and Sustainability: The Case of the North Atlantic," *Fish and Fisheries* 3, December (2002): 233–50.
28. Garrett Hardin, "The Tragedy of the Commons," *Science* 162 no. 3859 (1968): 1243–48.
29. Colin Clark, *The Worldwide Crisis in Fisheries: Economic Models and Human Behavior* (Cambridge: Cambridge University Press, 2006).
30. Ragnar Arnason, "Minimum Information Management in Fisheries," *Canadian Journal of Economics* 23, no. 3 (1990): 630–53.
31. Frank Asche, Trond Bjorndal, and Daniel V. Gordon, "Resource Rent in Individual Quota Fisheries," *Land Economics* 85, no. 2 (2009): 279–91.
32. Cindy Chu, "Thirty Years Later: The Global Growth of ITQs and Their Influence on Stock Status in Marine Fisheries," *Fish and Fisheries* 10, no. 2 (2009): 217–30. doi:10.1111/j.1467–2979.2008.00313.x; Ragnar Arnason, "Property Rights in Fisheries: Iceland's Experience with ITQs," *Reviews in Fish Biology and Fisheries* 15, no. 3 (2005): 243–64. doi:10.1007/s11160–005–5139–6.
33. Wilf Swartz and Gakushi Ishimura, "Baseline Assessment of Total Fisheries-Related Biomass Removal from Japan's Exclusive Economic Zones: 1950–2010," *Fisheries Science* 80, no. 4 (2014): 643–51. doi:10.1007/s12562–014–0754–6.
34. Colin Clark, *The Worldwide Crisis in Fisheries*; Daniel Bromley, "Abdicating Responsibility: The Deceits of Fisheries Policy," *Fisheries* 34, no. 6 (2009): 280–94.
35. U. Rashid Sumaila, Ahmed S. Khan, Andrew J. Dyck, Reg Watson, Gordon Munro, Peter Tydemers, and Daniel Pauly, "A Bottom-Up Re-Estimation of Global Fisheries Subsidies," *Journal of Bioeconomics* 12, no. 3 (2010): 201–25. doi:10.1007/s10818–010–9091–8.
36. FAO, *The State of World Fisheries and Aquaculture 2014*.
37. Colin Clark, *The Worldwide Crisis in Fisheries*; Sumaila et al., "A Bottom-Up Re-Estimation of Global Fisheries Subsidies"; Munro and Sumaila, "The Impact of Subsidies upon Fisheries Management and Sustainability."
38. Wilf Swartz and Rashid Sumaila "Fisheries governance, subsidies and the World Trade Organization." In Ekeland I et al. (eds) *The Ocean as a Global System: Economics and Governance of Fisheries and Energy Resources*. (2013): 30–44.
39. FAO, *The State of World Fisheries and Aquaculture 2014*; Wilf Swartz, U. Rashid Sumaila, Reg Watson, and Daniel Pauly, "Sourcing Seafood for the Three Major Markets the EU, Japan and the USA," *Marine Policy* 34, no. 6 (2010): 1366–73. doi:10.1016/j.marpol.2010.06.011.
40. Sarika Cullis-Suzuki and Daniel Pauly, "Failing the High Seas: A Global Evaluation of Regional Fisheries Management Organizations," *Marine Policy* 34, no. 5 (2010): 1036–42. doi:10.1016/j.marpol.2010.03.002.

41. Frederic Le Manach Mialy Andriamahefazafy, Sarah Harper, Alasdair Harris, Gilles Hosch, Glenn-Marie Lange, Dirk Zeller, Ussif Rashid Sumaila, "Who Gets What? Developing a More Equitable Framework for EU Fishing Agreements," *Marine Policy* 38 (2013): 257–266.
42. Swartz, Sumaila, et al., "Sourcing Seafood for the Three Major Markets."
43. Carolyn Fischer, "Does Trade Help or Hinder the Conservation of Natural Resources?" *Review of Environmental Economics and Policy* 4, no. 1 (2010): 103–21. doi:10.1093/reep/rep023.
44. Jean-Marc Fromentin, "The Fate of Atlantic Bluefin Tuna," *Science* 327, no. 5971 (2010): 1325–26. doi:10.1126/science.327.5971.1325-c.
45. Jacquet and Pauly, "Trade Secrets"; Peter B. Marko, Holly A. Nance, and Kimberly D. Guynn, "Genetic Detection of Mislabeled Fish from a Certified Sustainable Fishery," *Current Biology* 21, no. 16 (2011): R621–22. doi:10.1016/j.cub.2011.07.006.
46. Sven M. Anders and Julie A Caswell, "Standards as Barriers Versus Standards as Catalysts: Assessing the Impact of HACCP Implementation on U.S. Seafood Imports," *American Journal of Agricultural Economics* 91, no. 2 (2009): 310–21. doi:10.1111/j.1467–8276.2008.01239.x; Jason Grant and Sven M. Anders, "Trade Deflection Arising from U.S. Import Refusals and Detentions in Fishery and Seafood Trade," *American Journal of Agricultural Economics* 93, no. 2 (2010): 573–80. doi:10.1093/ajae/aaq150.
47. Daniel Pauly, "Anecdotes and the Shifting Baseline," *Trends in Ecology and Evolution* 10, no. 10 (1995): 430.
48. Loren McClenachan, "Documenting Loss of Large Trophy Fish from the Florida Keys with Historical Photographs," *Conservation Biology* 23, no. 3 (2009): 636–43. doi:10.1111/j.1523–1739.2008.01152.x.

RECOMMENDED READINGS/ SOURCES

Berkes, F., T. P. Hughes, R. S. Steneck, J. A. Wilson, D. R. Bellwood, B. Crona, C. Folke, L.H. Gunderson, H.M. Leslie, J. Norberg, M. Nystrom, P. Olsson, H. Osterblom, M. Scheffer, B. Worm2015. "Globalization, Roving Bandits, and Marine Resources." *Science* 311 (5767): 1557–58.

Cheung, William W. L., Vicky W. Y. Lam, Jorge L. Sarmiento, Kelly Kearney, Reg Watson, and Daniel Pauly. 2009. "Projecting Global Marine Biodiversity Impacts Under Climate Change Scenarios." *Fish and Fisheries* 10 (3): 235–51.

Clark, Colin. 2006. *The Worldwide Crisis in Fisheries: Economic Models and Human Behavior*. Cambridge: Cambridge University Press.

Clark, Colin, Gordon Munro, Rashid Sumaila. 2005. "Subsidies, Buybacks, and Sustainable Fisheries." *Journal of Environmental Economics and Management* 50 (1): 47–58.

Pauly, Daniel. 1995. "Anecdotes and the Shifting Baseline." *Trends in Ecology and Evolution* 10 (10): 430.

Pauly, Daniel, Villy Christensen, Johanne Dalsgaard, Rainer Froese, and Francisco Jr. Torres. 1998. "Fishing Down Marine Food Webs." *Science* 279 (5352): 860–63.

Pauly, Daniel, Villy Christensen, Sylvie Guenette, Tony J. Pitcher, U. Rashid Sumaila, Carl J. Walters, Reg Watson, and Dirk Zeller. 2002. "Towards Sustainability in World Fisheries." *Nature* 418: 689–95.

Sumaila, U. Rashid, William W. L. Cheung, Andrew Dyck, Kamal Gueye, Ling Huang, Vicky Lam, Daniel Pauly, et al. 2012. "Benefits of Rebuilding Global Marine Fisheries Outweigh Costs." *PLoS One* 7 (7): e40542. doi:10.1371/journal.pone.0040542.

Swartz, Wilf, Enric Sala, Sean Tracey, Reg Watson, and Daniel Pauly, 2010. "The Spatial Expansion and Ecological Footprint of Fisheries (1950 to Present)." *PLoS ONE* 5: e15143.

Walters, Carl, and Steve Martell. 2004. *Fisheries Ecology and Management*. Princeton: Princeton University Press.

Climate Change

by **THOMAS B. FOWLER**

CHAPTER FIVE

INTRODUCTION

Global warming or "climate change," has become a highly contentious issue, with political, economic, social, ecological, and scientific implications. The hapless observer is bombarded with books and documentaries replete with apocalyptic images, such as Al Gore's *An Inconvenient Truth*[1] and *Earth in the Balance*,[2] as well as writings by James Hansen[3] and other climate action activists, portraying a world overcome with famine, flooding, and destruction. Some reputable scientists doubt these conclusions and argue for a more nuanced position[4,5]; meanwhile, others denounce the whole global warming theory as a cruel hoax that will condemn many to lives of deprivation and starvation.[6] Unfortunately, such issues drive partisans to employ divisive rhetoric and obfuscating arguments, making it difficult for an objective observer—who simply wants to understand the issues at stake—to make a reasoned judgment. Global warming has, to some degree, displaced evolution as the subject where disagreement over scientific questions has turned into politicized controversy.

This chapter addresses the following issues, which are important to the energy consumer, the political decision maker, the corporate executive, and the government regulator.

1. What are the scientific facts and the scientific theories regarding climate change?
2. Why is there such controversy about the climate?
3. What are the likely outcomes of climate change?

4. Should fossil fuel usage policy be linked to climate change?
5. Which energy policies and mitigation strategies are most appropriate, given the state of our knowledge and the political realities?

The goal is to give the reader enough understanding of the problem to be able to hear and evaluate properly arguments, evidence, and conclusions, and thus to make intelligent judgments about matters relating to global warming and climate change.

OVERVIEW

The global warming/climate change controversy is not about the question of whether the Earth's climate is undergoing change, because we know from historical records and paleoclimatology research that the Earth's climate has always been changing. Rather, the current controversy is about the effect of human activity on the Earth's climate, and in particular, whether human activity is causing the Earth's climate to warm significantly. By "significantly," we mean enough to cause potentially serious, deleterious, and widespread changes to geography, flora, and fauna. This is known as anthropogenic global warming (AGW).

The present high level of concern about global warming arose because of temperature measurements made during the late 20th century that suggested an accelerated warming rate, presumably too rapid to be caused by natural processes (see Figure 5.1). Clearly, a long-term warming trend of this magnitude could spell major trouble, so it is very important to understand causal connections and, if possible, to predict the future of our climate. Predictions can be made on the basis of simple extrapolation, but the large variability of temperature data, and the short time span of instrument-based measurements, make this approach too crude to be useful for serious policy decisions. Climate change research, therefore, has two directions: looking back at past climate trends, primarily temperature, to improve the database; and looking forward to possible changes in the future. Past temperature trends can be reconstructed from proxy data and historical records until the late 19th century, when reliable instrument-based temperature measurements began to be recorded. For the future, computer-based climate simulation models, known as general circulation models (GCMs), are preferentially employed to project the effect of various types and degrees of climate change, based on recent trends and assumptions about climate dynamics.

The GCMs are bottom-up models, analogous to microeconomic models, which seek to describe climate and its trajectory based on assumptions and formulae about

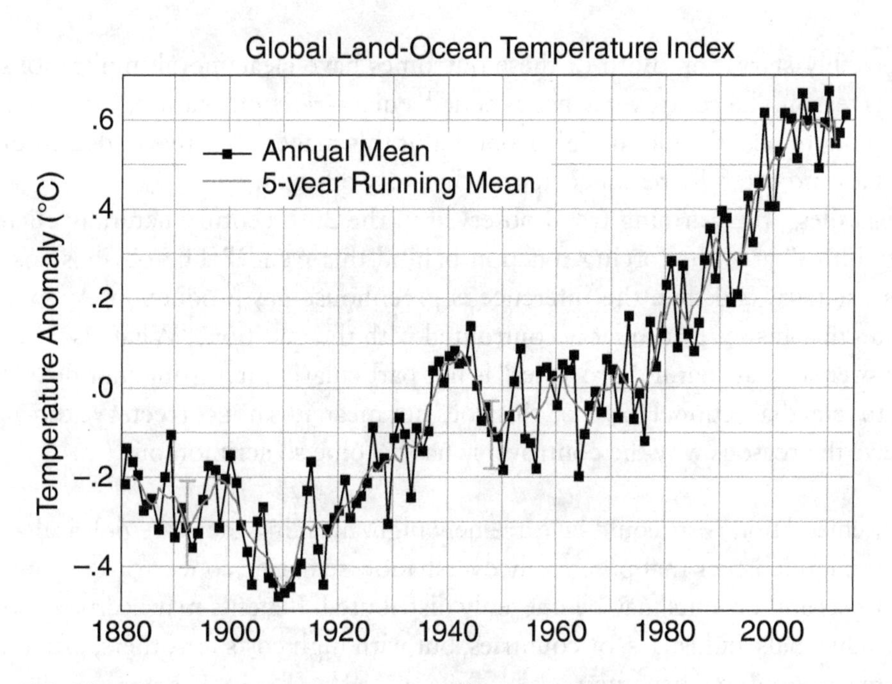

Figure 5.1. Global temperature changes over the past 130 years.

temperatures, wind, currents, and other data on very small scales. These models are extremely complex and employ huge databases, requiring supercomputers for their execution. They are run by various organizations around the world, but employ the same general assumptions about the climate system, and tend to arrive at similar conclusions. Top-down models, analogous to macroeconomic models, also exist and are much simpler, able to run on a PC. However, these models are not used by most climate researchers. It is the predictions of the GCMs that are driving the current policy discussions about global warming and climate change. If their more pessimistic predictions about the Earth's temperature are correct, the inference usually drawn is that action on a global scale is required to mitigate warming to avoid undesirable changes like widespread coastal flooding, extinctions, and possibly famine. The action envisioned usually involves significant reduction in the use of carbon-based fuels, since warming is generally attributed to excess carbon dioxide emissions produced by burning these fuels. Obviously any program to accomplish this goal would involve coercive measures on a very large scale, and would cause significant remediation expenses and efforts, as well as disruptions in individual ways of living, social organization, business practices, and other areas. Conversely, taking action when none is warranted will inevitably condemn many—especially the poor—to lives of unnecessary deprivation and possibly starvation. Both of these outcomes have clear moral implications, and for this reason, the controversy has assumed a quasi-religious nature, with both sides attempting to take the moral high ground. But this makes objective understanding of the issues and carefully reasoned approaches very difficult.

Regardless, the warming trend observed in the 20th century naturally elicits the question, "What is the forcing function behind this trend?" The obvious answer is human activity, and then the inference is greenhouse gas production. Anyone who disputes this answer is justifiably confronted with the question, "What else is there?" An answer such as "natural processes" is not particularly interesting, nor does it lend itself to remedial action. However, this does not mean it is not correct. We can already perceive the reasons why the controversy has become so acrimonious.

- Remediation costs could be extremely high, meaning there are political and economic issues that potentially overshadow scientific concerns.
- Costs and benefits may be unevenly distributed. Benefits may accrue to some individuals, industries, or countries, but with high costs for others, often with few or no direct benefits.
- Significant—even drastic—lifestyle changes could be required, especially for the industrialized countries.
- Dire predictions cause the controversy to assume a quasi-religious nature, since some are genuinely convinced global warming is a threat to the planet and humanity.
- GCMs are still evolving and subject to dispute, especially about causal influence and drivers. Thus the magnitude and timing of effects of climate change are very uncertain.
- Comprehensive measured data are only available for a relatively short period (a few decades), compared to the known time constants for climate change.
- Reputations of many prominent individuals and organizations are staked on one position or other, making any concessions potentially embarrassing and career-wrecking.

In many ways, money is the primary driver of much of the controversy surrounding global warming. If remediation costs and concomitant changes in the way we live were small, there would be little or no objection to any mitigation program, if for no other reason than as an insurance policy. No one wants to take unnecessary chances with Mother Nature. But the higher the potential cost for remediation, the greater the certainty needed, at least with respect to political action. No elected politician will impose onerous new laws or taxes without something close to irrefutable evidence; and even then, a crisis sometimes must be imminent. And few if any businesses will voluntarily assume a large cost burden in the absence of compelling reasons and, in most cases, some guarantee that other businesses are required to do the same.

Reductions envisioned (or considered desirable) for the United States are 83 percent by 2050 from 2005 levels.[7] In 2005, per capita emissions in the United States were about 5.4 tons. Assuming a projected U.S. population of 439 million by 2050, it will be necessary to reduce per capita emissions to a level of about 0.7 tons. This is approximately the per capita emission level of the U.S. in 1870, and about the level in Nigeria today, where half the population does not have access to electricity, and only 3 percent have cars. It is difficult to say what sort of technology or social change would be required to achieve this goal, or what the cost would be. However, this does not mean the goal is impossible. Assuming all U.S. energy needs were met by solar power, and assuming an efficiency of 30 percent for solar cells (high but not unachievable), the current energy consumption level of 97.5 quads (quadrillion BTUs/year) could be met by covering an area of about 17,500 square miles with solar cells. (This is roughly 0.5% of the U.S. land area; but factoring in the need for roads and supporting infrastructure, the area needed would be at least double). Such a shift would require huge changes in power distribution, home, and office systems, industrial processes, transportation, and other areas, as well as enormous capital for investment. Renewable energy sources such as solar currently account for around 10 percent of U.S. energy production.[8] If fusion power became practical, it could displace all other methods with almost no pollution.

The Scientific Case

The scientific case for climate change is ultimately based on empirical observations, as well as assumptions and theories about the physics of the atmosphere and of the oceans. For the sake of clarity, matters not in dispute will be followed by those that are in dispute.* First, points *not* in dispute and *not* rejected by either climate change deniers or climate change supporters:

1. The rise in global temperatures, between about 1980 and 1997, which is well attested by both ground-based and satellite measurements

*There are irrational people on both sides of the climate debate, of course, people who make absurd pronouncements and claims. Here we are concerned with rational people who are sincerely interested in understanding the issues, and fortunately that includes most scientists on both sides.

2. The steady global temperatures from about the year 2000 to the present
3. Increased carbon dioxide levels in the atmosphere, from 290 parts per million (ppm) in 1900,[9] to more than 390 ppm in 2012[10] (though CO_2 is less than 0.1% of the atmosphere by volume)[11]
4. Human activity as the principal source of the increase in CO_2 and other greenhouse gases
5. Carbon dioxide and other greenhouse gases as climate forcing functions, which cause heating of the atmosphere[†]
6. Feedback loops in the climate system that can amplify or diminish climate forcing

What is in dispute is the explanation for recent rise in temperature, involving these factors.

1. The temperature record over the past 1000 years
2. The nature of the feedback loops in the climate system (resulting in amplification or diminution)
3. The impact of factors other than greenhouse gases on the atmosphere
4. The overall dynamics of the climate system
5. The degree of natural variability in the climate system

Those who support the AGW hypothesis believe the dynamics of the climate system are such that they amplify the greenhouse gas effect, causing an increased rate of warming; those who reject it believe that the dynamics cause the greenhouse gas effect to be diminished, and possibly outweighed by other factors, resulting in little or no new warming. However, the fact of late 20th century warming requires explanation, regardless of whether one agrees with the prevailing opinion that it is ultimately caused by human activity. But recent steady temperatures also require an explanation, and it obviously isn't greenhouse gas emission.

In this problem, as in others, one must be aware of the orders of magnitude involved. Warming of the atmosphere is measured in terms of watts/square meter of effect. Solar irradiance (energy from the sun) is about 1,368 watts/square meter at the top of the Earth's atmosphere, when the sun is overhead. Taking into account the

[†]"Forcing function" in climatology is something that causes climate changes (warming or cooling), measured in watts/square meter. This refers to the equivalent energy increase from the sun that would be required to achieve the same warming effect.

lower angle of the sun in most locations, reflection by the atmosphere, the absence of sun at night, and other factors, the amount of solar energy actually incident on the Earth averages about 240 watts/square meter. This means that energy from the sun puts about 240 watts on average continuously on every square meter of the Earth's atmosphere, considered as a very thin shell around the Earth. Most of this passes through the atmosphere to the Earth's surface. For reference, the Earth's current level of CO_2 is usually rated at 1.5 watts/square meter of forcing, methane at 0.5 watts/square meter, and all greenhouse gases together (excluding water vapor) at about 2.4 watts/square meter. These numbers mean that if there were no greenhouse gases, the same warming effect would result if the sun delivered an additional 2.4 watts/square meter of energy to the Earth. In other words, greenhouse gases are about 1 percent of the sun with respect to forcing. If the greenhouse gases' effects do not include amplification or diminution of the warming, a doubling of them (expected over the next 50–100 years) would raise the Earth's temperature by about 1°C. Forecasts predict increases about 2 to 3 times higher. Other influences on climate that can act as forcing functions (positive or negative) include Earth's albedo (reflectivity of sunlight by clouds) and, in the long term, solar activity (possibly correlated with sunspots).

The organization primarily responsible for coordinating and collecting research on climate change, and formulating policies, is the United Nations Intergovernmental Panel on Climate Change (IPCC), established in 1988. Its mission is to "provide the governments of the world with a clear scientific view of what is happening to the world's climate."[12] It has issued five major reports, called assessments, the most recent in 2013.[13] The IPCC assessments are detailed, with contributions from climate scientists worldwide; they are the product of an enormous amount of research and data collection. The IPCC assessments try to synthesize the best knowledge we have about the Earth's climate, and make judgments accordingly. For this reason, the assessments are often taken, not without justification, as the final word on the subject. The IPCC's general position is that naturally driven climate change occurs over relatively short periods; a sustained temperature rise lasting 20 to 30 years is unprecedented, and therefore must be the result of a non-natural forcing function. The pause in global warming since 2000 has caused the IPCC to dial back some of its predictions, but its views have not changed. The IPCC does not publish dissenting views, despite acknowledged uncertainties in climate science and the brevity of the instrumented climate record. Nor does it employ researchers who do not agree with its general position, or utilize their research and conclusions, which often directly contradict its own.

Greenhouse effect and greenhouse gases

Much of the debate about the explanation of global warming is concerned with the greenhouse effect and greenhouse gases, which are atmospheric gases that contribute to the greenhouse effect. The greenhouse effect refers to the fact that many substances—not just glass used in real greenhouses, but also gases such as CO_2 and water vapor—will transmit light at certain wavelengths but block it at others. Sunlight enters a real greenhouse and warms the objects inside. When the objects are heated, they begin to radiate energy, by the laws of thermodynamics; but they radiate energy at wavelengths to which glass is opaque. Thus, that energy just reflects off of the glass, and back into the greenhouse. So a greenhouse heats up, because most of the energy it receives from the sun remains trapped inside it.

The Earth's atmosphere behaves similarly, trapping the heat from sunlight. The Earth's surface is heated and then radiates energy outward that is reflected off of the atmosphere. This is desirable to a certain degree. It prevents the dark side of the Earth (the side facing away from the sun at any time) from cooling too quickly, as does the dark side of the moon, for instance. Without greenhouse gases, the Earth's temperature would be about -18°C (0°F). Greenhouse gases raise our average temperature to about +15°C (59°F). With respect to global warming, the question is whether human activity is creating dangerously high levels of these gases, and the associated warming, thus triggering potential catastrophic effects.

The gases in the Earth's atmosphere responsible for the greenhouse effect include water vapor, CO_2, nitrous oxide, ozone, and methane, among others. Water vapor is by far the most important greenhouse gas, contributing about 75 percent of the greenhouse effect. But attention is concentrated on carbon dioxide, which contributes somewhere between 10 and 25 percent, because we can conceivably control its production—something we cannot realistically do for water vapor. Moreover, this fits with the wider environmentalist agenda of reducing pollutants that result from burning fossil fuels, and of reducing consumption of non-renewable resources. Methane production is 5 to 10 percent of the total greenhouse gas contribution. It could be reduced by curtailing agriculture or slaughtering livestock, but this (and the resulting mass starvation) is not a politically or ethically viable solution.

Measurement of warming trends

There are two basic ways to measure global temperatures: direct and indirect. The direct method requires measurement and recording of temperatures across the globe at regular intervals. This is now done with ground-based and precision satellite instruments. Records exist in the West going back about 200 years. In China, carefully kept records of first frost and other phenomena allow inference of temperatures for East Asia, going back a thousand years or more.[14] The indirect method uses proxies—directly measurable quantities correlated with temperature—when direct measurements are not available. For example, sediment cores from the Gulf of Mexico have been used to infer sea surface temperatures over the past 1,400 years.[15] Some proxies (such as tree rings) can be difficult to interpret and are subject to much controversy.

Looking back: temperature trend analysis

Temperature trends are the major focus of the global warming controversy. Temperature trend analysis can be broken into three periods, which reflect different evidence and different measurement methods and models.

- Recent temperatures, roughly 100 years, for which good instrumented data are available
- Temperature trends since the year 1,000 AD
- Temperature trends before the year 1,000 AD, back several hundred thousand years

Though of quite unequal length, these three periods have been chosen because they correspond closely to the degree of controversy surrounding temperature trend measurement. The first is relatively uncontroversial, since it is based on data from modern measuring instruments around the globe. The third is not very controversial, since it is based primarily on ice core samples which go back hundreds of thousands of years. Only the second is highly controversial, due in large measure to the now famous "hockey stick" graph, the work of climatologist Michael Mann, first published in 1998.[16] Mann and his graph will be considered in more detail below.

Recent temperature trends

Figure 5.1 shows the temperature trend over the past 130 years, from the end of the Little Ice Age (16th–19th centuries) to the present. This is the graph usually cited when evidence of global warming is needed, and when action is called for, based on the clear trend from the late 1970s to about 2000. First, note that the temperature anomaly (deviation from assumed normal) is less than 1°C over the period. Second, there was an actual decrease from about 1940 to 1975, probably forming the basis for

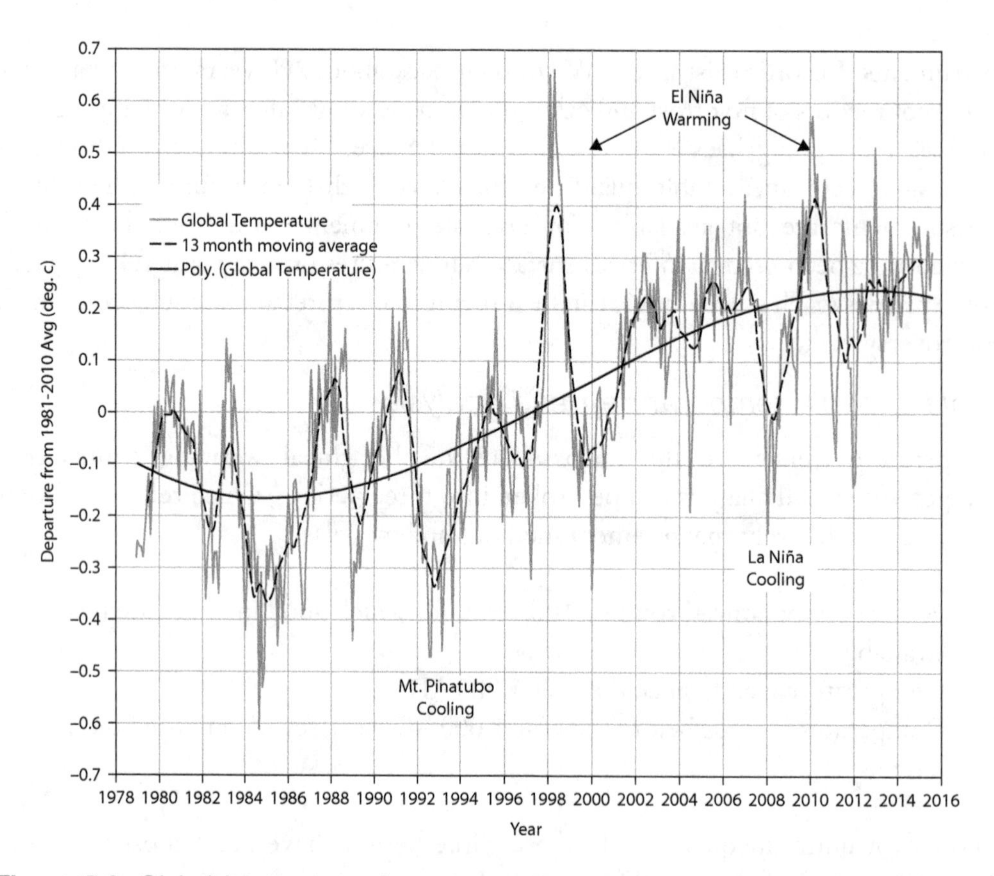

Figure 5.2. Global lower atmosphere temperature averages using satellite data, with polynomial regression line added (solid). Dashed curve is 13- month moving average.

predictions, made at that time, of a new ice age. Third, this graph begins at the end of the Little Ice Age, when temperatures were significantly cooler than today, so some warming is to be expected as part of normal climate cycles. A key question—and it is difficult and controversial—is how to remove the effects of this period. Fourth, the trend from 2000 to the present is actually slightly downward. A more detailed graph for the period 1978 to 2014, based only on precision satellite data covering the entire Earth, is shown in Figure 5.2. This graph illustrates the peaking and relatively flat temperatures over the past decade, though the month-to-month variations make it difficult to pick out long-term trends. Various techniques, such as moving averages and regression analysis, can be employed, but they do not give consistent results, especially for recent years. The graph shows a 13-month moving average—essentially year-to-year changes, and a fourth order regression, which is just a data smoothing technique. The reader should be aware that a fifth order regression curve shows a slight uptick at the end.‡

The recent pause in warming—now 15 or more years—has (or should have) affected our policy choices, or at least their urgency. A 2008 report from the National Oceanic and Atmospheric Administration (NOAA) is explicit about the GCMs:

> Near-zero and even negative trends are common for intervals of a decade or less in the simulations, due to the model's internal climate variability. The simulations rule out (at the 95% level) zero trends for intervals of 15 yr or more, suggesting that *an observed absence of warming of this duration is needed to create a discrepancy with the expected present-day warming rate.*[17]

In other words, a steady temperature for a long period casts doubt on the models upon which current policy is being built. Various explanations that do not require wholesale rejection of the GCMs have been proposed for the pause.[18] Global warming advocates do not seem interested in addressing the obvious methodological question if how long you maintain a theory that fails to make successful predictions. Given the stakes, it may be best to await more data before making irreversible policy decisions.

The intermediate term

Is the temperature rise shown in Figures 5.1 and 5.2 unusual or just normal variability? That is the key driver of the global warming controversy—if normal variability, we have nothing to worry about; if abnormal, then possibly catastrophic results could ensue. If an abnormality exists, it is presumed to be due to human action altering the climate. To begin to answer this question, we must examine temperature records going back a millennium. Unfortunately, records become spotty more than 200 years in the past, and measurements back to the Middle Ages require proxies of various types. This has led to the most heated disputes in the global warming controversy, because it is directly relevant to the question of contemporary anthropogenic warming, and because it involves disputed methods and data for temperature reconstructions over the past 1,000 years.

The temperature reconstruction task was undertaken by, among others, Michael Mann, then at the University of Virginia. He sought to gather data from locations

‡A similar dataset maintained by the British, HadCRUT4, is also in wide use.

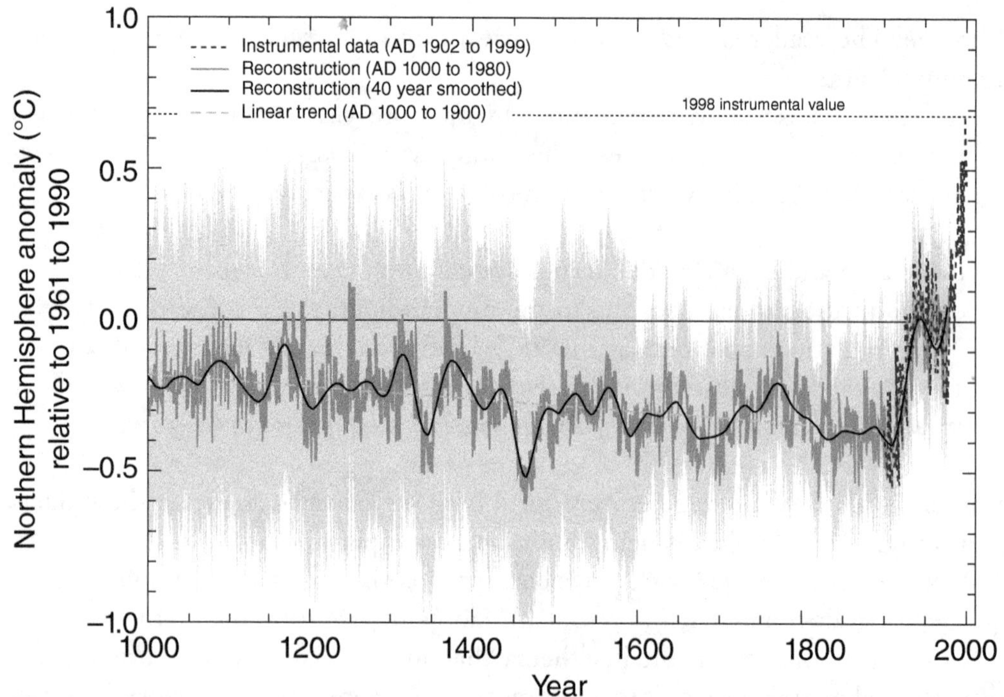

Figure 5.3. The "hockey stick" graph showing rapid and extraordinary 20th-century warming from IPCC. See original source for color version. Intergovernmental Panel on Climate Change, IPCC Third Assessment Report, http://www.ipcc.ch/ipccreports/tar/wg1/069.htm#fig220. Copyright © 2001 by Intergovernmental Panel on Climate Change.

worldwide, rather than just Europe and eastern North America. His results achieved a great deal of notoriety, and became known as the "hockey stick." This temperature graph is shown in Figure 5.3, in the form published by the IPCC. Prior to Mann's work, it was generally accepted that there was a Medieval Warm Period or Medieval Maximum, where temperatures were several degrees warmer, on average, than in the preceding half a millennium or so. Evidence for this exists across North America and Europe.[19] The Medieval Warm Period was followed, beginning about the year 1500, by the Little Ice Age, which lasted until the late 19th century. Both of these climate anomalies are well documented. During the warm period, grapes, for example, were grown in England; and the many reports of bitterly cold winters, combined with oil paintings of winter scenes during the Little Ice Age, such as those by Brueghel, clearly show it was abnormally cold during that period.

What Mann sought to demonstrate is that these two anomalies were restricted to Europe, or perhaps Europe and parts of North America, but were not global phenomena—an assertion disputed by other scientists.[20] In this way, he believed he could show that global temperatures were fairly steady for about 900 years, only to rise steeply in the 20th century. He did this by assembling a large database of temperature record proxies (mainly tree rings) going back 1,000 years. Mann's results fit with prevailing concerns about climate, and as a result were widely touted as the basis for calls to reduce greenhouse gas emissions. The graph was remarkable because it effectively eliminated the well-known Medieval Warm Period, and scarcely showed the Little Ice Age (15th–19th centuries), thus making present-day temperatures appear to be extraordinarily high.

There were, however, doubts on the part of many researchers with respect to the data sets used.[21] Tree ring data is suspect because examination of tree rings from the late 20th century has shown that they do not demonstrate sensitivity to the unusual warmth during that period. If this is true generally, it would entail that the tree rings underestimate warming in the past, and temperature reconstructions based on them would thus show less variation than actually existed, especially on the high side—precisely what the hockey stick shows.[22]

It is troubling that Michael Mann's famous hockey stick graph was not immediately scrutinized by climate scientists worldwide. Those who favor the idea of anthropogenic global warming must surely have been aware that a well-documented and consistently duplicated result would have been a much more potent weapon than a poorly documented result that could not be easily duplicated. As it happens, the first person who actually attempted to verify Mann's work, and replicate his data analysis and results, quickly discovered that it was not a straightforward process, and that Mann himself had little interest in enabling this crucial scientific step. He also discovered that it was not very robust with respect to data sets, thus calling into question its value. This action led to a review by the National Academy of Sciences, which determined that the graph was the result of flawed methodology.[23] A subsequent version of the graph had the Medieval Warm Period and the Little Ice Age reappearing.

However, the graph had already been adopted by IPCC for its Third Assessment Report (2001), and was widely circulated. This gave clear evidence that the warming of the late 20th century was unprecedented, and quickly led to calls for political action. But in 2009 the Climategate scandal broke. This incident involved the unplanned release of emails among various climate researchers, including those involved with the hockey stick graph. The emails made it appear, at least, that the climate scientists were more concerned with a political agenda than with objective science, and were trying to suppress views that contradicted their own.[24]

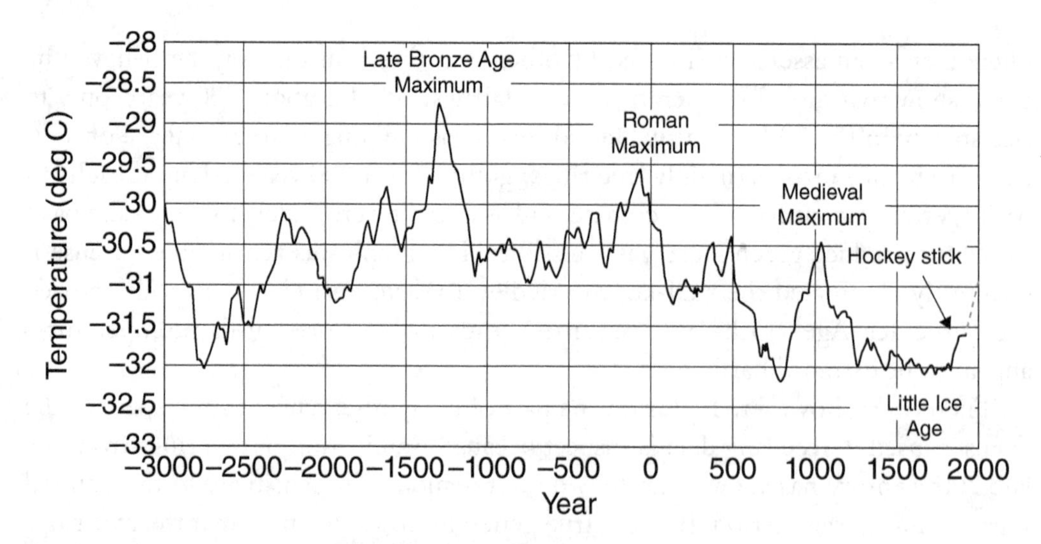

Figure 5.4. Temperature change since 3000 BC based on ice core samples, with recent instrumental record (dashed) and other annotations.

The net result of this incident was a significant increase in the skepticism already surrounding the claims for anthropogenic global warming. It became clear that despite claims of consensus and settled science—something essential if coordinated worldwide abatement efforts are to gain traction—the matter of explanation of the recent temperature rise is still far from being resolved. This is compounded by the fact that the rise has paused for about 15 years. It appears at least 10 to 20 more years of data will be needed to state with any confidence whether the pause in warming since 2000 is temporary, or represents some sort of top. At this point, the IPCC appears to be backing away from the hockey stick as the primary impetus to action (though it still supports its basic finding of unprecedented 20th-century warming).[25] The focus is now on other aspects of their scientific case, primarily the mechanisms believed responsible, mechanisms that operate regardless of whether the hockey stick is true or not, and the question of where all the global warming heat has gone.

Longer-term findings

The best way to put the current global warming controversy into perspective is to examine temperature records over longer historical periods. These records are obtained by proxies, the main one being ice core samples from central Greenland, made by NOAA. Refer to Figure 5.4, covering the period from 3000 BC to the present.

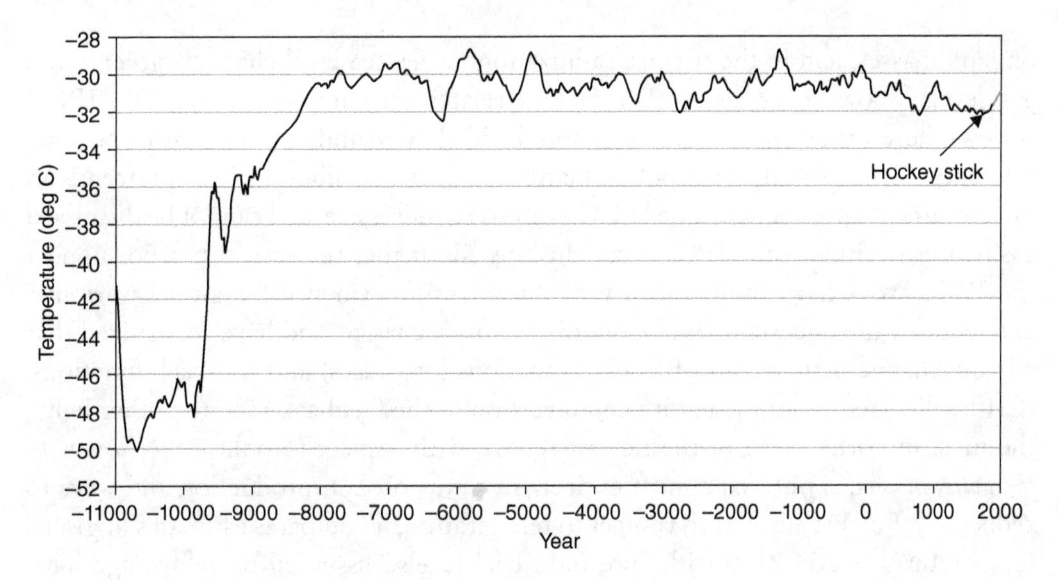

Figure 5.5. Temperature change since 11,000 BC based on ice core samples, with recent instrumental record (dashed) and other annotations.

Key trends are apparent in this graph. In particular, there is a peak corresponding to the Roman Empire, well documented, around the year 50 BC, known as the Roman Maximum, which dwarfs the Medieval Maximum; and an even larger peak at the time of the late Bronze Age, about 1200 BC, which dwarfs even the Roman Maximum. The late Bronze Age was also a very fertile period for human activity. There is also a smaller peak during the period usually called Late Antiquity, around the years AD 400–500. Note that even the dip between the Roman Maximum and this Late Antiquity peak had temperatures that equal or exceed that of the recent past, as did the dip in temperatures from the end of the Late Bronze Age peak to the Roman Maximum.

Going back to 11,000 BC, as shown in Figure 5.5, the last Ice Age clearly comes into view, a cold period that ended about 10,000 BC. There are several other peaks prior to the Late Bronze Age, but now the record makes the peaks and dips from about 8000 BC to the present look like noise on top of a much larger signal. It is possible to go back further, but these graphs suffice for our purposes.

Looking Forward: The IPCC and the GCMs

The IPCC report (latest is the fifth, 2013, available publicly on the Internet) collects a large amount of data on climate change, including temperatures in the atmosphere, on land masses, and in the oceans; salinization levels; sea level changes; greenhouse gas levels; snow cover; and other factors related to climate change. The IPCC reviews these with respect to causality and the likelihood and extent of anthropogenic influences. It also deals with policy matters and the likelihood of major trends in greenhouse gas production. The IPCC analysis is impressive, and cannot be dismissed easily. Even critics of the IPCC's conclusions admit that the scientists who support the IPCC work have summarized well the scientific evidence for global warming, and many of the uncertainties surrounding climate change, and have recognized that climate change is the result of forcing functions (or causes) and feedback functions. (Critics disagree about the nature and direction of the feedback.) On the other hand, the most important part of the newest report, with respect to policy, the *Summary for Policymakers*, is phrased almost entirely in terms of CO_2 production and ways to reduce it.[26] Furthermore, with respect to temperature, it compares estimates of global temperatures in AD 2100 with "pre-industrial levels," assumed to be average temperatures between 1850 and 1900. This is odd since the world was just emerging from the Little Ice Age at that time, so significant warming would be expected. There does not seem to be any attempt to quantify this in the IPCC report. The pre-industrial level of CO_2 was about 280 ppm; current levels are about 395 ppm. The IPCC report stresses the need to keep levels by AD 2100 around 450 ppm or less, so that global temperatures will not exceed the pre-industrial level by more than 2°C. However, the report concedes this is unlikely to happen: "At present, emissions are not on track for stabilization let alone deep cuts.... This reality has led to growing research on possible extreme effects of climate change and appropriate policy responses."[27] Few will dispute the IPCC estimates of global CO_2 under their various scenarios. What will be disputed is the effect of these levels on global temperatures, especially in light of the increase from about 365 ppm in 2000 to 395 ppm in 2014 (about 10%), with no concurrent rise in global average temperature.

In 2007 the IPCC projected future temperature ranges, and assuming a doubling of CO_2 concentrations over the next century or so, concluded that the global average temperature increase "is likely to be in the range 2°C to 4.5°C, with a best estimate of about 3°C, and is very unlikely to be less than 1.5°C. Values substantially higher than 4.5°C cannot be excluded."[28] The assessment specifically projected an increase of 0.2°C per decade for the next two decades (to 2027), and claimed that even if greenhouse gas emissions remained at year 2000 levels, there would still be an increase of 0.1°C per decade. This is a significant increase, which would affect glacial melting, agriculture, ocean currents and salinization, and many other climate elements, most in a negative way with respect to human interests. We are now 7 years into that 20-year prediction period, and there has been no increase. The IPCC admits that there are large uncertainties regarding clouds and their effect,[29] and indeed a change in average cloud cover of 3 percent (resulting in a change in albedo of about 0.01) could account for warming or cooling of the magnitude seen in the 20th century.[§]

This pause in global warming, despite the continual dumping of large amounts of CO_2 into the atmosphere, is causing consternation among supporters of the IPCC and the global warming hypothesis, and casting doubt on the validity of the GSMs, none of which predicted it. James Lovelock, British environmentalist and originator of the Gaia theory of the Earth as a single, integrated organism, has recanted: "There's nothing much really happening yet. We were supposed to be halfway toward a frying world now. The world has not warmed up very much since the millennium. Twelve years is a reasonable time. The temperature has stayed almost constant, whereas it should have been rising. Carbon dioxide is rising, no question about that."[30]

Case studies

Unfortunately, there are no case studies of climate change actions in the past to guide us, because this is the first time humanity has become aware of the problem, and has the ability to pursue or at least contemplate global action. It is, however, not the first time that climate change has had significant impact. As a cautionary tale, consider the situation in Europe about the year 1300:

> For five centuries, Europe basked in warm, settled weather, with only the occasional bitter winters, cool summers, and memorable storms, like the cold year of 1258 caused by a distant volcanic eruption.... Summer after summer passed with long, dreamy days, golden sunlight, and bountiful harvests. Compared with what was to follow, these centuries were a climatic golden age.... Nothing prepared [the Europeans] for the catastrophe ahead.[31]

[§]Some estimates of the effect of albedo put its forcing much higher.

**The Little Ice Age is generally considered to begin around 1500, but temperatures began falling 200–300 years earlier, and other effects of the climate shift, such as the bad weather of the early 14th century, had significant effects on the population.

That catastrophe was the Little Ice Age, ushered in by the unprecedented cold and rain of the year 1315, which caused widespread crop failures and famine.** The lower temperatures and reduced crop yields of the 14th century were a direct contributor to a weakened populace in the face of the Black Death of 1346 to 1355. While our economic and food production systems are more robust than in those days, a sharp temperature shift—either up or down—could have similar disastrous consequences, especially for the poor of the world.

Policy options

Policy questions are at the forefront of any discussion of climate change, since everyone would like to know what we should do (if anything). At this point in time there are several policy options available.[32] The basic dichotomy is between 1. minimal action (i.e., assuming the temperature fluctuations we have seen are normal), and 2. instigating a mitigation program. Under the first, we can a) literally do nothing, or b) take a wait-and-see attitude. Under the second, we can a) take aggressive action to reduce carbon emissions, and/or b) pursue a geo-engineering strategy. Regardless of which of these is followed, we can 3. take important actions that are largely independent of 1. and 2. These actions, any or all of which can be done, include a) conduct research and build our knowledge base, b) pursue an adaptation strategy, and c) reduce consumption of non-renewable resources. The options are shown in Figure 5.6.

Minimal action. We could choose the path of minimal action on account of (1) disagreement about temperature reconstructions for the past, and thus about the seriousness of the recent rise; (2) disagreement about the validity of the GCMs, and in particular about the sensitivity of the climate system with respect to greenhouse gas forcing (negative versus positive feedback); and (3) the large sums of money and the economic and social dislocations necessary for any effective mitigation strategy, including the degree of coercion required. This implies that unwarranted actions to reduce CO_2 by reducing fossil fuel consumption will lead to catastrophe, including starvation and significantly reduced living standards, especially for the poor, since the richer countries will be able to afford the higher prices for food, energy, and other goods stemming from greenhouse gas abatement efforts. So we could a) write off the whole climate change scenario as overhyped. On the other hand, we could be more cautious and, following the famous dictum of the Hippocratic Oath, *primum non nocere*,[33] and b) suspend judgment, on account of the relatively short period of time over which we have reliable measurements and thus the ability to make accurate climate models and forecasts. Under this view, we assume that the degree of certainty

Box 5.1 Major International Treaties and Agreements on Climate Change

Geneva Convention on Long-Range Transboundary Air Pollution. Treaty adopted in 1979 to deal with air pollution. Not specifically directed at climate change but relevant. Four protocols directed at specific pollutants (Helsinki, 1985; Sofia, 1988; Geneva, 1984 and 1991).

United Nations Framework Convention on Climate Change (UNFCCC). International environmental treaty negotiated in 1992. Objective is to "stabilize greenhouse gas concentrations in the atmosphere at a level that would prevent dangerous anthropogenic interference with the climate system." Not binding, but provides framework for negotiating specific international treaties (called "protocols") to set binding limits on greenhouse gases. As of 2014, has 196 parties including all United Nations member states.

Kyoto Protocol (1997). An international treaty extending UNFCCC that commits state parties to reduce greenhouse gases emissions, based on the premise that a) global warming exists, and b) manmade CO2 emissions have caused it. Commitment period ended in 2012. At time of writing not extended. Not ratified by the United States.

Copenhagen Accord (2009). Calls for countries to implement action plans directed at reducing global warming to 2°C. Made part of UNFCCC process by *Cancun Agreements* (2010). The United States pledged to reduce emissions by 17 percent compared to 2005.

Durban Platform for Enhanced Action (2011). From UNFCCC meetings held in 2011. Calls for new binding protocol to succeed Kyoto, to be adopted in 2015 and implemented in 2020.

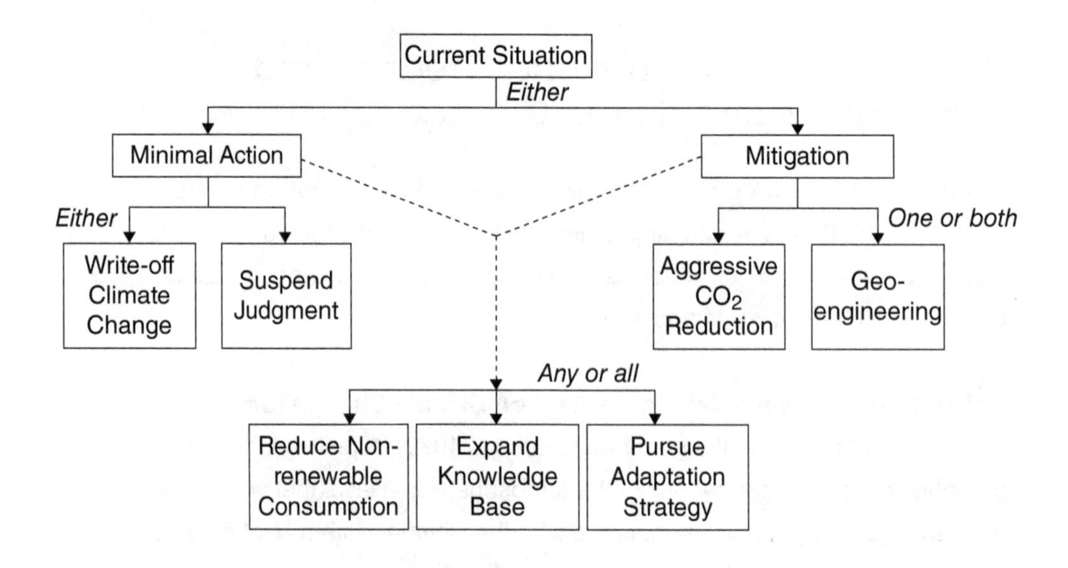

Figure 5.6. Possible strategies and actions with respect to climate change.

needed for difficult and possibly irreversible political, social, and economic changes is lacking. The next ten years will give us much more information about the Earth's climate, and in particular, about temperature trends. Most likely we shall have to wait that long before there is any certainty regarding the effect of CO_2, and thus the need for a mitigation strategy. So under this view, a wait-and-see attitude for now is the best course. This course of action is not without risk, however, because global warming could escalate, rendering mitigation far more difficult.

Institute a mitigation program. Here we assume that despite acknowledged uncertainties, we know enough to warrant immediate action. Two courses of action are available, either or both of which could be done: a) Take worldwide action to reduce fossil fuel use immediately. To many, including the IPCC, historical trends and climate models strongly indicate there will be global catastrophe, including flooding, famine, property destruction, and reductions in the habitability of the Earth unless CO_2 emissions are sharply curtailed, which means fossil fuel use must be significantly reduced. This reduction does not necessarily mean a return to 1870s living standards. As noted above, a relatively small portion of the U.S. surface area covered with solar panels could generate enough power for current needs, and many uses of fossil fuel, like space heating, ground transportation, cleaning/drying, and others could be shifted to electricity, especially since the life of much of the equipment is about 10 to 15 years. This assumes a goal of reducing CO_2 production by 80 percent or so by 2050. Other areas like air travel will be more difficult because of the extremely high energy density of fossil fuels. Realistically, this will be a difficult course to follow because of the lack of consensus, the need for global cooperation, the enormous cost, disruption to lifestyles, and the uncertainties in technology needed to implement it. However we could at the same time, or alternatively, b) pursue geo-engineering. Geo-engineering is the deliberate manipulation of some aspects of the climate system to reduce global temperatures.[34] In particular, carbon sequestration on a large scale could counteract the increase in atmospheric CO_2. Methods to achieve this goal include reforestation, fertilizing the oceans, capturing and storing CO_2 from the air, and adding minerals to the oceans to increase alkalinity and thus ability to dissolve CO_2. Another strategy is to reduce the sun's radiation at the Earth's surface. Methods to achieve this include seeding clouds to make them more reflective, use of large mirrors in space, whitening rooftops, and injecting aerosols into the stratosphere. Geo-engineering is a high-risk strategy; as Higgins has noted, "the complexity of the climate system makes it challenging for scientists to fully identify and quantify the potential consequences associated with geo-engineering. As a result, the approach could cause unintended and adverse consequences."[35] For example, if global temperatures begin to decrease due to natural factors, amplifying that decrease could be catastrophic.

Undertake worthwhile additional actions. Advocates of either minimal action or mitigation agree that several actions can be taken immediately, none of which requires difficult political decisions or worldwide strictures: a) Do research and build our knowledge base. The more we know, the better positioned we are to decide what action to take and how to go about it. b) Pursue an adaptation strategy. This involves making preparations for climate change and perhaps even taking advantage of it. For example, if global temperatures are increasing, many northern areas could grow food crops and more southern areas could shift to different crops. It might also include changes in land use and occupancy, such as reducing settlement in flood-prone areas. Many of the actions could also protect against severe weather or other natural disasters. While these kinds of actions in most cases would require some political commitment, it would be local and/or national, rather than international. c) Reduce consumption of non-renewable resources. Despite fracking and other new recovery technologies, fossil fuels will eventually run out, so they should not be squandered. The world consumes about 10 trillion tons of fossil fuels annually (coal, oil, natural gas), producing a great deal of CO_2 and other airborne pollutants. This level of consumption is undesirable for several reasons that have nothing to do with global warming: we need to husband resources for future generations—the supply of fossil fuels is not unlimited (sustainability); use of fuels imported from unstable regions of the world leaves us vulnerable to geopolitical events that could interrupt supply; and we should reduce pollution, and burning of fossil fuel leads to relatively high pollution levels. This means that the question of fossil fuel use and conservation should be decoupled from that of global warming. The ideal solution would be to fund alternative energy research to find alternative heat and carbon-neutral ways of generating power.

CONCLUSION

The Earth's climate is always changing. Climate research seeks to understand it by looking back to past events and trends, and forward by modeling the climate and projecting future trends. Several conclusions are not in dispute:

1. The high rate of temperature increase observed in the late 20th century
2. The fairly steady temperatures since then
3. The increase in atmospheric CO_2 and other greenhouse gases
4. The responsibility of human activity for increases in greenhouse gases
5. The climate forcing of CO_2 and other greenhouse gases
6. The existence of positive and negative feedbacks in the Earth's climate system

What *is* in dispute is explanation of the temperature rise, the nature of the feedbacks in the climate system, and future temperature projections. The prevailing position is that of the IPCC, that the warming is unprecedented and must be the result of climate forcing from human-originated greenhouse gas emissions, amplified by feedback in the Earth's climate system. The primary remedy is curtailment of these emissions. Critics claim that the feedback on balance is negative, reducing the impact of greenhouse gas emissions.

At this time, the Climategate scandal and the pause in global warming have adversely affected the credibility of climate change advocates, and cast some doubt on their scientific case. The global recession that began in 2008 has effectively killed serious global efforts at CO_2 mitigation. As for future action, opinion polls on the subject of global warming vary considerably, and depend on the particular questions asked. The percentage of the population that believes global warming is happening or is a threat ranges from 30 to 70,[36,37] with a recent Yale poll putting the number at 60 percent, at least in the United States.[38] A Nature Conservancy poll from 2008 disclosed that only 18 percent of respondents thought that global warming was real, harmful, and due to human activity.[39] These numbers are inconsistent, which suggests support is below the threshold needed for sustained aggressive political action.

Climate change has become the focus of much attention because of the prestige of the IPCC and its predictions of significant future temperature increases if CO_2 production is not curtailed. The controversy has assumed a religious nature, in part because of biblical passages interpreted as enjoining environmental stewardship on mankind, and because for some environmentalism has become a surrogate religion: "We are going to destroy the creation," James Hansen has warned us.[40] Indeed both sides are claiming the moral high ground: those aligned with the IPCC contend that our failure to curtail greenhouse gas production will result in a catastrophe for the Earth and humanity; those opposed argue that there will be a catastrophe, but of a different sort, especially for the poor, if the abatement proceeds.

The basic policy options are minimal action or aggressive intervention. The choice made will depend mainly upon how certain one is of the predictions of future temperature increases. There is also a set of actions that can be taken independently of either option, including further research, better husbanding of resources, and pursuit of an adaptation strategy.

The old Chinese curse seems appropriate here: "May you live in interesting times!" We do, thanks in part to the global warming controversy. The next decade or so will tell the tale: either science (or at least establishment science) will enjoy one of its greatest triumphs and save humanity, or suffer its most embarrassing and humiliating failure.

ENDNOTES

1. Al Gore, *An Inconvenient Truth* (Emmaus, PA: Rodale Books, 2006). Also a well-known film.
2. Al Gore, *Earth in the Balance* (Emmaus, PA: Rodale Books, 2006).
3. James Hansen, *Storms of My Grandchildren* (London: Bloomsbury, 2010).
4. Roy Spencer, *The Great Global Warming Blunder* (New York: Encounter Books, 2010).
5. Robert Carter, *Climate: The Counter Consensus* (London: Stacey International, 2010).
6. Steve Goreham, *The Mad, Mad, Mad World of Climatism* (New Lenox, IL: New Lenox Books, 2012).
7. White House Press Release, November 25, 2009. Available at http://www.whitehouse.gov/the-press-office/president-attend-copenhagen-climate-talks.

8. U.S. Energy Information Administration, http://www.eia.gov/totalenergy/.
9. J. Farmer and M. Baxter, "Atmospheric Carbon Dioxide Levels as Indicated by the Stable Isotope Record in Wood," *Nature* 247 (February 1974): 273–75.
10. NOAA Earth Research Laboratory, "Recent Mauna Loa CO_2," available at http://www.esrl.noaa.gov/gmd/ccgg/trends/.
11. "Air," *Encyclopedia Britannica*, available at http://www.britannica.com/EBchecked/topic/10582/air.
12. Intergovernmental Panel on Climate Change History (IPCC), http://www.ipcc.ch/organization/organization_history.shtml#.T5agnNmQOeY.
13. Available at http://www.ipcc.ch/report/ar5/wg1/.
14. Quansheng Ge et al., "Winter Half-Year Temperature Reconstruction for the Middle and Lower Reaches of the Yellow River and Yangtze River, China, During the Past 2000 Years," *The Holocene* 13 (2003): 933–40.
15. Julie Richey, "1400 Yr Multiproxy Record of Climate Variability from the Northern Gulf of Mexico," *Geology* vol. 35, no. 5 (May, 2007): 423–26.
16. Michael Mann, R. Bradley, and M. Hughes, "Global-Scale Temperature Patterns and Climate Forcing over the Past Six Centuries," *Nature* 392 (1998): 779–87.
17. T. C. Peterson and M. O. Baringer, eds., "State of the Climate in 2008," Special Supplement to the *Bulletin of the American Meteorological Society* 90, no. 8 (2009): S22. The report was prepared under the auspices of NOAA.
18. Matt Ridley, "Whatever Happened to Global Warming?" *Wall Street Journal*, September 4, 2014.
19. C. Woodhouse, D. Meko, G. MacDonald, D. Stahle, and E. Cook, "A 1,200-Year Perspective of 21st Century Drought in Southwestern North America," *Proceedings of the National Academy of Sciences* 107, no. 50 (2010): 21283–88.
20. The papers by Quansheng and Richey, cited above, confirm the Medieval Warm Period in their respective locations (east Asia and North America).
21. Fred Pearce, "Hockey Stick Graph Took Pride of Place in IPCC Report, Despite Doubts," *Guardian*, February 9, 2010. Available at http://www.guardian.co.uk/environment/2010/feb/09/hockey-stick-graph-ipcc-report.
22. Roy Spencer, *The Great Global Warming Blunder* (New York: Encounter Books, 2010), 11.
23. Gerald North, Franco Biondi, Peter Bloomfield, *Surface Temperature Reconstructions for the Last 2000 Years* (Washington, DC: National Academies Press, 2006).
24. Andrew W. Montford, *The Hockey Stick Illusion* (London: Stacey International, 2010), 402–20.
25. Intergovernmental Panel on Climate Change, *Climate Change 2007: The Physical Science Basis* (New York: Cambridge University Press, 2007), Figure TS.20, 55. The figure shows 12 different reconstructions of northern hemisphere temperatures, most of which show some medieval

warming, and some subsequent cooling. But all show that current temperatures are significantly higher than the medieval period, by 0.5°C or more.

26. IPCC, Climate Change 2014: Mitigation of Climate Change, *Summary for Policymakers*, http://report.mitigation2014.org/spm/ipcc_wg3_ar5_summary-for-policymakers_approved.pdf.
27. IPCC Working Group III-Mitigation of Climate Change, AR5, 2014, Chapter 1 Introductory Chapter, 19. Available at http://report.mitigation2014.org/drafts/final-draft-postplenary/ipcc_wg3_ar5_final-draft_postplenary_chapter1.pdf.
28. Ibid., 12.
29. Intergovernmental Panel on Climate Change, *Climate Change 2007: The Physical Science Basis*, 88.
30. "Climate Change Alarmist Recants: 'I Made a Mistake'," report from MSNBC, reported in *Newsmax*, http://www.newsmax.com (April 29, 2012).
31. Brian M. Fagan, *The Little Ice Age: How Climate Made History 1300–1850* (New York: Basic Books, 2000), 21.
32. Some of these positions and their discussion are taken from Paul Higgins, "How to deal with Climate Change," *Physics Today* 67, no. 10 (2014): 32ff.
33. "First do no harm."
34. Higgins, "How to deal with Climate Change."
35. Ibid.
36. Richard Gray and Ben Leach, "New Errors in IPCC Climate Change Report," *The Telegraph*, February 6, 2010. Available at http://www.telegraph.co.uk/Earth/environment/climatechange/7177230/New-errors-in-IPCC-climate-change-report.html.
37. Juliet Eilperin, "Fewer Americans Believe in Global Warming, Poll Shows," *Washington Post*, November 25, 2009. Available at http://www.washingtonpost.com/wp-dyn/content/article/2009/11/24/AR2009112402989.html.
38. Stephanie Pappas, "New Poll Shows 63 Percent of Americans Believe Global Warming Is Occurring," *LiveScience*, December 4, 2011. Available at http://www.mnn.com/Earth-matters/climate-weather/stories/new-poll-shows-63-percent-of-americans-believe-global-warming-.
39. "What Do Americans Believe About Climate Change?" The Nature Conservancy, October, 2008. Available at http://www.nature.org/initiatives/climatechange/features/art26253.html.
40. Scott Rothschild, "NASA Climate Expert Warns Kansans of Dire Consequences of Global Warming," *Lawrence Journal-World*, September 23, 2008.

RECOMMENDED READINGS/SOURCES

Carter, Robert M. 2010. *Climate: The Counter Consensus: A Paleo-climatologist Speaks*. London: Stacey International.

Eggleton, Tony. 2012. *A Short Introduction to Climate Change*. Cambridge: Cambridge University Press.

Fagan, Brian. 2000. *The Little Ice Age: How Climate Made History 1300–1850*. New York: Basic Books.

Gardiner, Stephen M. 2013. *A Perfect Moral Storm: The Ethical Tragedy of Climate Change*. Oxford: Oxford University Press.

Gardiner, Stephen, and Simon Caney, eds. 2010. *Climate Change: Essential Readings*. Oxford: Oxford University Press.

Giddens, Anthony. 2011. *The Politics of Climate Change*, 2nd ed. Cambridge, UK: Polity.

Gore, Al. 2006. *An Inconvenient Truth: The Planetary Emergancy of Global Warming and What We Can do About It.*. New York: Rodale

Gore, Al. 2006. *Earth in the Balance*. Emmaus, PA: Rodale.

Goreham, Steve. 2012. *The Mad, Mad, Mad World of Climatism*. New Lenox, IL: New Lenox Books.

Hansen, James. 2010. *Storms of My Grandchildren: The Truth About the Coming Catastrophe and Our Last Chance to Save Humanity*. New York: Bloomsbury USA.

Intergovernmental Panel on Climate Change (IPCC). 2014. *Fifth Assessment Report (2014)*. Geneva: IPCC. Available at http://www.ipcc.ch/.

Montford, Andrew W. 2010. *The Hockey Stick Illusion*. London: Stacey International.

Spencer, Roy W. 2010. *The Great Global Warming Blunder*. New York, Encounter Books.

Toxic Waste

by **TOBIAS LANZ**

CHAPTER SIX

INTRODUCTION

Human and animal waste, waste from mining and metallurgy, and other economic practices have created health and environmental problems for millennia. Toxic waste is nothing new. What is different today is the amount and types of waste that now enter the ecosystem. Moreover, the health and environmental effects of many of these toxins are still unknown.

The term hazardous is often preferred to toxic waste, because the sheer quantity and quality of the toxins is such that it now presents a major hazard (real or potential) to people and the environment. Moreover, toxic waste can be natural (e.g., arsenic in ground water), whereas hazardous waste is the result of modern industry. Humans alone produce toxins on a scale and consistency to create hazardous conditions that are anomalous in nature. And, as the number of industrial products and processes continues to grow, so does the amount of hazardous waste.

The United States Environmental Protection Agency (EPA) defines hazardous waste:

> Waste that is dangerous or potentially harmful to our health or the environment. Hazardous wastes can be liquids, solids, gases or sludges. They can be discarded commercial products, like cleaning fluids or pesticides, or the by-products of manufacturing processes.[1]

Hazardous waste can pollute the air, soil, water, and ground water. There are also different categories of waste, and specific procedures determining how hazardous waste is identified and properly managed. In the United States, the EPA defines these categories and procedures (see Box 6.1).

THE HAZARDOUS WASTE PROBLEM

Hazardous waste is a serious problem because it is so lethal to humans, plants, and animals. But dealing with hazardous waste is also a dilemma, because industrially produced chemicals are essential to the comfort, ease, wealth, and security of the modern world. There is no aspect of modern life that does not involve industrial chemicals. Modern life would be unthinkable without them.

Our water supply is treated with fluoride, and we brush our teeth with toothpaste made of fluoride compounds. The food we eat is preserved with chemicals, and chemical fertilizers, pesticides, herbicides, and fungicides are used to produce our food supply. All of our medicines are chemical concoctions. Clothing is made of chemical compounds like rayon and polyester, and is cleaned with an array of chemicals. Cars are filled with plastics and metals, all chemical compounds, and require many chemical fluids to run. Building materials, from insulation to flooring, are made of chemical compounds. And the products that keep our buildings clean are chemicals. The list goes on.

Many of these products are toxic, and many are the result of industrial manufacturing processes that use toxic chemicals. It is the disposal of all these chemical waste products that first began to alert the general public to the more general problem of the real and potential dangers of our modern reliance on industrially produced chemical products.

People already knew in the 19th century about industrial waste. Companies routinely dumped waste into rivers and lakes, or simply buried it. The effects were largely local and as such did not garner much attention from the general public. Medicine was not yet aware of the toxicity of industrial chemicals. And government likewise did not respond. Even if local citizens objected to local dumping, government often sided with the wealthy and influential companies that produced and disposed of the waste.

The 20th century saw a change. First, the amount and toxicity of industrial waste began to increase, especially after World War II. Industry was expanding rapidly, and it produced a vast and dizzying array of new products, as well as new types of waste. Much of it was connected to the production of military armaments and the petroleum industry. And much of it, like nuclear waste, was highly toxic and difficult to dispose.

Box 6.1 Hazardous Waste Definitions

Listed Wastes

By definition, the Environmental Protection Agency (EPA) determined that some specific wastes are hazardous. These wastes are incorporated into lists published by the EPA. These lists are organized into three categories:

1. The F-list (non-specific source wastes): This list identifies wastes from common manufacturing and industrial processes, such as solvents that have been used in cleaning or degreasing operations. Because the processes producing these wastes can occur in different sectors of industry, the F-listed wastes are known as wastes from non-specific sources.
2. The K-list (source-specific wastes): This list includes certain wastes from specific industries, such as petroleum refining or pesticide manufacturing. Certain sludges and wastewaters from treatment and production processes in these industries are examples of source-specific wastes.
3. The P-list and the U-list (discarded commercial chemical products): These lists include specific commercial chemical products in an unused form. Some pesticides and some pharmaceutical products become hazardous waste when discarded.

Characteristic Wastes

Waste that has not been specifically listed may still be considered a hazardous waste if exhibits one of the four characteristics—ignitability, corrosivity, reactivity, or toxicity.

1. Ignitability: Ignitable wastes can create fires under certain conditions, are spontaneously combustible, or have a flash point less than 60°C (140°F). Examples include waste oils and used solvents.
2. Corrosivity: Corrosive wastes are acids or bases (pH less than or equal to 2, or greater than or equal to 12.5) that are capable of corroding metal containers, such as storage tanks, drums, and barrels. Battery acid is an example.

Continued...

3. Reactivity: Reactive wastes are unstable under "normal" conditions. They can cause explosions, toxic fumes, gases, or vapors when heated, compressed, or mixed with water. Examples include lithium-sulfur batteries and explosives.
4. Toxicity: Toxic wastes are harmful or fatal when ingested or absorbed (e.g., containing mercury, lead, et cetera). When toxic wastes are land disposed, contaminated liquid may leach from the waste and pollute ground water. May be harmful to human health or the environment.

Universal Wastes

The EPA's universal waste regulations streamline hazardous waste management standards for federally designated universal wastes, which include batteries, pesticides, mercury-containing equipment, and bulbs (lamps).

Source: Environmental Protection Agency, http://www.epa.gov/waste/hazard/wastetypes/index.htm.

Citizens and government recognized that waste was no longer a local problem. It was a national problem, requiring political action.

The first changes occurred in the 1960s. The environmental movement now went beyond simply protecting wildlife and wilderness. These were still important issues, but now the environmental movement broadened. It had a distinctive focus on industry, industrial pollution, and its impact on public health and the environment. And it is significant that, for the first time, urban poor people became aware of pollution and toxins in their neighborhoods and work places. Similar developments occurred in Europe and industrializing countries in Asia.

In the United Sates, Congress passed the Clean Air Act in 1963 and the Solid Waste Disposal Act in 1965, which dealt with waste disposal in general. It was the Nixon administration that then pursued the most active policies to date. The Clean Water Act was signed in 1972. Most importantly, the administration created the Environmental Protection Agency (EPA) in 1970. Its explicit goal is to protect human health and the environment from hazardous wastes. It writes and enforces

Box 6.2 The Main Pollution and Hazardous Waste Laws in the United States

Solid Waste Disposal Act (1965): Required environmentally sound methods for disposal of household, municipal, commercial, and industrial waste.

National Environmental Protection Act (1969): Empowered the U.S. Environmental Protection Agency (EPA) and the National Environmental Quality Control Council (NEQCC) to establish environmental regulations and legislation.

Clean Air Act (1970): Protects and enhances national air quality.

Federal Insecticide, Fungicide, and Rodenticide Act (1972): Regulates the disposal and storage of excess pesticides and pesticide containers.

Safe Drinking Water Act (1974): Ensures quality of public drinking water.

Hazardous Materials Transportation Act (1975): Regulates the transportation of hazardous materials.

Resource Conservation and Recovery Act (1976): Regulates management and disposal of hazardous wastes.

Toxic Substances Control Act (1976): Provides a broad range of risk reduction actions to accommodate the EPA's control of toxic substance use and disposal.

Clean Water Act (1977): Restores and maintains the chemical, physical, and biological quality of all of the nation's water resources.

Comprehensive Environmental Response, Compensation and Liability Act (1980): Also known as "Superfund." Establishes a broad authority to deal with hazardous wastes, especially remediation of hazardous waste sites.

Asbestos Hazardous Emergency Response Act (1986): Requires local educational agencies to inspect schools for asbestos and helps them reduce asbestos hazards.

Emergency, Planning, and Community Right to Know Act (1986): Helps communities protect public health, safety, and the environment from chemical hazards.

Continued...

Oil Pollution Act (1990): Strengthens the EPA's ability to prevent and respond to oil pollution accidents.

Pollution Prevention Act (1990): Establishes pollution prevention as the national policy for controlling industrial waste at its source.

Sources: Environmental Protection Agency, http://www2.epa.gov/laws-regulations; D. Kofi asante-Duah and Imre V. Nage. 1998. International Trade in Hazardous Waste. *London: Routledge Publishers.*

environmental regulations. The main federal law regulating hazardous wastes is the Resource Conservation and Recovery Act (RCRA), signed in1976 (see Box 6.2).[2]

The first great challenge to the EPA and the RCRA came from a place called Love Canal, which has become synonymous with hazardous waste. The Love Canal neighborhood in Niagara Falls, New York, became a national crisis in 1978, after it was discovered that an entire community was being ravaged by the negligent disposal of hazardous waste. The scale and severity of the health problems started the national debate on hazardous waste in America (see Case 6.1). Since that date, other cases have emerged in America and around the world. After Love Canal, the hazardous waste problem could no longer be denied.

By the 1980s, the production, use, and transport of hazardous materials and waste had become global. Two international industrial accidents focused attention on the global presence of hazardous waste, how quickly toxins could be released, and their lethal consequences. One was a massive explosion at a Union Carbide pesticide plant in Bhopal, India, in 1984. It injured over 500,000 people and killed over 3,000. It remains the worst industrial disaster ever.[3]

The other was the accident at the Chernobyl nuclear facility in the Soviet Union in 1986 (see Case Study 6.2). It killed dozens, exposed hundreds of thousands of people to toxic radiation, and poisoned thousands of acres of forest and farmland. It created international furor and fear, because after Chernobyl it became clear that hazardous waste was also a transnational problem. It could no longer be contained to specific regions and nations. Global political action would be required.

HAZARDOUS WASTE AS A GLOBAL PROBLEM

The global trade in hazardous waste has become an international waste issue—one of the main transnational environmental problems today.[4] The trade has grown because advanced industrial nations developed stricter controls over disposal. As a result, the United States, Japan, China, and the European Union now ship much of their hazardous waste overseas—to poor nations, where it is disposed. The phenomenon has also been prompted by globalization, which created new markets and opportunities to dispose of hazardous waste.

The problem is that waste management regulations in the developing countries where the waste is disposed are weak to non-existent. So while the health and environmental problems from toxic waste once found in the industrial nations have been greatly reduced, many are now exported to the developing world. And the rate of waste disposal in these countries often grows more rapidly than the ability of governments or the markets to deal with it.

The disposal of toxic wastes has become a major global industry. It also involves many actors. First there are governments—both the wealthy Global North and poor Global South are involved. They make the policies that promote waste disposal. Governments of poor nations are often willing to receive the waste because they receive substantial payments for this service. Those of the wealthy nations are relieved to have the hazardous material leave their territory.

Transnational corporations (TNCs) are another important actor. They are involved in every stage of the product cycle. They manufacture and ship the hazardous materials. They are involved in negotiating policies and practices with governments that receive and dump hazardous waste. Many critics thus believe that TNCs bear the greatest responsibility to properly dispose of hazardous waste, because of this intimate involvement—an involvement that is also highly profitable.

Nongovernmental organizations (NGOs) may be the most important international actors on this issue, especially from an environmental standpoint. In many cases they are the only organizations that monitor the hazardous waste trade, its health and environmental consequences. And it is NGOs that have forged international agreements to regulate the trade and disposal of hazardous wastes. The Basel Convention was the first and most important of these agreements.

The Basel Convention on the Control of Transboundary Movements of Hazardous Waste and their Disposal was adopted in 1989 and went into force in 1992. The goal of the treaty has been to reduce the amount of hazardous waste traded between nations, to reduce the toxicity of that waste, and to help developing nations better manage hazardous waste. Currently, 181 countries have signed the treaty. The United States has not.[5]

The international trade in hazardous waste has also sparked debates over economic policy and theory. Liberal economics (capitalism) and its emphasis on free trade is the basis of contemporary globalization. Advocates argue that the disposal of toxic waste in poor nations provides them with much needed income. And because of limited regulation and inexpensive dumpsites, these countries have a "comparative advantage"—a trade advantage in hazardous waste over advanced industrial nations.

This argument is strongly rejected by other economists and environmentalists, who see the global hazardous waste trade as another way in which wealthy countries exploit the poor. The trade also raises questions about the growing power and influence of TNCs, and their ability to manipulate government policy (of rich and poor countries alike) to their advantage—but to the disadvantage of the poor and the environment.

TYPES OF HAZARDOUS WASTE

More than 20,000 hazardous waste generators produce over 40 million tons of hazardous waste in the United States every year. The EPA reports that the world's total is about three times that amount.[6] Hazardous waste is produced by small businesses like dry cleaners and gas stations, and large industries that produce chemicals, petroleum products, and energy.

There are different classes of hazardous waste. Some of the most important are as follows.

Asbestos

Asbestos is a general term for a group of materials that contains calcium or magnesium silicates. These compounds form long, thin fibers, which can be blended with other materials to create many different products. The most important quality of asbestos is its high resistance to heat and fire. Because it is a fire retardant, it has been widely used in electrical products, insulation, and building materials.

Another asbestos quality is that it is not subject to biological or chemical change. This stability is good for products, but creates a hazard for living things. Asbestos's toxicity is in its physical structure—the long threads. When ingested, and especially inhaled, they become lodged in the lungs and other body tissues. They cause long-term health problems, including respiratory problems and lung cancer (mesothelioma), since the body cannot assimilate them.

The most serious asbestos hazards have been in urban environments. People living in buildings with asbestos products and those working in asbestos manufacturing have contracted many diseases from exposure. The Environmental Working Group, a toxic waste research and advocacy organization, estimates that over 10,000 Americans die every year from asbestos-related illnesses, mainly lung cancer.[7] Many of these illnesses do not develop until years after exposure.

People knew for decades that asbestos caused illness and death. But it was not until the 1970s that lawsuits related to asbestos exposure at home or the workplace were filed in large numbers, including several major class action lawsuits. This occurred throughout the industrial nations. The result was that many asbestos and asbestos product manufacturers stopped production. Some even went bankrupt because of the large settlements they paid to asbestos victims.[8]

Since then, considerable asbestos production has moved to the newly industrializing countries of the Global South. Yet most nations, including the United States, strictly regulate asbestos production. Materials that are friable—meaning they readily produce airborne particles—are banned in most of the world. Some countries have banned all asbestos production and products. Currently the Basel Convention lists asbestos as a controlled waste.

Synthetic Organic Chemicals

Synthetically produced chemicals, especially organic chemicals, are the most abundant and some of the most lethal types of hazardous waste. Organic chemicals are carbon compounds found naturally in the environment. It is the manufacture of new organic chemicals, especially from coal, petroleum, and natural gas, which is unprecedented. Many of these have environmental and health impacts that are still unknown. And the number of synthetic organic chemical products is enormous.

This chemical revolution began slowly in the 19th century, with the development of the petroleum industry. It exploded after World War II, as chemists discovered many ways to manipulate and change naturally occurring carbon compounds. Total synthetic organic chemical production in the United States totaled one billion pounds in 1940. By 1976, it was 300 billion pounds. By 2005 it was over 25 trillion pounds.[9] The industry is now global, and continues to grow.

The most toxic synthetic organic chemicals are known as persistent organic pollutants (POPs). There were originally 12 such chemicals, which earned them

Box 6.3 Persistent Organic Pollutants—"The Dirty Dozen," Their Uses and Human Health Effects

1. Aldrin: Insecticide. Linked to skin irritation.
2. Chlordane: Insecticide. Carcinogen.
3. Dichlorodiphenyltrichloroethane (DDT): Insecticide. Carcinogen and neurotoxin. Linked to diabetes and reproductive problems.
4. Dieldrin: Insecticide. Neurotoxin. Linked to Parkinson's disease.
5. Dioxins: Byproducts of various industrial manufacturing processes. Carcinogen. Linked to immune and enzyme disorders.
6. Endrin: Insecticide. Neurotoxin.
7. Furan: Byproduct of various industrial manufacturing processes. Carcinogen.
8. Heptachlor: Insecticide. Carcinogen. Linked to reproductive problems.
9. Hexachlorobenzene (HCB): Fungicide. Byproduct of various industrial manufacturing processes. Linked to reproductive problems, intestinal problems, and metabolic disorders.
10. Mirex: Insecticide and fire retardant in plastics, rubber, and electrical goods. Carcinogen.
11. Polychlorinated biphenyls (PCBs): Heat exchange fluid in electrical transformers. Additive to paints, sealants, and plastics. Linked to reproductive problems.
12. Toxaphene: Insecticide. Carcinogen.

Source: Environmental Protection Agency, Persistent Organic Pollutants: A Global Issue, A Global Response. *Available at http://www2.epa.gov/international-cooperation/persistent-organic-pollutants-global-issue-global-response.*

the name "the Dirty Dozen" (see Box Three). They are used in many products and manufacturing processes, which leads to high volumes of waste. And because they are very stable compounds, they also persist in the environment for years, accumulating in soil, water, or living organisms.

Dichlorodiphenyltrichloroethane (DDT) is the most famous POP. It is an insecticide that can remain in the soil for 15 years after application. It bioaccumulates in fish, birds, and people. It interrupts birth cycles, causes birth defects, and is a carcinogen. Most countries have banned the production and use of DDT. The United States banned it in the 1970s. But a few nations in the tropics still use it to control malaria. Ironically, the World Health Organization (WHO), which is part of the United Nations, has endorsed DDT, as it is argued that malaria control is impossible without it.

Because of their persistence and toxicity, POPs have become a leading global environmental problem and policy issue. Another United Nations agency, the United Nations Environmental Programme, called for global action on the POPs problem in the 1990s. As a result, the Stockholm Convention on Persistent Organic Chemicals was created and signed by 178 countries and the European Union in 2001. Subsequent treaty conferences have added new POPs to be eliminated or restricted.[10]

The Stockholm Conference has had some clear successes, especially in getting advanced industrial nations to eliminate the production of these toxic chemicals. But it is an ongoing process, as new POPs are constantly being developed by the chemical industry. It often takes years for these materials to be recognized as toxic. Proper regulation and control over POP usage in Global South nations is another challenge.

Heavy Metals

Heavy metals are another class of hazardous materials. The most toxic to human health and the environment are arsenic, zinc, copper, cadmium, lead, and mercury. Their chemical composition makes them inherently toxic, unlike other hazardous materials, which are dangerous because of a particular molecular form or combination. Moreover, heavy metals do not change their composition due to heat or biological processes. So when they enter a living organism, they are not assimilated, retaining their chemical structure and toxicity.[11]

Heavy metals were among the first toxic materials encountered by human societies. Mining and smelting exposed people directly to these metals, and water was polluted by mining waste (tailings). And people also worked with these materials and used products made from them. For example, mercury was used in ancient Greece, and lead pipes supplied drinking water in ancient Rome. Both caused illness.

The use and disposal of heavy metals has increased dramatically since the Industrial Revolution in the 18th century. Today these toxins are found in a wide range of products and production processes. Lead and mercury are the two most hazardous heavy metals. Lead is a powerful neurotoxin that can cause nerve and brain damage. It also destroys human organs. It was commonly used in paints and gasoline before being banned. But it is still widely used in batteries and electronic devices, and is a byproduct of mining.

Mercury is even more toxic. Small doses—less than a gram—can kill people, and long-term exposure can cause kidney, brain, and heart problems. More people are poisoned by mercury than any other hazardous material in the world today. Over three million people suffer from severe health problems and early deaths. People often consume mercury through their diet, as the metal is stored in the fat of animals and fish, but most come into contact with it through work, especially the mining industry.[12]

Mercury is critical to the mining of precious metals, as it is used to separate the metal from surrounding rock and silt. The resulting amalgam is then heated to vaporize and remove the mercury. Miners inhale this vapor. The mercury-laden tailings also pollute waterways and thus afflict entire ecosystems. The mercury process is widespread because it is cheap and easy. It is thus used by small-scale miners the world over, few of whom understand the health risks. The process continues to spread because of the growing value of precious metals, especially gold.[13]

Most cases are from the Global South, where there is little regulation or proper healthcare for afflicted people. Ironically, the mercury hazard is relatively easy and inexpensive to control. Special devices can easily be built to capture the toxic fumes, thus greatly reducing health risks. It is usually NGOs that now educate miners and implement controls. It is an enormous logistical problem because mining operations are literally spread all over the world.

Nuclear Waste

Nuclear or radioactive waste is the most toxic class of hazardous waste. Its lethal and destructive potential is well known. Thus the thought of a nuclear military attack, or simply an accident at a nuclear facility, evokes fear in most people. Even people who have no knowledge of other types of toxic waste know about the dangers of nuclear waste.

To understand radioactive waste, one must understand its chemical properties. Every chemical element is composed of protons and neutrons. The number of protons determines the type of element (e.g., hydrogen has one proton and is listed first on the periodic table of chemical elements). But some elements have varying numbers of neutrons. These variants are known as isotopes. And some isotopes are unstable, meaning they are radioactive and spontaneously disintegrate and release energy.

This spontaneous energy release is what makes nuclear materials so dangerous. When radiation makes contact with matter, it is converted into other forms of energy. This conversion process is highly destructive, destroying tissues, organs, and cells in living things. The mass chain reaction released by nuclear weapons destroys every physical object in range. Contact with high doses of radiation leads to instant death. Exposure to low levels, even minute levels, for long periods of time, leads to cancer, reproductive problems, skin diseases, and more.

Humans have found many ways to harness nuclear materials and use them for many purposes—x-rays and other medical procedures, electricity, and weapons production. But it is the energy and weapons industries that produce the most hazardous types and levels of nuclear waste, so-called high level waste and transuranic waste. These waste types include spent nuclear reactor fuel, obsolete nuclear weapons, solids generated in fuel processing, and all equipment contaminated by high radiation levels.[14]

Some types of nuclear waste can be recycled, but most is buried on the bottom of deep cooling ponds at nuclear facilities. Other waste is locked into sealed containers that are usually buried in deep underground vaults, or inside stable rock formations. Sealed and secure disposal is critical for nuclear waste, because it takes decades to centuries for the waste to degenerate into a non-toxic form.

In the United States, the EPA, the Nuclear Regulatory Commission (NRC), the Department of Energy (DOE), and the Department of Transportation (DOT) share the responsibilities for nuclear waste management. The EPA sets standards for exposure, and the NRC regulates and licenses all waste. The DOT monitors all aspects of the waste movement, and the DOE manages clean-up programs, regulates contracts, and licenses nuclear facilities.[15]

All nations with nuclear industries have governmental bodies that regulate and manage nuclear materials. At the international level there are several organizations that do the same. The International Atomic Energy Organization is the foremost nuclear international organization (IO). It was founded in 1957 to promote the safe and peaceful development of nuclear technology. The Nuclear Energy Agency is another IO that is part of the Organization for Economic Cooperation and Development. Its focus is research and technology development. The International Nuclear Regulatory Association focuses on safety and comprises individuals from key nuclear nations.[16]

While the specter of nuclear war faded with the end of the Cold War, there is still fear that nuclear destruction could be unleashed by a terrorist attack or an accident at a nuclear facility. This has already occurred at Three Mile Island (USA), Chernobyl (Soviet Union; see Case Study Two) and recently Fukushima Daiichi (Japan). But the greater concern is the routine disposal of nuclear waste from industry. Currently, 12,000 tons are produced annually, and all must be stored with the utmost safely and security.[17] As more nations turn to nuclear energy and nuclear products, this amount will grow and the question over how and where to store this most hazardous of wastes will become more pressing.

A NEW WASTE INDUSTRY

Electronic or E-Waste

Information technology—computers, television, telephones, and other electronic devices—has been heralded as a higher and better phase of industrialization. It is seen as "higher" because it is more complex than the old steel and iron industries. It is also seen as higher because it is believed to more efficient, ethereal, and thus more environmentally friendly.

This has proven false. The information technology industry is a resource- and energy-intensive industry that produces a considerable amount of hazardous waste. Few people are aware of how much waste is generated in the production process and at the consumer end. Computers, for example, use 50 pounds of fossil fuels, 50 pounds of chemicals and 1.5 tons of water for every unit produced.[18] The industry creates some unique environmental problems because of the complex nature of the products and production processes.

There are many complex stages in the electronic product cycle, and all use resources. This begins at the mining stage. Computers use 20 different metals.[19] And, as in all mining, this uses considerable energy in extraction and transportation, and produces considerable toxic waste, like sulfuric acid, in the tailings (materials left behind after valuable ores have been removed).

The next stage—manufacturing—is equally wasteful. The complexity of electronic devices requires equally complex production techniques. To make a simple one-ounce microchip—the "brain" of computers and every other electronic device—requires up to 70 pounds of water and 500 to 1,000 different chemicals, including phosphoric, sulfuric and nitric acids; ammonia; and a host of other toxic chemicals.[20] Other computer components are no different, with computer screens using toxic metals like lead and mercury.

An example of the toxic consequences of high-tech manufacturing is Silicon Valley. It is the center of the high-tech industry, and one of the wealthiest and most beautiful places in America. It is also one of the most polluted. Miles of ground water supplies are contaminated with a host of toxic chemicals. And the EPA has declared 29 areas in the Silicon Valley as Superfund sites (those with the worst levels of pollution). The high-tech industry has been the direct cause of 20 of these.[21]

Energy and waste are also present in the consumption part of the cycle. Energy use per electronic unit keeps improving, but lower costs make electronic devices ever cheaper and more popular, with billions now in use worldwide. This is worsened by their short product life cycle—usually two or three years. This is the result of Moore's Law—that computer processing capacity doubles every two years, causing the constant development of new products.

As the technology and capabilities of electronic devices increase, so does energy usage. This is especially the case with wireless devices like smartphones. Some researchers claim that at maximum use, these phones consume more electricity than an energy efficient refrigerator.[22] All of this energy use produces hazardous waste. Energy is electricity, which is produced, in most cases, by nuclear power or burning coal. Both produce significant waste.

Environmental groups have leveled many criticisms at high technology industries in recent years—especially as these industries have become pervasive and are known to be energy intensive. Companies like Google and Apple have responded to these challenges by building more efficient data centers. Much of the problem also lies with consumers, who use high technology with little understanding of its health or environmental costs.

The waste that has garnered the most attention—e-waste—comes at the end of the cycle, when products are discarded. Electronic devices must be dumped or recycled. By 2010, 3 billion electronic devices (mainly televisions, phones, and computers) had already been discarded in America. Most of this e-waste went to landfills. The rate is expected to stay at about 400 million units per year.[23] To this must be added the e-waste of Europe and Asia. The latter may eventually produce the most e-waste, given its large populations, many of whom desire electronic goods.

The future of high technology may not be so much about processing and storing information as it will be over how to manage the increasing amount of energy the industry uses, and the hazardous waste it produces. It will also require consumers to understand that high technology is not some new or magical industry. It is simply another type of industrial production that uses energy and resources, and produces

Box 6.4 Hydraulic Fracturing and Hazardous Waste

Fracking was developed decades ago but was not widely used until recently. Better technology and high oil and gas prices made the process economically feasible. Today over 2 million wells have been fracked worldwide. The process injects high pressure chemical solutions deep into well bores. These fluids fracture rock formations, which releases oil and gas. There are many toxic chemicals used in the process, including methanol, isopropyl, various acids, and salt solutions.

Environmental concerns over fracking are 1. the poisoning of ground water by the chemical solutions; 2. the large amounts of water used in the process, which also becomes polluted; 3. surface and air pollution caused by the chemical solutions; 4. noise pollution; and 5. seismic disturbances caused by the fracturing of deep rock formations.

Reports about the impact of hydraulic fracturing have been mixed. Yet many countries have banned the process and opposition to it, especially by local communities, is growing.

Source: United Kingdom Department of Energy and Climate Changes. 2013. Developing Onshore Shale Gas and Oil—Facts about "Fracking." London: Crown Publishing.

a considerable amount of waste, much of it hazardous.

Hydraulic Fracturing

Hydraulic fracturing, or "fracking," is a new and widely used method of oil and gas production. The process uses many chemicals that are injected into wells to release oil and gas. The impact of these chemicals on the environment is still unknown, and concerns many environmentalists.

THE FUTURE OF HAZARDOUS WASTE

One of the positive trends in hazardous waste management is the vast improvement in treatment, storage, and disposal. In decades past, hazardous materials were simply dumped anywhere (often illegally). Growing evidence of the negative health and environmental effects of hazardous waste forced dramatic changes in waste management in the last few decades.

As a result, hazardous waste management has matured into a sophisticated modern industry. Today there are many hazardous waste treatment, storage, and disposal methods, which vary greatly depending on the type of material. Waste can be treated biologically, thermally, and chemically. It can be in incinerated. It can be stored in containers and buried in landfills. And more toxic materials can be buried deep underground in vaults or injection wells. Hazardous waste can also be recycled.

Some experts argue that hazardous waste management must be viewed more objectively, as a legitimate business and also as an important ecological process. The proper treatment, storage and disposal facilities act as the "kidneys" of the entire industrial world.[24] They help clean and control waste, and thus keep the human-created industrial world from polluting the natural environment. Rather than a pariah to be shunned, many observers believe the waste industry must be understood as necessary to good human health and clean ecosystems. As such, it must be properly developed and regulated.

It is also for this reason that many analysts advocate a global trade in hazardous wastes, even to poor nations. It is a legitimate economic endeavor, and one that, if performed properly, can help keep the environment and human health safe, and generate jobs and economic development. Hazardous waste must be reexamined in this light.

Yet despite all these positive trends, experts also believe the most important phase in hazardous waste management will be 1. the overall reduction of the amount and toxicity of waste, and 2. the elimination of certain classes of waste, especially highly toxic ones. The future of hazardous waste will focus more on pollution prevention rather than pollution control—the current situation. This endeavor will involve many political and economic actors, the least of which will be citizens, consumers, and workers—those who will pay the price if the hazardous waste problem is not properly addressed.

CASE STUDY 6.1

Love Canal

Love Canal is synonymous with hazardous waste. Located in the famous town of Niagara Falls, New York, the canal made the town infamous. For it is here that the Hooker Chemical Company dumped 21,000 tons of chemical poisons that ruined the health and lives of hundreds of people. Love Canal became the national scandal that first made the American public aware of the dangers and pervasiveness of toxic waste.

The canal was constructed in the 1890s as part of a plan to promote industry in the region. The power generated by Niagara Falls had already attracted a good amount of industry, and with it, industrial waste. Tourists were already complaining of foul-smelling water, dead fish, birds, and vegetation at this early date. But development proceeded.

The canal was never finished, as its promoters went bankrupt in the economic crash of the 1890s. But a long, deep, and open pit was left behind, and had to be used for something or by someone. That someone was the Hooker Chemical Company, one of the town's largest companies and maker of chlorine and 100 other chemical products. This produced a tremendous amount of hazardous waste, which had to be disposed of.

Hooker began dumping toxic materials in Niagara Falls shortly after its first factory was built in 1906. The company grew rapidly and expanded throughout the country. It reached over US$1 billion in net sales by the 1970s. But those chemical sales meant more hazardous waste disposal. All of that waste was buried or discharged into rivers and streams in close proximity to the Hooker factories. Benzene, dioxins, and polychlorinated biphenyls (PCBs)—some of the most toxic materials ever manufactured—were found in every Hooker dumpsite throughout the United States.

Health problems and environmental damage from these dump sites were being reported to authorities in the 1950s. But they were sporadic. No action was taken. Much of this was due to ignorance. Few people, even professionals, understood toxic waste and its effects. But the evidence kept growing. And the evidence that finally brought action and change was Love Canal.

The Love Canal dumping began in the 1940s and continued into the early 1950s, when it was filled up and covered with soil. The site garnered little attention until 1953, when the company deeded the land to the city council, which wanted it for a new school. The canal site was now a bucolic setting, with grass and trees that would attract families who would build homes and create a neighborhood. And all were directly on top of 21,000 tons of hazardous waste.

As the baby boom community grew, so did the reports of problems. Cancer rates were higher than normal, as were birth defects and miscarriages. Suicide, anxiety, and depression rates were also high. Residents, especially children who played outdoors, complained of dizziness, nausea, headaches, swellings, and strange rashes. Strong odors were common in the neighborhood, as was the seepage of odd-colored liquids and sludges into nearby creeks. Something was obviously wrong.

The story was not made public until 1978, when investigative journalists from the local *Niagara Falls Gazette* reported it. They and other activists helped Love Canal residents form protest groups, who took the issue to the city council. The council, which had bought and developed the land, was in denial. This intensified the furor. New York state health authorities finally addressed the problem and declared a state of emergency in 1978.

But the story kept growing, as more health and environmental problems became known. It became a national scandal and a national problem. President Jimmy Carter declared a federal emergency. It was the first time in American history that disaster funding was provided for something other than a natural disaster. In 1980, the United States government passed the Comprehensive Environmental Response, Compensation, and Liability Act (CERCLA) or "superfund" as it is commonly known.

The Hooker Chemical Company was eventually fined over $120 million to provide compensation and clean up Love Canal and four other hazardous waste sites in Niagara Falls. The company was not held liable, for it had disclosed the presence of the waste to the school board at the time of the deed. But they were deemed negligent because they disposed of such quantities of toxic material in an irresponsible way.

The Love Canal case is one of the most important in American environmental history. Hazardous waste had become a legal and political problem because companies could now be held liable for their industrial waste products. More importantly, the general public was now keenly aware that the problem of hazardous waste was not only pervasive, it was permanent. It was the cost of living in a modern industrial society.

Source: Brown, Michael H. 1983. *Laying Waste: The Poisoning of America by Toxic Chemicals.* New York: Pantheon Books.

CASE STUDY 6.2

The Chernobyl Nuclear Disaster

One of the world's greatest nuclear disasters occurred on April 26, 1986, in the Soviet Union. Chernobyl, the name of the power plant where the accident occurred, has become synonymous with nuclear disaster. And it still evokes fear that such an event could be repeated through human error, as was the case at Chernobyl, and more recently at the Fukushima Daiichi power plant in Japan. Even greater is the fear that nuclear disaster could result from war or a terrorist attack.

The Chernobyl nuclear power plant was located in what was then the Ukrainian SSR (now the independent nation of Ukraine). The reactor was undergoing a routine test when an unexpected power surge occurred. This destroyed one of the four reactors, and led to a massive explosion and fire. A giant cloud of highly toxic radioactive material was released into the atmosphere and then drifted westward across the Soviet Union and eastern Europe, and into western Europe.

The severity of the accident was worsened by the Soviet government's decision not to report it immediately. It was not announced until two days later, and only then was the nearby city of Pripyat evacuated. Death and illness had already been reported. The international community did not find out until Swedish scientists, while monitoring their own nuclear power plant at Forsmark, noticed extremely high rates of radioactivity. When they discovered their plant was not the source, it became clear that an enormous disaster had occurred somewhere in the Soviet Union.

The entire world was soon watching the event unfold. The Soviet government tried to make comparisons with America's Three Mile Island nuclear accident in 1979. But Chernobyl was much worse. It emitted 520 toxic radionuclides and 100 times the toxic nuclear waste of Hiroshima. The scale of the disaster became more evident as time went on.

Within months, 31 people had died as a direct result of the accident, and thousands were permanently disabled or chronically ill. In all, over 8 million people were exposed to radiation, and 40,000 had to be evacuated and resettled. Contaminated land totaled 150,000 acres. Countless numbers of crops, livestock, and forest were destroyed immediately, and remained contaminated and unproductive for years.

The financial costs were equally high. The Soviet government spent 18 billion rubles (roughly US$18 billion) to clean up and contain the hazardous nuclear waste. Some observers believe this massive expenditure was a financial burden so great that it helped bring down the entire Soviet system five years later. Even today, the governments of Ukraine and neighboring Belarus spend a significant percentage of national budgets dealing with various Chernobyl-related problems.

One of the bright spots in the entire Chernobyl debacle was at the international level. It led to new levels and types of cooperation. One example was between American and Russian nuclear scientists, who overcame ideological differences to find solutions to this and future nuclear disasters. The Soviet government, realizing it needed additional help in dealing with the accident, has worked closely with the UN since 1990.

The UN has passed several resolutions and programs dealing with various aspects of the disaster. The Office for the Coordination of Humanitarian Affairs helped establish a special trust fund to mobilize resources and better channel humanitarian aid. More recently, in 2003, the Chernobyl Recovery and Development Programme was created to focus on problems in Ukraine. In 2001 the UN announced a new strategy to promote economic development rather than purely humanitarian assistance.

To date, hundreds of research and assistance projects, many coordinated with NGOs, have been launched to deal with a broad range of problems in the aftermath of the Chernobyl nuclear disaster.

Sources: The United Nations and Chernobyl, http://www.un.org/ha/chernobyl/history.html; Yablokov, Alexey V., Vassily B. Nesterenko, and Alexey V. Nesterenko. 2009. *Chernobyl: Consequences for People and the Environment.* Boston: Blackwell.

ENDNOTES

1. EPA website, www.epa.gov/osw/hazard/.
2. William C. Blackman Jr., *Basic Hazardous Waste Management*, 3rd ed. (Boca Raton, FL: CRC, 2001), 20–25.
3. For policy and legal consequences, see Kim Fortun, *Advocacy After Bhopal: Environmentalism, Disaster, New Global Orders* (Chicago: University of Chicago Press, 2001); and Sheila Jasanoff, *Learning from Disaster Risk Management After Bhopal* (Philadelphia: University of Pennsylvania Press, 1994).
4. For an overview, see Jennifer Clapp, *Toxic Exports: The Transfer of Hazardous Wastes from Rich to Poor Countries* (Ithaca, NY: Cornell University Press, 2001).
5. "Parties to the Convention," http://www.basel.int/Countries/StatusofRatifications/Parties Signatories.
6. "Introduction to Generators," http://www.epa.gov/osw/inforesources/pubs/training/gen05.pdf.
7. See the Environmental Working Group website at http://www.ewg.org/key-issues/toxics/asbestos.
8. For a history of asbestos bankruptcy cases, see Crowell and Moring at http://www.crowell.com/Practices/Bankruptcy-Creditors-Rights/History-of-Asbestos-Bankruptcies.
9. Environmental Protection Agency, *Control of Volatile Organic Compound Emissions from Air Oxidation Processes in Synthetic Organic Chemical Manufacturing Industry* (Research Triangle Park, NC: EPA, Office of Air and Radiation, Office of Air Quality Planning and Standards, 1984).
10. See Stockholm Convention website at http://chm.pops.int/default.aspx.
11. Samuel Epstein, Lester O. Brown, and Carl Pope, *Hazardous Waste in America* (San Francisco: Sierra Club, 1982), 17–19.
12. David Biello, "World's 10 Worst Toxic Pollution Problems," slide 1. Available at http://www.scientificamerican.com/article/10-worst-toxic-pollution-problems-slide-show/.
13. Ibid.
14. Blackman, *Basic Hazardous Waste Management*, 291–98.
15. Ibid., 292–93.
16. See the Nuclear Regulatory Commission website at http://www.nrc.gov/about-nrc/ip/intl-organizations.html.
17. World Nuclear Association, "Radioactive Waste Management." Available at http://www.world-nuclear.org/info/Nuclear-Fuel-Cycle/Nuclear-Wastes/Radioactive-Waste-Management/.
18. National Resources Defense Council, "Your Computer's Lifetime Journey." Available at http://www.nrdc.org/living/stuff/your-computers-lifetime-journey.asp.
19. Ibid.
20. Ibid.
21. Environmental Protection Agency, "Final National Priorities List (NPL) Sites—by State." Available at http://www.epa.gov/superfund/sites/query/queryhtm/nplfin.htm#CA.

22. The iPhone–refrigerator comparison has received many critiques. It began with this report: Mark Mills, "The Cloud Begins with Coal: Big Data, Big Networks, Big Infrastructure, and Big Power. An Overview of the Electricity Used by the Global Digital Ecosystem." Available at http://www.tech-pundit.com/wp-content/uploads/2013/07/Cloud_Begins_With_Coal.pdf?c761ac.
23. International Association of Electronics Recyclers, *IAER Electronic Recycling Industry Report* (Albany, NY: IAER, 2004), 7.
24. H. G. Bhatt, R.M. Sykes, and T. L. Sweeney, eds., *Management of Toxic and Hazardous Wastes* (Chelsea, MA: Lewis, 1986).

RECOMMENDED READINGS/SOURCES

Adeola, Francis O. 2012. *Industrial Disasters, Toxic Waste, and Community Impact: The Health Effects and Environmental Justice Struggles Around the World.* Lanham, MD: Lexington.

Blackman, William. C. Jr. 2001. *Basic Hazardous Waste Management*, 3rd ed. Boca Raton, FL: CRC Press.

Brown, Michael H. 1983. *Laying Waste: The Poisoning of America by Toxic Chemicals.* New York: Pantheon.

Brunnengräber, Achim. *Nuclear Waste Governance.* Berlin: Springer VS, 2015.

Clapp, Jennifer. 2001. *Toxic Exports: The Transfer of Hazardous Wastes from Rich to Poor Countries.* Ithaca, NY: Cornell University Press.

Environmental Protection Agency (EPA). 1991. *Hazardous Waste Management.* Washington DC: USEPA, Office of Research and Development.

Epstein, Samuel, Lester O. Brown, and Carl Pope. 1982. *Hazardous Waste in America.* San Francisco: Sierra Club.

Fortun, Kim. 2001. *Advocacy After Bhopal: Environmentalism, Disaster, New Global Orders.* Chicago: University of Chicago Press.

Gabrys, Jennifer. 2011. *Digital Rubbish: A Natural History of Electronics.* Ann Arbor, MI: University of Michigan.

Goodman, Helen. 2008. *Toxic Waste.* Green Bay, WI: Worldwide.

Kummer, Katharina. 1994. *International Management of Hazardous Wastes: The Basel Convention and Related Legal Rules.* Oxford: Clarendon.

Pellow, David Naguib. 2007. *Resisting Global Toxins.* Boston: MIT Press.

Szasz, Andrew. 1994. *Ecopopulism: Toxic Waste and the Movement for Environmental Justice.* Minneapolis: University of Minnesota.

Yablokov, Alexey V., Vassily B. Nesterenko, and Alexey V. Nesterenko. 2009. *Chernobyl: Consequences for People and the Environment.* Boston. MA: Blackwell.

Air Pollution/ Acid Rain

by **PALASH SANYAL**

CHAPTER SEVEN

Air pollution is evident as far as human history stretches; the global impact of it is much more recent. It is a severe issue because it can affect us in many ways. Statistics from the World Health Organization (WHO) show outdoor air pollution causes about 16 percent of lung cancer deaths, 11 percent of deaths from chronic obstructive pulmonary disorder, and more than 20 percent of ischemic heart disease and stroke.[1] Although this type of pollution can affect everyone, young children and elderly people are at an especially high risk. Air pollution can also damage materials and agriculture, and is a component of climate change.

Air pollution can result from both human and natural activities. Natural occurrences that pollute the air consist of pollen dispersal, forest fires, volcanic eruptions, wind erosion, evaporation of organic compounds, and other natural activities. But compared to human causes of air pollution, natural factors are negligible.

It has been over 40 years since the United States federal government enacted the Clean Air Act of 1970 to address the acute air pollution that was facing numerous urban areas. Air pollution emissions continue to persist at high levels, with several U.S. urban regions facing seemingly intractable poor air quality.

In recent years, thinning ozone layer and acid rain have emerged as critical consequences of air pollution. This chapter will talk about overall air pollution, with the focus on these two factors. To solve the problem of air pollution, it's necessary to understand the issues and look for ways to counter it. But, to understand the reasons better, we first need to understand the air, atmosphere, and their interaction.

WHAT IS AIR?

To understand air pollution, first we need to define what air is.

To answer simply—air is life. Without it we could survive only a few minutes. Air constitutes the close physical environment of living entities. It is a mixture of various gases such as nitrogen, oxygen, and carbon dioxide, along with water vapor. And there are other gases not in substantial amounts.

The atmosphere is layered in to four distinct zones of distinct temperature, due its constituent and energy absorption difference. The four atmospheric layers are troposphere, stratosphere, mesosphere, and thermosphere. Understanding how these layers differ and what creates them helps us understand atmospheric function.

Troposphere

The layer of air immediately adjacent to the Earth's surface is called the troposphere. Most of the mass (about 80%) of the atmosphere is in the troposphere due to the force of gravity and the compressibility of gases. Most types of clouds are found in the troposphere, and almost all weather occurs within this layer. The troposphere extends upward to about 6.2 miles above sea level. The height of the top of the troposphere varies with latitude (it is lowest over the poles and highest at the equator) and by season (it is lower in winter and higher in summer). It can be as high as 12 miles near the equator, and as low as 4 miles over the poles in winter.

Air is warmest at the bottom of the troposphere, near ground level. Air gets colder as one rises through the troposphere. That's why the peaks of tall mountains can be snow-covered even in the summertime.

Air temperature drops rapidly with increasing altitude in this layer, reaching about –76°F at the top of the troposphere. A sudden reversal of this temperature gradient creates a sharp boundary, the tropopause, which limits mixing between the troposphere and the upper zones.

Stratosphere

The stratosphere is the second layer, as one moves upward from Earth's surface, of the atmosphere. The top of the stratosphere occurs at 31 miles of altitude. The boundary between the stratosphere and the mesosphere above is called the stratopause. The altitude of the bottom of the stratosphere varies with latitude and the seasons, occurring between about 5 and 10 miles. The bottom of the stratosphere is around 10 miles above Earth's surface near the equator, around 6 miles at mid-latitudes, and around 5 miles near the poles. It is slightly lower in winter at mid- and high-latitudes, and slightly higher in the summer.

Ozone, an unusual type of oxygen molecule that is relatively abundant in the stratosphere, heats this layer as it absorbs energy from incoming ultraviolet radiation from the sun. Temperatures rise with increasing altitude in the stratosphere. This is exactly the opposite of the behavior in the troposphere, where temperatures drop with increasing altitude. Because of this temperature stratification, there is little convection and mixing in the stratosphere, so it is quite stable. Commercial jet aircraft fly in the lower stratosphere to avoid the turbulence, which is common in the troposphere below.

The stratosphere contains little water vapor. Because of this, few clouds are found in this layer; almost all clouds occur in the lower, more humid troposphere. Polar stratospheric clouds are the exception. They appear in the lower stratosphere near the poles in winter. They are found at altitudes of 9.3 to 15.5 miles and form only when temperatures at those heights dip below –108.4°F. They appear to help cause the formation of the infamous holes in the ozone layer by ensuring certain chemical reactions that destroy ozone. These clouds are also called nacreous clouds.

Air is roughly a thousand times thinner at the top of the stratosphere than it is at sea level. Because of this, jet aircraft and weather balloons reach their maximum operational altitudes within the stratosphere.

Due to the shortage of vertical convection within the layer, materials that get into the layer will stay there for a long time. Such is the case for the ozone-destroying chemicals known as CFCs (chlorofluorocarbons). Giant volcanic eruptions and major meteor impacts exert aerosol particles up into the layer, where they can linger for months or years, typically neutering Earth's climate.

Mesosphere

The mesosphere starts at 31 miles above Earth's surface and goes up to 53 miles high. As you get higher up in the mesosphere, the temperature gets colder. The top of the mesosphere is the coldest part of Earth's atmosphere. The temperature there is around –130°F. The boundary between the mesosphere and the thermosphere above it is called the mesopause.

Most meteors from space burn up in this layer. A special type of clouds, called night clouds, sometimes form in the mesosphere near the North and South Poles. These clouds are strange because they form far higher up than any other type of cloud. There are also odd types of lightning in the mesosphere. These types of lightning, called sprites and elves, appear dozens of miles above thunderclouds in the troposphere below.

In the mesosphere and below, different kinds of gases are all mixed together in the air. Above the mesosphere, the air is so thin that gas atoms and molecules rarely collide. The gases get separated some, depending on the kinds of elements (like nitrogen or oxygen) that are in them.

Waves can form in the ocean or other bodies of water. But waves of air also form in the atmosphere. Some start in the lower atmosphere, the troposphere and stratosphere, and move upward into the mesosphere. The waves carry energy to the mesosphere. Most of the movement of air in the mesosphere is caused by these waves.

Thermosphere

The thermosphere is directly above the mesosphere and below the exosphere. It extends from about 56 miles to between 311 and 621 miles above our planet.

Temperatures climb sharply in the lower thermosphere, then level off and hold fairly steady with increasing altitude above that height. Solar activity strongly influences temperature in the thermosphere. The thermosphere is typically about 360°F hotter in the daytime than at night, and roughly 900°F hotter when the sun is very active than at other times. Temperatures in the upper thermosphere can range from about 932°F to 3,632°F or higher.

The boundary between the thermosphere and the exosphere above it is called the thermopause.

Although the thermosphere is considered part of Earth's atmosphere, the air density is so low in this layer that most of the thermosphere is what we normally think of as outer space. In fact, the most common definition says that space begins at an altitude of 100 km (62 miles), slightly above the mesopause at the bottom of the thermosphere. The space shuttle and the International Space Station both orbit Earth within the thermosphere!

Below the thermosphere, gases made of different types of atoms and molecules are thoroughly mixed together by turbulence in the atmosphere. Air in the lower atmosphere is mainly composed of the familiar blend of about 80 percent nitrogen molecules (N_2) and about 20 percent oxygen molecules (O_2). In the thermosphere and above, gas particles collide so infrequently that the gases become somewhat separated based on the types of chemical elements they contain. Energetic ultraviolet and x-ray photons from the sun also break apart molecules in the thermosphere. In the upper thermosphere, atomic oxygen (O), atomic nitrogen (N), and helium (He) are the main components of air.

The aurora (the southern and northern lights) primarily occurs in the thermosphere. Charged particles (electrons, protons, and other ions) from space collide with atoms and molecules in the thermosphere at high latitudes, exciting them into higher energy states. Those atoms and molecules shed this excess energy by emitting photons of light, which we see as colorful auroral displays.

Understanding atmospheric layers helps us to visualize the interaction between air elements. Let us now look at how air is polluted, and our focus factors: ozone layer and acid rain.

AIR POLLUTION

Air pollution refers to the contamination of the atmosphere by harmful chemicals or biological materials. According to the Blacksmith Institute in 2008, two of the worst pollution problems in the world are urban air quality and indoor air pollution.[2]

Air pollution is most common in large cities, where emissions from many different sources are concentrated. Sometimes mountains or tall buildings prevent air pollution from spreading out. This air pollution often appears as a cloud, making the air murky. It is called smog. The word smog comes from combining the words smoke and fog.

Clean, dry air consists primarily of nitrogen and oxygen—78 percent and 21 percent, respectively, by volume. The remaining 1 percent is a mixture of other gases, mostly argon (0.9%), along with trace (very small) amounts of carbon dioxide, methane, hydrogen, helium, and more. Water vapor is also a normal, though quite variable, component of the atmosphere, normally ranging from 0.01 to 4 percent by volume; under very humid conditions the moisture content of air may be as high as 5 percent.

The gaseous air pollutants of primary concern in urban settings include sulfur dioxide, nitrogen dioxide, and carbon monoxide; these are emitted directly into the air from fossil fuels such as fuel oil, gasoline, and natural gas that are burned in power plants, automobiles, and other combustion sources. Ozone (a key component of smog) is also a gaseous pollutant; it forms in the atmosphere via complex chemical reactions occurring between nitrogen dioxide and various volatile organic compounds.

Airborne suspensions of extremely small solid or liquid particles, called particulates (e.g., soot, dust, smoke, fumes, mists), especially those less than 10 micrometers in size, are significant air pollutants because of their very harmful effects on human health. Various industrial processes, coal or oil-burning power plants, residential heating systems, and automobiles emit them. Lead fumes are particularly toxic.

Global Air Pollution Scenario

Seven million people died throughout the world as a result of air pollution in 2012, the World Health Organization estimates.[3] One in eight global deaths in 2012 was linked with air pollution, making it "the world's largest single environmental health risk."[4] Nearly 6 million of the deaths were in Southeast Asia and the WHO's Western Pacific region.[5] Outdoor air pollution was responsible for the deaths of some 3.7 million people under the age of 60 in 2012. The WHO also emphasized that indoor and outdoor air pollution combined are among the largest risks to health worldwide.

The World Health Organization considers fine particulate matter (PM) pollution levels higher than 10 micrograms per cubic meter to be unsafe. $PM_{2.5}$ is particulate matter with an aerodynamic diameter of up to 2.5 µm, referred to as the fine particulate matter. PM_{10} is particulate matter with an aerodynamic diameter of up to 10 µm, i.e. the fine and coarse particulate matter combined. Most U.S. cities' average pollution level is 9.6,[6] and 33 percent of cities are above the WHO standard. Those cities tend to be geographically dispersed throughout the United States, but are predictably cities with heavy industry and driving, like Cleveland, Chicago, Los Angeles, and Philadelphia. Outside of the WHO, the United States has its own particulate matter standard of 12 micrograms per cubic meter. The pollution in 13 percent of American cities is higher than that.

In Europe, the average European city has pollution levels that are double what the WHO considers safe, at 21.7 micrograms per cubic meter.[7] In total, 93 percent of Europe's cities have unsafe levels of pollution when measured against the WHO standards. The EU standard, against which member countries base their regulations, considers 25 micrograms per cubic meter safe. Only a quarter of the EU's cities fail to meet that standard.

Only 8 of the 74 Chinese cities monitored by the central government managed to meet official minimum standards for air quality in 2014.[8] The three cities that met the standards were Haikou, Zhoushan, and Lhasa. The dirtiest cities were in northern China, where coal-powered industries are concentrated, including electricity generation and steel manufacturing. In the broad northern region that includes the large cities of Beijing and Tianjin, as well as the province of Hebei, which surrounds Beijing, the air quality standards were met on only 37 percent of days in 2013.[9] Beijing, with 20 million people, did so on only 48 percent of days.

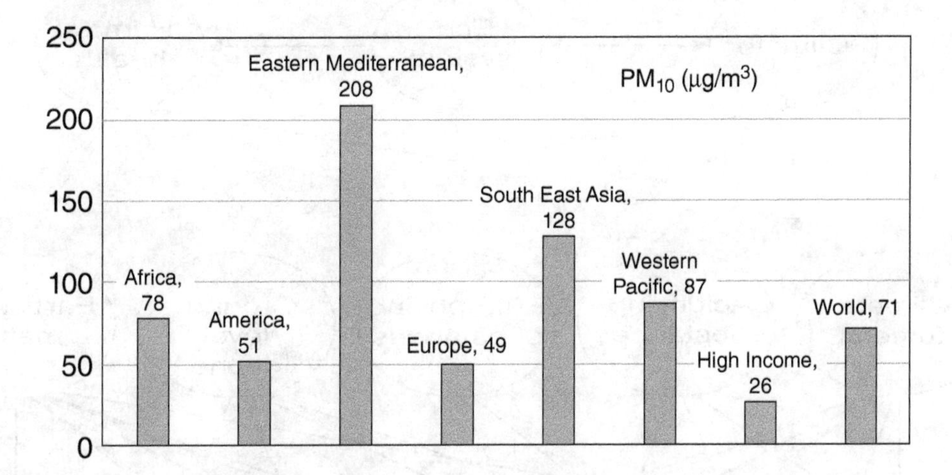

Figure 7.1. PM_{10} levels by region, for the last available year in the period 2008–2012.
Source: *WHO fact sheet, 2014.*[10]

The Yale Environmental Performance Index ranked India 174th out of 178 countries on air pollution in 2014. The WHO examined pollution levels in nearly 1,600 cities in 91 countries for the years 2008 to 2013, and found that the annual mean for particulate matter $PM_{2.5}$ concentrations in Delhi was 153 micrograms per cubic meter.[11] The cities of Patna, Gwalior, and Raipur followed Delhi for the worst air pollution readings. Delhi's reading was almost three times that of Beijing. According to India's Central Pollution Control Board, in 2010, particulate matter in the air of 180 Indian cities was six times higher than World Health Organization standards.

And the impact of these pollutions is visible. In 2014, Europe was the hottest in 500 years. California had record heat, which created its most severe drought in the last 1,200 years. Australia broke heat records across the continent (for the second year running). In January 2014, temperatures soared higher than 120°F. Much of Siberia defrosted in spring and early summer under temperatures more than 9°F above its 1981 to 2010 average as Live Science noted.[12] This is the second exceptionally hot summer in a row for the region, and scientists now think the huge crater discovered this year in the area was probably caused by thawing permafrost.[13]

Air pollution causes damage to crops, animals, forests, and bodies of water. It also contributes to the depletion of the ozone layer, which protects the Earth from the sun's ultraviolet (UV) rays. Another negative effect of air pollution is the formation of acid rain, which harms trees, soils, rivers, and wildlife. We will now look at both of the phenomena and try to understand them.

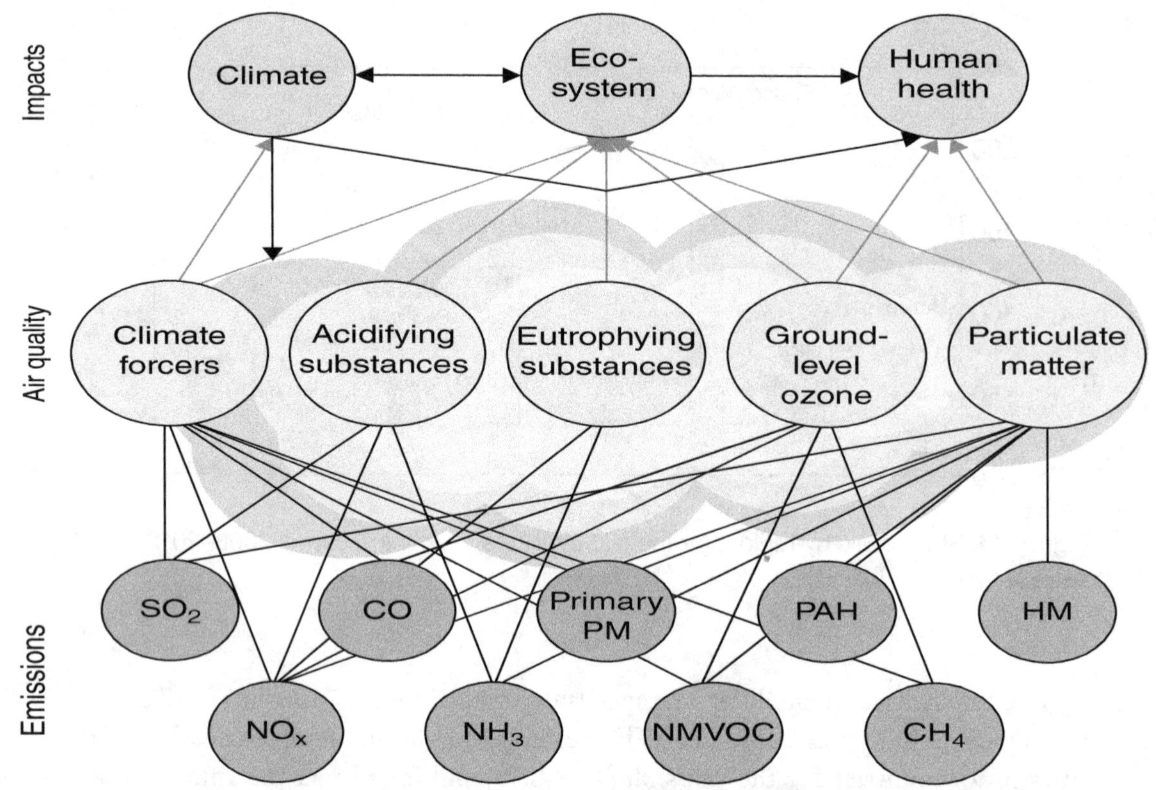

Note: From left to Right the pollutants shown are followings: sulphur dioxide (SO_2), nitrogen oxide (NO_x), carbon monooxide (CO), Ammonia (NH_4), particulate matter (PM), non-methane volatile organic compounds (NMVOC), polycyclic aromatic hydrocarbon (PAH), methane (CH_4), heavy metal (HM).

Figure 7.2. Relationship between emission, air quality and impacts. From left to Right the pollutants shown are followings: sulphur dioxide (SO_2), nitrogen oxide (NO_x), carbon monooxide (CO), Ammonia (NH_4), particulate matter (PM), non-methane volatile organic compounds (NMVOC), polycyclic aromatic hydrocarbon (PAH), methane (CH_4), heavy metal (HM). Source: Air Pollution Fact Sheet 2014, European Union (EU-28), pp. 3. Copyright © 2014 by European Environment Agency.

OZONE DEPLETION

The ozone layer refers to a region of Earth's stratosphere that absorbs most of the sun's UV radiation. It contains high concentrations of ozone (O_3) relative to other parts of the atmosphere. Ozone depletion describes two distinct but related phenomena that have been observed since the late 1970s: a steady decline of about 4 percent per decade in the total volume of ozone in Earth's stratosphere, and a much larger springtime decrease in stratospheric ozone over Earth's polar regions.

Scientific evidence indicates that stratospheric ozone is being destroyed by a group of manufactured chemicals containing chlorine and/or bromine. These chemicals are called ozone-depleting substances (ODS).

ODS are very stable, nontoxic, and environmentally safe in the lower atmosphere, which is why they became so popular in the first place. However, their very stability allows them to float up, intact, to the stratosphere. Once there, they are broken apart by the intense ultraviolet light, releasing chlorine and bromine. Chlorine and bromine demolish ozone at an alarming rate, by stripping an atom from the ozone molecule. A single molecule of chlorine can break apart thousands of molecules of ozone.

The main ODS are chlorofluorocarbons (CFCs), hydrochlorofluorocarbons (HCFCs), carbon tetrachloride, and methyl chloroform. Halons (brominated fluorocarbons) also play a large role. Their application is quite limited: they're used in specialized fire extinguishers. But the problem with halons is they can destroy up to 10 times as much ozone as CFCs can.

Hydrofluorocarbons (HFCs) are being developed to replace CFCs and HCFCs, for uses such as vehicle air conditioning. HFCs do not deplete ozone, but they are strong greenhouse gases. CFCs are even more powerful contributors to global climate change, though, so HFCs are still the better option until even safer substitutes are discovered.

CFCs were invented in the late 1920s. These chemicals were not poisonous, and didn't harm fabrics, plants, or people. Companies thought they were great and used them in refrigerators, air conditioners, Styrofoam packaging, and spray cans.

From the 1920s to the 1970s, billions of CFC molecules were released into the air. In 1974, Sherry Rowland and Mario Molina published a laboratory study demonstrating the ability of CFCs to catalytically breakdown ozone in the presence of high frequency UV light. Further studies estimated that the ozone layer would be depleted by CFs by about 7 percent within 60 years, and based on such studies, the United States banned CFCs in aerosol sprays in 1978. Slowly, various nations agreed to ban CFCs in aerosols, but industry fought the banning of valuable CFCs in other applications.

Impact of Ozone Depletion

Stratospheric ozone filters out most of the sun's potentially harmful shortwave UV radiation. If this ozone becomes depleted, then more UV rays will reach the Earth. Exposure to higher amounts of UV radiation could have serious impacts on human beings, animals, and plants:[16]

- It causes skin cancers, sunburns and premature aging of the skin.
- UV radiation can damage several parts of the eye, including the lens, cornea, retina, and conjunctiva.

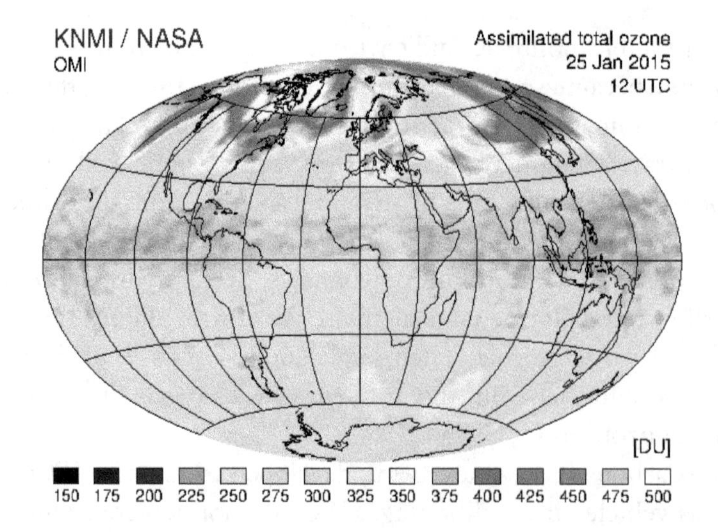

Figure 7.3. Total ozone from the ozone monitoring instrument (OMI) using the Differential optical absorption spectroscopy (DOAS) technique. Source: KNMI / NASA, http://www.temis.nl/protocols/o3field/data/omi/2015/01/o3col2015012512_gl.gif. Copyright © 2015 by KNMI/TEMIS.

- Cataracts (a clouding of the lens) are the major cause of blindness in the world. A sustained 10 percent thinning of the ozone layer is expected to result in almost two million new cases of cataracts per year, globally.
- Several of the world's major crop species are particularly vulnerable to increased UV, resulting in reduced growth, photosynthesis and flowering. These species include wheat, rice, barley, oats, corn, soybeans, peas, tomatoes, cucumbers, cauliflower, broccoli, and carrots.
- Only a few commercially important trees have been tested for UV (UV-B) sensitivity, but early results suggest that plant growth, especially in seedlings, is harmed by more intense UV radiation.
- In particular, plankton (tiny organisms in the surface layer of oceans) are threatened by increased UV radiation. Plankton are the first vital step in aquatic food chains.
- Decreases in plankton could disrupt the fresh and saltwater food chains, and lead to a species shift in waters.
- Loss of biodiversity in oceans, rivers, and lakes could reduce fish yields for commercial and sport fisheries.

- In domestic animals, UV overexposure may cause eye and skin cancers. Species of marine animals in their developmental stage (e.g., young fish, shrimp larvae, and crab larvae) have been threatened in recent years by the increased UV radiation under the Antarctic ozone hole.
- Wood, plastic, rubber, fabrics, and many construction materials are degraded by UV radiation.
- The economic impact of replacing and/or protecting materials could be significant.

ACID RAIN

Any rainfall that has a pH (measure of the acidity) value less than 5.6 is characterized as acid rain. Solutions with a pH less than 7 are said to be acidic, and solutions with a pH greater than 7 are basic or alkaline.

Acid rain has been an observed phenomenon since the very earliest years of the Industrial Revolution. In 1872, English scientist Robert Angus Smith wrote of its corrosive effect on buildings and plants. As large amounts of chemicals are released into the atmosphere through such processes as the burning of coal, they become bonded with water vapor held in clouds and are subsequently released to the Earth in the form of highly acidic rainfalls. While acid rain only causes indirect damage to living human beings, primarily through its reactions with volatile organic compounds to form ground-level ozone (smog), it causes tremendous damage to soil fertility, aquatic life, and durable inorganic materials such as stone and metals.

Some of the greatest measurable effects of acid rain can be observed on human constructions, particularly old buildings with facades built of corrosion-prone metals, such as copper, and porous stone, such as limestone. In the last 30 years some 1,000-year-old stained glass windows have been damaged by acid rain.[17] The damage of many big buildings in the developing world indicates that acid pollution is a global phenomenon.

Unfortunately, buildings and monuments at most of the world's most important heritage sites were not built to withstand such toxic punishment, and as many of these great sites are located in or near burgeoning industrial cities, they have sustained considerable damage. In our modern global economy, as developing countries such as China and India become increasingly industrialized without implementing the stringent pollution controls mostly adopted decades ago by older industrialized nations, many of their greatest cultural treasures are at risk from their own runaway national economic success. These hazards are not, however, limited in any sense to the rapidly industrializing world. Countries such as Australia have also experienced terrible conflicts between cultural preservation and industrial concerns, while the chemical-laden clouds themselves know no borders and have the potential to float over a large area.

Sources of Acid Rain

Although there are naturally occurring emissions of SO_2 (e.g., volcanoes) and NO_X (e.g., forest fires, soil, and lightning), human activities are responsible for the majority of the emissions put into the air. Globally, half of all SO_2 and most NO_X emissions are produced as a result of burning fossil fuels, such as coal, oil, and gas. Fossil fuels are made up of layers of once-living organisms that have accumulated over thousands of years.

The bodies of these organisms contain chemical elements, such as carbon (C), hydrocarbons (HC), sulfur (S), and nitrogen (N). When fossil fuels are burned, these elements are released into the atmosphere as sources of acid rain waste products. Oxygen, present in the air, combines with the sulfur and nitrogen in fuel to form many different compounds of sulfur and nitrogen, including sulfates and nitrates, sulfuric and nitric acids, and the two nitrogen compounds that compose NO_X.

Effect of Acid Rain

Together, biological organisms and the environment in which they live are called an ecosystem. The plants and animals living within an ecosystem are highly interdependent. For example, frogs may tolerate relatively high levels of acidity, but they may be affected indirectly, if they eat insects highly susceptible to acid rain. They may disappear if their food supply disappears. Because of the connections between the many fish, plants, and other organisms living in an aquatic ecosystem, changes in pH or aluminum levels affect biodiversity as well. Thus, as lakes and streams become more acidic, the numbers and types of fish and other aquatic plants and animals that live in these waters decrease.

The ecological effects of acid rain are most clearly seen in the aquatic, or water, environments, such as streams, lakes, and marshes. Acid rain flows into streams, lakes, and marshes after falling on forests, fields, buildings, and roads. Acid rain also falls directly on aquatic habitats. Most lakes and streams have a pH between 6 and 8, although some lakes are naturally acidic even without the effects of acid rain. Acid rain primarily affects sensitive bodies of water, which are located in watersheds whose soils have a limited ability to neutralize acidic compounds (called "buffering capacity").

Lakes and streams become acidic (i.e., the pH value goes down) when the water itself and its surrounding soil cannot buffer the acid rain enough to neutralize it. In areas where buffering capacity is low, acid rain releases aluminum from soils into lakes and streams; aluminum is highly toxic to many species of aquatic organisms.

Some types of plants and animals are able to tolerate acidic waters. Others, however, are acid-sensitive and will be lost as the pH declines. Generally, the young of most species are more sensitive to adverse environmental conditions than adults. At pH 5, most fish eggs cannot hatch. At lower pH levels, some adult fish die. Some acid lakes have no fish.

The impact of nitrogen on surface waters is also critical. Nitrogen plays a significant role in episodic acidification, and new research recognizes the importance of nitrogen in long-term chronic acidification as well. Furthermore, the adverse impact of atmospheric nitrogen deposition on estuaries and near-coastal water bodies is significant. Scientists estimate that 10 to 45 percent of the nitrogen produced by various human activities that reach estuaries and coastal ecosystems is transported and deposited via the atmosphere. For example, about 30 percent of the nitrogen in the Chesapeake Bay comes from atmospheric deposition. Nitrogen is an important factor in causing eutrophication (oxygen depletion) of water bodies.

The symptoms of eutrophication include blooms of algae (both toxic and non-toxic), declines in the health of fish and shellfish, loss of sea grass beds and coral reefs, and ecological changes in food webs. According to the National Oceanic and Atmospheric Administration, these conditions are common in many of our nation's coastal ecosystems. These ecological changes impact human populations by changing the availability of seafood and creating a risk of consuming contaminated fish or shellfish, reducing our ability to use and enjoy our coastal ecosystems, and causing an economic impact on people who rely on healthy coastal ecosystems, such as fishermen and those who cater to tourists.

Both natural vegetation and crops are affected by acid rain. The roots are damaged by acidic rainfall, causing stunted growth or death. Nutrients present in the soil are destroyed by the acidity. Useful microorganisms, which release nutrients from decaying organic matter into the soil, are killed off, resulting in fewer nutrients being available for the plants. The acid rain falling on the plants damages the waxy layer on the leaves and makes the plant vulnerable to disease. The cumulative effect means that even if the plant survives, it will be very weak and unable to survive climatic conditions like strong winds, heavy rainfall, or short dry periods. Plant germination and reproduction is also inhibited by the effects of acid rain.

All living organisms are interdependent on each other. If a lower life form is killed, other species that depended on it will also be affected. Every animal up the food chain will be affected. Animals and birds, like waterfowl or beavers, which depended on the water for food sources or as a habitat, also begin to die. Due to the effects of acid rain, animals that depend on plants for their food also begin to suffer. Tree-dwelling birds and animals also begin to languish due to loss of habitat.

Mankind depends upon plants and animals for food. Due to acid rain, the entire fish stocks in certain lakes have been wiped out. The economic livelihood of people who depended on fish and other aquatic life suffers as a result. Eating fish that may have been contaminated by mercury can cause serious health problems. In addition to loss of plant and animal life as food sources, acid rain gets into the food we eat, the water we drink, and the air we breathe. Due to this, asthmatic adults and children are directly affected. Urban drinking water supplies are generally treated to neutralize some of the effects of acid rain, and therefore, city dwellers may not directly suffer due to acidified drinking water. But out in the rural areas, those depending upon lakes, rivers, and wells will feel the effects of acid rain on their health. The acidic water moving through pipes causes harmful elements like lead and copper to be leached into the water. Aluminum, which dissolves more easily in acid rain as compared to pure rainfall, has been linked to Alzheimer's disease. The treatment of urban water supplies may not include removal of elements like aluminum, and so it is a serious problem in cities, too.

CONCLUSION

The biggest problem concerning pollution reduction, especially air pollution, is industrial development. And burning energy—especially coal and fossil fuels—is the main cause of air pollution. But burning energy is also critical to economic development. Naturally, few governments are willing to reduce or modify energy use at the domestic level because it would undermine development and wealth creation.

There is also little agreement at the international level. This is why many countries are not in binding with the Kyoto Protocol. This international agreement is based on common but differentiated responsibilities. It puts the obligation to reduce current emissions on developed countries, on the basis that they are historically responsible for the current levels of emissions in the atmosphere. The Kyoto Protocol was adopted in Kyoto, Japan, on December 11, 1997, and entered into force on February 16, 2005.

Kyoto is not the first of its kind. Efforts at global air pollution control have been underway since 1970, to make the governments realize and enact laws. By 1980, public awareness and knowledge about ozone depletion had grown. The Convention on Long-range Transboundary Air Pollution was the first international, legally binding instrument to deal with problems of air pollution on a broad regional basis. It was signed in 1979 and entered into force in 1983. In 1987, leaders from many countries came together to sign the Montreal Protocol on Substances that Deplete the Ozone Layer. The Montreal Protocol bound countries from producing and releasing ozone depletion chemicals. Currently, 197 countries are under the treaty.

China took action on air pollution prevention and control in 2013, and updated its Environmental Protection Law in 2014. The Hong Kong government implemented a host of measures to cut vehicular emissions after 1999. Compared with 1999, the roadside concentrations of respirable suspended particulates, sulfur dioxide (SO_2), and nitrogen oxides (NO_x) have decreased by 37 percent, 59 percent, and 29 percent, respectively, in 2013.

Global efforts are not only limited to protocols and action plans. Concepts like sustainable development (see Chapter Ten) and the development of green technologies are beginning to influence public policy and industry. Also, countries like India, Canada, and the United States are working together to deal with the situation. The United States and Canada have successfully worked on the transboundary acid rain problem. From 2003 to 2010, the U. S. Environmental Protection Agency has been engaged in India to support science-based air pollution control strategies in Indian cities. With Mexico, the United States created the Border 2020 plan, which aims to reduce pollutant emissions in order attain ambient air quality standards on particular regions of both countries.

Many analysts think these efforts are is still insufficient. Bolder and further-reaching efforts must be pursued. Developing countries will face the worst consequences. As they pursue development, they must often compromise environmental integrity. Growth has to be sustainable, with minimal effect on air. On the other side, developed world has to provide guidance to the developing world, by implementing strict actions against emission sources.

CASE STUDY 7.1

Acid Rain and World's Most Populated Country

Seven of the ten most polluted cities in the world are located in China. Air pollution alone claims 300,000 lives prematurely every year.[1] The problem of air pollution was first observed in the 1970s, with industrial emissions of sulfur dioxide (SO_2) and total suspended particulates.

In the 1980s, acid rain was detected in major cities in the northern part of the country, and this was mainly caused by SO_2 from coal combustion, which accounts for more than 70 percent of the fuel consumption in China.[2] In the 1990s, the number of vehicles on roads increased very rapidly, especially in medium-sized and large cities. In Beijing alone, the number of vehicles increased by a factor of 10, from 0.5 million in 1990 to 5 million in 2012.[3]

In addition, the emission factor (the amount of pollution emitted by one car) in China is much higher than in developed countries, because China has much lower emission standards for automobiles. Thus, the drastic rise in the number of vehicles and rapid development of industries in cities has led to worsening air quality, and concentrations of nitrogen oxides (NO_x) and particulates are especially high. Now, acid rain falls on two-thirds of the territory. China faces a severe acid rain problem due to its air pollution status.

In 2003, acid rain fell on more than 250 cities in China and caused direct annual economic losses of 110 billion yuan (US$13.3 billion), equal to nearly 3 percent of the country's gross domestic product.[4] Prior to the 2008 Olympics, the government poured money into moving polluting industries out of the capital in an effort to clean up Beijing.

The regional acid rain pollution is very intense in some southern cities, especially in the southwestern areas, due to heavy industrialization. In fact, the areas suffering from acid rain are actually expanding, with some already reporting increased acidity. In 2011, monitoring stations in the Pan-Bohai Bay area in northeast China recorded the highest frequency and acidity of acid rains in 15 years. The average pH value of the central districts was lower than 5.0, and the acid rain frequency was 7 out of 10 times.[5] The coastal city of Dalian in Liaoning province, also a popular summer resort, reported an acid rain frequency of 51.6 percent in 2007.[6]

Acid rain poses a threat to China's environment, ecological systems, forests, and humans, with cost estimates varying from US$1–32 billion. It costs 30 billion yuan in crop damage and 7 billion in material damage annually. It is estimated that acid rain causes over 30 billion yuan in damages to crops, primarily vegetable crops (about 80% of the losses). This amounts to 1.8 percent of the value of agricultural output.

According to a 2014 report by Greenpeace, acid rain led by air pollution affected more than 10 percent of China's land area, whilst industrial and agricultural pollution reduced arable land by more than 80,000 hectares, with more than 30 percent of China's land area suffering from soil erosion.[7]

Damage to building materials in the south imposed a cost of 7 billion yuan on the Chinese economy in 2003.[8] The Leshan Buddha, an ancient statue carved from a cliff in southern China, is slowly dissolving because of acid rain. Since being chiseled in the Tang dynasty (8th century), it has remained intact for 1,200 years. In 1996, the Buddha was named a UNESCO World Heritage Site. Now, its nose is black, hair curls have fallen from its head, and its reddish body is becoming a charred gray color.

In the 1980s and 1990s, as the coal industry in Shanxi Province powered growth throughout China, the impact of acid rain and air pollution on the statues in the Yungang Grottoes was also severe. A national highway ran in front of the grottoes, where 51,000 statues stand in 254 niches and caves. Up to 20,000 coal trucks passed each day. Villagers burned coal for cooking and heating. Restoration efforts, prompted by a bid for UNESCO World Heritage List status, started in the late 1990s. Officials moved the highway in 1998 and barred coal trucks from using it. About 10 small coalmines were ordered shut. Officials also moved six villages from the area, a total of 4,750 households.

Increasing coal combustion and pollutants derived from agriculture, industry, and transportation accompanied the exponential economic growth witnessed in China over the latter part of the 20th century. Major causes of acid rain are the rapidly growing number of cars on the roads, and the increasing consumption of cheap, abundant coal, as the country struggles to cope with energy shortages and meet power demand. The growth of nitrates, due to a swift rise of automobile and coal consumption, plus overuse of fertilizers, is playing an increasing role in the country's acid rain pollution. China is the world's largest source of soot and sulfur dioxide (SO_2) emissions from coal, which fires three-quarters of the country's power plants. More than 21 tons of SO_2 were discharged in China in 2003, a rise of 12 percent on the previous year.[9]

The Chinese government has made significant efforts and progress in energy saving and consumption reduction. Energy consumption has gone down year by year over the past two decades. However, China's environment has been ravaged by two decades of breakneck growth, and by the pressures of feeding and housing a population of 1.4 billion. With its annual steady growth of over 8 percent, China is paying the ultimate price of industrialization. China's explosive economic growth is outpacing environmental protection efforts. The government is trying to balance the growth and environment.

In industry, the rate of smoke and dust removal from industrial waste gas has been reduced, and the government has taken measures such as the introduction of levying charges for pollution emissions, and issuing licenses for discharging air pollutants. It has also promoted the adoption of clean coal, energy conservation and desulphurization technologies to help with the prevention of acid rain.

Data from 2005 to 2009 indicates a 13 percent decrease in SO_2 emissions, which is a good sign, as China is aggressively pursuing promises made in late 2009 to cut the intensity of carbon dioxide emissions per unit of gross domestic product in 2020 by 40 to 45 percent, compared with 2005 levels. China is also committed to increasing the share of non-fossil fuels in primary energy consumption to around 15 percent, to have 40 million more hectares of forest by 2020, according to the Copenhagen Accord.

Despite China's pledge to rely more on renewable energy sources, it was recently projected that the annual coal consumption will reach 3.8 billion tons by 2015, an increase of 800 million tons compared to 2009. But it hopes to control the emission. This will be achieved by setting quotas for SO_2 emissions from thermal power plants and urging them to install desulphurization facilities. China has already banned the use of coal in the areas most severely affected by SO_2 emissions, but sulfur is not the only enemy in the fight against acid rain. The country has also passed strict laws regarding emissions, but China will not see any drastic change in their weather or rain due to the damage already done.

ENDNOTES

1. Edward Wong, "Air Pollution Linked to 1.2 Million Premature Deaths in China", *New York Times*, April 1, 2013. Retrieved February 13, 2015, from http://www.nytimes.com/2013/04/02/world/asia/air-pollution-linked-to-1–2-million-deaths-in-china.html?_r=0.
2. Dongyong Zhang, Junjuan Liu, and Bingjun Li, "Tackling Air Pollution in China: What Do We Learn from the Great Smog of 1950s in London," *Sustainability 6, no. 8 (2014):* 5322–38.
3. Ibid.
4. James Gustave Speth and Peter Haas, *Global Environmental Governance: Foundations of Contemporary Environmental Studies* (Washington DC: Island Press, 2006).
5. Zentrum fur Bioinformatik (ZBH), "Acid Rain," State of the Environment, China '97. Retrieved February 13, 2015, from http://english.mep.gov.cn/SOE/soechina1997/acid/acids1.htm.
6. "A Hard Rain is Falling as Acid Erodes Beauty," *China Daily*, January 12, 2011. Retrieved February 13, 2015, from http://usa.chinadaily.com.cn/2011–01/12/content_11833224.htm.

7. Damina Kahya, "Chinese Environment Ministry Warns on Water Pollution," Green Peace, June 5, 2014. Retrieved February 13, 2015, from http://www.greenpeace.org.uk/newsdesk/energy/news/chinese-environment-ministry-warns-water-pollution.
8. The World Bank, *Cost of Pollution in China* (Washington DC: The World Bank, 2007).
9. Gordon, Ruth, "The Environmental Implications of China's Engagement with Sub-Saharan Africa," *Environmental Law Reporter News & Analysis* 42 (2012): 11,109.

CASE STUDY 7.2

Ozone Hole over Antarctica

Life at the margins may be extreme, but it is also fragile. The British Antarctic Survey's first documentation of the Antarctic ozone hole in 1985, and subsequent National Science Foundation–funded study of the phenomenon, alerted the world to the danger of chlorofluorocarbons, or CFCs, to the world's ozone layer. That research team, led by 1999 National Medal of Science winner Susan Solomon, conducted observations that have significantly advanced our understanding of the global ozone layer, and changed the direction of ozone research.

Stratospheric ozone, located 12 to 20 miles above the Earth, protects against ultraviolet radiation. The breakdown of this ozone layer by CFC molecules can have harmful effects on a range of life forms, from bacteria to humans. The long, cold, dark Antarctic winters allow the formation of polar stratospheric clouds, the particles of which form an ideal surface for ozone destruction. The returning sunlight provides energy to start the complex chemical reaction that results in ozone destruction. The ozone hole above Antarctica typically lasts about four months, from mid-August to late November.

During this period, increased intensity of ultraviolet radiation has been correlated with extensive DNA damage in the eggs and larvae of Antarctic fish. Embryos of limpets, starfish, and other invertebrates do not grow properly. Other species have developed defenses. The Antarctic pearl wort, a moss like plant on rocky islands, developed a pigment called flavonoid that makes it more tolerant of ultraviolet radiation.

The ozone hole appeared first over the colder Antarctic because the ozone-destroying chemical process works best in cold conditions. The Antarctic continent has colder conditions than the Arctic, which has no landmass. As the years have gone by the Ozone Hole has increased rapidly, and is now as large as the continent of Antarctica. The hole lasts for only two months, but its timing could not be worse. Just as sunlight awakens activity in dormant plants and animals, it also delivers a dose of harmful ultraviolet radiation. After eight weeks, the hole leaves Antarctica, only to pass over more populated areas, including the Falkland Islands, South Georgia, and the tip of South America. This biologically damaging, high-energy radiation can cause skin cancer, injure eyes, harm the immune system, and upset the fragile balance of an entire ecosystem. News about the ozone hole that forms over Antarctica each October has spread around the world. The ozone hole can be as big as 1.5 times larger than the United States.

Ozone levels in the early 1990s measured 10 percent lower than those estimated in the late 1970s in the northern polar regions. The Arctic does experience ozone depletion, but to a lesser degree than the Antarctic. Unlike the Antarctic, large-scale weather systems disturb the wind flow in the Arctic and prevent the temperature in the stratosphere from being as cold. Therefore, fewer stratospheric clouds are formed to provide surfaces for the production of ozone-depleting compounds. Some clouds do form, however, and allow the chemical reactions to occur that deplete ozone. Ozone depletion has a direct effect on human inhabitants, but research has only just begun on the effects of increased ultraviolet radiation on terrestrial and aquatic ecosystems, and societies and settlements in the Arctic.

The good news is that countries around the world have agreed to ban the manufacture of CFCs through the Montreal Protocol. The contributions of Antarctic researchers led to swift policy action, and because of that, the ozone layer should recover in the future. In the meantime, however, research funded by the National Science Foundation continues to monitor the level of the CFCs still lingering in the atmosphere. The polar regions will continue to play an important role as early warning systems for the rest of the globe.

Source: http://www.nsf.gov.

ENDNOTES

1. World Health Organization (WHO), "Ambient Air Pollution." Retrieved February 13, 2015, from http://www.who.int/gho/phe/outdoor_air_pollution/en.
2. Blacksmith Institute, "List Identifies Toxins and Activities Contributing to Death and Disability." Retrieved February 13, 2015, from http://www.blacksmithinstitute.org/the-2008-top-ten-list-of-world-s-worst-pollution-problems.html.
3. WHO, "7 Million Premature Deaths Annually Linked to Air Pollution." Retrieved February 13, 2015, from http://www.who.int/mediacentre/news/releases/2014/air-pollution/en/.
4. Ibid
5. Ibid.
6. WHO, "WHO Fact Sheet." Retrieved February 13, 2015, from http://www.who.int/mediacentre/factsheets/en/.
7. Ibid.
8. British Broadcasting Service (BBC), "Most China Cities Fail to Meet Air Quality Standards" *BBC News*, February 3, 2015. Retrieved February 13, 2015, from http://www.bbc.com/news/world-asia-china-31110408.
9. Edward Wong, "Most Chinese Cities Fail Minimum Air Quality Standards, Study Says," *New York Times*, March 27, 2014. Retrieved February 13, 2015, from http://www.nytimes.com/2014/03/28/world/asia/most-chinese-cities-fail-pollution-standard-china-says.html?_r=0.
10. Burden of disease from Household Air Pollution for 2012", World Health Organization, Retrieved February 13, 2015, from http://www.who.int/phe/health_topics/outdoorair/databases/FINAL_HAP_AAP_BoD_24March2014.pdf
11. "WHO Fact Sheet. 2014), World health Organization, Retrieved February 13, 2015 from http://www.who.int/phe/health_topics/outdoorair/databases/cities/en/
12. Hottest Year Ever: 5 Places Where 2014 Temps Really Cooked", Live Science, Retrieved February 13, 2015 from http://www.livescience.com/49295–2014-hottest-year-countdown.html
13. Ibid
14. "Air pollution fact sheet 2014 European Union", European Environment Agency, Retrieved February 13, 2015 from http://www.eea.europa.eu/themes/air/air-pollution-country-fact-sheets-2014/eu-27-air-pollutant-emissions/at_download/file
15. Tropospheric Emission Monitoring Internet Service Retrieved January 25, 2015, from http://www.temis.nl/protocols/o3field/data/omi/2015/01/o3col2015012512_gl.gif
16. "The Impacts of Ozone Depletion," British Columbia Air Quality. Retrieved February 13, 2015, from http://www.bcairquality.ca/101/ozone-depletion-impacts.html.
17. Kenneth Mellanby, *Air Pollution, Acid Rain and the Environment Report, Number 18* (New York: Springer, 1988).

RECOMMENDED READINGS/SOURCES

Christie, Maureen. 2000. *The Ozone Layer: A Philosophy of Science Perspective.* Cambridge: Cambridge University Press.

Dessler, Andrew. 2000. *Chemistry and Physics of Stratospheric Ozone.* Hong Kong: Elsevier Limited.

Fabian, Peter. 2014. *Ozone in the Atmosphere: Basic Principles, Natural and Human Impacts.* New York: Springer.

Hoffman, Matthew J. 2005. *Ozone Depletion and Climate Change: Constructing a Global Response.* Albany: State University of New York.

Jacob, Daniel. 1999. *Introduction to Atmospheric Chemistry.* Princeton: Princeton University Press.

Jacobs, Chip, and William Kelly. 2008. *Smogtown: The Long-Burning History of Pollution in Los Angeles.* New York: Overlook.

Park, Chris C. 2013. *Acid Rain (Routledge Revivals): Rhetoric and Reality.* London: Routledge.

Seinfeld, John H., and Spyros N. Pandis. 2006. *Atmospheric Chemistry and Physics: From Air Pollution to Climate Change.* Hoboken, NJ: Wiley-Interscience.

Somers, Warren. 2013. *Acid Precipitation: Results of the Nation's Acid Rain Program and Further Considerations.* New York: Nova Science.

United States Department of Commerce, National Oceanic and Atmospheric Administration. "Nonpoint Source Pollution: A Brief History." Available at http://oceanservice.noaa.gov/education/kits/pollution/02history.html.

United States Environmental Protection Agency. "Acid Rain." Available at http://www.epa.gov/acidrain/.

United States Environmental Protection Agency. "The Ozone Problem." Available at http://www.epa.gov/region1/airquality/oz_prob.html.

Weatherhead, Elizabeth C., and Signe Bech Andersen. "The Search for Signs of Recovery of the Ozone Layer." *Nature* 441 (2006): 39–45.

White, James C. 1998. *Acid Rain: The Relationship Between Sources and Receptors.* New York: Springer.

Agriculture and the Environment

by **TOBIAS LANZ**

CHAPTER EIGHT

INTRODUCTION

The most intimate human relationship with the environment is agriculture or farming—the raising of plants and animals. Hunting and gathering involves intimate human–environmental relationships, but agriculture goes even further because it entails transforming the environment—forests, wetlands, and grasslands—for human use.

Agriculture is central to the environmental debate because it simplifies ecosystems, which reduces biodiversity. And as human populations increase, more land is converted to farming, which further threatens biodiversity. Thus the struggle of modern agriculture is not just how many people can the Earth feed, but how many people can it feed and still maintain biodiversity and the proper functioning of ecosystems. Modern agriculture also uses many synthetic chemical inputs which creates pollution problems.

Balancing agriculture and ecology will be one of the greatest challenges of the 21st century. And it is one that has many ethical, political, technological, and cultural dimensions.

THE BEGINNINGS OF AGRICULTURE

Hunter–gatherer peoples cultivated plants and animals for thousands of years. But about 10,000 years ago, new ways to obtain food from the environment were developed, in what has been dubbed the Neolithic Revolution. It was not an immediate transformation, but a slow, incremental process in which hunter–gatherer peoples found new ways of growing crops and raising livestock.

It was the intensification of plant and animal production (increased yield per land area) that marked such a dramatic shift from the past. Historians offer many explanations for this—population growth, conflict, climate change, and so on. But there is no debate over the consequence of this transition—more people could subsist from a given area of land. Once populations grew, the need to maintain these new production systems was established. Humans could now create and sustain artificial ecosystems. And that was revolutionary.

Southwest Asia is the first place in the world where people developed artificial ecosystems on which they depended for almost all of their food needs. Grains and legumes were among the first domesticated crops, and sheep and goats among the first animals. China and South America were two other areas of agricultural innovation. Pigs, horses, chickens, rice, and millet were cultivated in China and corn, squash, tomatoes, peppers, and potatoes in South America.[1]

The plants and animals developed in these three centers, then spread slowly to other parts of the world through trade, conquest, or population growth. Agriculture became the economic basis of all the world's great ancient civilizations, from Egypt and Rome to China and Hindu India, to the Maya and Inca of South America. And the size and longevity of all these civilizations (some endured for millennia) was due to the extensive areas of arable land available to them.

The expansion of agricultural production to feed growing populations throughout the world was still largely through the conversion of wilderness to cultivation (extensive agriculture). As such, it had an explicit environmental cost. Yet farming methods that focused on increasing yields per land area (intensive agriculture) continued to increase slowly through the use of manure and other soil additives, crop rotation, irrigation, and improved crop and livestock varieties.

But the single most important factor in increasing agricultural productivity was the harnessing of new energy sources—namely human and animal labor. These were highly efficient energy converters, as they produced considerable labor output from relatively low food inputs. And they could transform large areas of land to productivity in a relatively short period, when aided by plows, hoes, and other tools. In this sense, the agrarian revolution was really an energy revolution.

Despite dramatic improvements in agricultural production, most of the world's agrarian peoples still lived on the brink of starvation, subsisting mainly on grains. Almost the entire population of agrarian societies was involved in food production, and many were slaves. But what was different from prior human societies was the emergence of a new social class—soldiers, religious personnel, merchants, and administrators—that was not involved in food production. It lived off of the economic surplus (profit) produced by the farming majority.

This class not only lived from the surplus, but also used it to develop institutions, laws, infrastructure, and technologies that could accumulate and concentrate increasing amounts of political and economic power. This, in turn, allowed human societies to control and conquer other peoples, as well as the environment. And as social complexity grew, the need for labor, land, and other natural resources grew in tandem. The advantage of humans over nature now became decisive.

EUROPEAN ECONOMIC EXPANSION AND THE PLANTATION COMPLEX

Agricultural civilization spread slowly for thousands of years, but did not change dramatically until the global expansion of European trade after 1500. North and South America, the Caribbean, Africa, southern and Southeast Asia and the Pacific islands—lands heretofore ecologically and culturally isolated—were now all integrated into a single economic system. The cultivation and trade of agricultural goods was central to this economic endeavor.

One positive consequence of the expansion of global agricultural trade was the qualitative improvement of the human diet. An array of crops, livestock, and other agricultural goods could now be grown or traded around the world. Native Latin American foods, namely potatoes, corn, squash, peppers, avocados, and tomatoes, changed the world diet more than food from any other region. Without the global production and trade of these crops, especially corn and potatoes, much of the world's population could not be adequately fed today.

But there were many negative consequences of global agricultural trade. This is especially true of plantation agriculture. The plantation complex became the first global production-consumption system. Most plantations were in the tropics or semi-tropics, their goods destined almost entirely for Europe, and their labor—slave or semi-slave—procured from many corners of the world.[2]

Slavery was essential to—indeed synonymous with—the plantation economy. Tens of millions of slaves were uprooted from their homelands and brought to work on plantations. Most came from Africa and were brought to the New World, but countless Chinese, Filipinos, and Indians were transported as well. As the plantation complex spread worldwide, so did slavery.

The inhumanity of slavery is well known. Most slaves died en route to their destination. Those that survived lived only a few years more, often under brutal conditions. Many relocated peoples simply died because they could not adapt to new climates or diseases. But the massive removal and relocation of people had other consequences. Small and isolated populations became extinct after all its peoples were sold into slavery. Other societies were so diminished by population decline that their cultural traditions were lost or they became politically and economically unstable, and vulnerable to a host of social ills.

The plantation complex was also environmentally destructive. First, plantations destroyed large areas of virgin forest, much of it species-rich rainforest. And because lands in the conquered colonies were essentially free (they were uninhabited or simply conquered), they were exploited to the fullest. Many plantations covered thousands of acres and were thus many times larger than any European farm or estate.

Second, the plantation replaced rich biomes with radically simplified ecosystems. While all farms simplify nature, traditional farming at least created stable, diverse and, resilient farms that used local or well-adapted crops. Traditional farms also included woodlands and grasslands for hunting and foraging. Plantations did not. Plantations sometimes grew two, but usually one crop (monocrop cultivation). Little regard for surrounding ecosystems was taken into account.

There was also little regard for local peoples—hunter–gatherers or traditional subsistence farmers. They were driven off the land or forced into plantation labor. This labor system was characterized by more than poor conditions. It was part of a radically new type of farming. It was the beginning of the modern assembly line, in which labor is routinized and production is exclusively for the market.[3] This model would be the basis of the Industrial Revolution, which would eventually transform the economies and ecosystems of the entire globe.

Plantations also produced cash crops, not food crops, which benefitted European trade and industry, especially the luxury market. New goods like bananas, cocoa, tea, and a host of spices were introduced. Others, like coffee, sugar, and tobacco, were already known but could now be grown in sufficient quantity to make them staple items. Cash crops undermined food production in the colonies where plantations were located. The best lands and labor were used for plantation agriculture. Food production was neglected, and poverty and social instability throughout the colonies increased.

The plantation complex grew even more rapidly after formal colonial empires were established in the 18th and 19th centuries. Although the global slave trade ended in the early 19th century, large pools of native labor could now be "employed" on plantations. The low pay and poor conditions were not much different from slavery. So, from the highlands of India, to the lowlands of Southeast Asia, to the African coasts, and throughout Latin America and the Caribbean islands, a monotonous monocrop ecosystem populated by impoverished peoples was created. And it endures into the present.

INDUSTRIAL AGRICULTURE

Agriculture changed once again with the Industrial Revolution, which began in the 18th century. Like the Neolithic Revolution, the Industrial Revolution was centered on new energy sources—coal, electricity, nuclear power, and especially, fossil fuels. Their application to transportation, communication, housing, medicine, and especially, agriculture, dramatically improved the human condition. It also created new and unforeseen social and environmental problems.

The impact of industry on agriculture did have positive impacts on production and productivity. The use of machinery (mechanization) allowed for more land to be cultivated with fewer labor inputs. As a result, farm laborers, especially slaves, were freed from difficult agricultural work. It is no accident that the end of slavery and the slave trade coincided with the spread of industrial agriculture.

Increases in production and productivity increased the food supply and thus lowered food prices. This especially benefitted the poor. More importantly, the quantity of food produced kept pace with population growth (which was sustained, in part, by more and better food). The world's human population grew seven-fold from 1800 to 2000—from one to seven billion. So did agricultural production.[4]

The large numbers of laborers that left farms moved to cities. Here they became an important labor pool in manufacturing, services, and other new economic sectors spawned by the Industrial Revolution. The standard of living of many of these city dwellers would improve greatly, and constituted part of the rise of the modern consumer or affluent society.

Industry also changed the way food was transported and stored. Rails and steamships, later trucks and airplanes, could transport food over great distances. Fresh fruits, vegetables, and meats could be shipped in greater quantities and variety than ever before with the development of refrigeration. As a result, agricultural production expanded across the globe.

But all of these benefits carried environmental costs. The first was associated with the expansion of agricultural production. As world population and agricultural commodity demand grew, so did the conversion of wilderness to cultivation. This was especially the case in the New World, where populations were low and land abundant. Between 1860 and 1920, 500 million acres of land were converted to agriculture worldwide. By the end of the 20th century, agricultural land composed one-third of the world's vegetated area.[5] This trend continues as world population continues to grow.

Cultivation also exposed land to soil erosion. Machines could till large areas of land, but this also exposed vast areas to massive soil erosion through wind and storms. Once lands were degraded in this manner, farmers were forced to convert new land to cultivation, creating a destructive cycle of expansion. This loss of precious topsoil continues wherever open till methods are still used.[6]

But it was the use of synthetic chemical additives in agriculture that would have the greatest impact on society and the environment. Farmers had long used natural (organic) additives like manure, compost, and lime to increase production. But with the Industrial Revolution, chemists and agronomists developed synthetic (inorganic and organic) additives. And they could be produced cheaply and in large quantities.

Fertilizers were the first artificial additives to be widely used, beginning in the 19th century. The main chemical fertilizers were nitrogen, phosphorus, and potassium. Production grew steadily and accelerated rapidly after World War I (many munitions factories were converted to fertilizer production, as both used the same chemicals). Total world artificial fertilizer production was only 360,000 tons in 1900. It increased to 140 million tons by 2000—a 400-fold increase.[7]

The initial effect of increased fertilizer use was increased production. But in the 20th century it was recognized that increased use had a point of diminishing returns, after which production did not increase significantly with greater fertilizer use. The negative environmental impact was also recognized. Many fertilizers were overused or were not sufficiently absorbed by the soil. The result was chemical runoff into streams and ground water, which contributed, along with other industrial runoff, to increased water pollution. Aquatic life died and drinking water was contaminated.

Water pollution was worsened by the use of pesticides, fungicides, and herbicides, which had become routine in industrialized agriculture by the mid-20th century.

Yet, the health and environmental consequences of these chemicals were completely unknown for years. It did worry some observers, because many of these chemicals (especially pesticides) used the same lethal neurotoxins found in chemical weapons.

These worries were confirmed by the 1950s, as bird and fish populations began to die in the rivers and lakes of the advanced industrial countries. The publication of the book *Silent Spring* by biologist Rachel Carson in 1963 confirmed the worst.[8] Her stirring tale of a spring without singing birds (all dead because of toxins) made the American public aware of the devastating effects of industrial pollution.

This was a watershed event. It made society question—for the first time—the costs and consequences of industrialization. As such, it initiated a new environmental awareness that went beyond simply conserving land and species, to developing poignant critiques and alternatives to industrial society. This was the beginning of contemporary environmentalism.

Environmentalists began criticizing industry for air and water pollution and its heavy energy use. Alternatives to the industrial lifestyle, which included industrial agriculture, were part of this movement. One such alternative was organic agriculture. Long considered marginal, even radical, its advocacy of non-synthetic chemical inputs and focus on healthy food made it appealing to the general public.

But organic agriculture was nothing new or radical. It is the way farmers had produced agricultural goods prior to the Industrial Revolution. What was different about the new generation of organic farmers is that they relied upon modern science—agronomy, horticulture, botany, and ecology—to enhance production. And this production had to be competitive with industrial chemical agriculture.

By the 1990s organic agriculture had become mainstream in America and Europe. Organic fruits, vegetables, meats, milk, and eggs were found in major grocery stores. Today, the largest seller of organic foods in America is the Wal-Mart Corporation, which has made organic a major focus of its grocery business.[9] Large-scale commercial agriculture has also shifted much of its production to the lucrative organic market.

Many environmentalists welcome these changes. But others charge that while organic farming benefits the environment, it does not solve all the problems of industrial agriculture; it only solves the synthetic chemical input problem. Organic agriculture, when practiced on a large scale, is still industrial agriculture. It still requires the same levels of mechanized and fossil fuel dependent production, transport, and storage. Critics argue that agriculture must change even further to be more environmentally sustainable.

First, new production methods are needed that reduce not just synthetic chemical inputs, but also energy inputs. The entire industrial production and consumption system is energy intensive. The amount of energy used to produce food in industrial societies is often greater than the energy (measured in calories) of the food output. In some crops, like fruits and vegetables, energy input actually exceeds energy output.[10] Transportation costs are equally high. The average food item in America travels 1,500 miles to reach its destination.[11]

The heavy reliance on irrigation has also created environmental problems. The massive movement of water, often over long distances, requires extensive networks of canals, aqueducts, pipes, and dams, which can destroy native habitat. This can also lead to political conflict over water rights and access, especially when water control involves neighboring nations. Long-term irrigation can also lead to salinization. Here naturally occurring salts rise and accumulate in surface soils, rendering them sterile.

The only way to change the energy and irrigation equation is to promote local and small-scale production. This realization has led to new types of organic production, like permaculture, agroforestry, and urban agriculture (see Boxes One and Two). These approaches often have political, social, and cultural goals, in that they try to reintegrate food production with human society, a connection that industrial agriculture has destroyed. Local production is also reliable because production and transportation are easier to manage. This helps reduce health and market risks.

Most environmentalists believe that reconnecting people with agriculture, and doing so in ecologically sound ways, is one of the best ways to create a more stable and sustainable world. There is an incentive here because all the world's peoples—rich and poor, in urban and rural settings, and across diverse cultures and religions—must eat. And all people prefer healthy foods from reliable sources.

AGRICULTURE AND THE MAKING OF THE CONSUMER SOCIETY

Other criticisms of industrial agriculture focus on the consumption side of the equation. Industrial agriculture produces an inexpensive, abundant, and diverse food supply, which is an important feature of affluence. And the very ability of a society to adequately feed its entire population is a sign of economic development. But there are costs to this abundance. And as consumer preferences increasingly influence

Box 8.1 Alternatives to Conventional Agriculture

Permaculture and urban agriculture are two of the most well-known alternatives to conventional farming. They focus on intensification of production and new production methods that are compatible with surrounding ecosystems. They are particularly suited to small land areas found in cities and suburbs. This is the essence of sustainability or sustainable development.

Permaculture

Permaculture is a holistic approach to farming, in which agricultural and livestock production are integrated into the ecosystem. It focuses on improved design to increase output and sustain it permanently (hence permaculture). Stability and diversity are other features of permaculture systems. The goal of permaculture goes beyond simply agricultural production. It seeks the reintegration and harmonization of human farming (and all human culture) with the ecosystem.

The idea of permaculture is not new, as many traditional farming peoples in Europe, Africa, and Asia have utilized its principles for centuries. What is new is the reapplication of these principles to modern agriculture and society—in both developed and developing societies. Areas with high population densities and limited land are especially suitable to permaculture methods—but so are areas with extensive lands. Here, production can be concentrated on smaller areas, allowing some farmlands to be returned to a wild state.

Two farming methods that have influenced permaculture are agroforestry and "hugelkultur." Agroforestry, or forest gardening, combines fruit- and timber-producing trees with shrubs, livestock, and crops to create diverse and resilient production systems. Hugelkultur, or hill farming, is an old German method that creates deep beds, filled with logs and branches that are then covered with soil and compost. This mixture retains a great amount of moisture, allowing crop production with almost no irrigation. It reduces labor and resources over the long term.

Two pioneers of permaculture are Bill Mollison and David Holmgren of Australia (Tasmania). They began writing about and teaching permaculture

Continued...

methods in the 1970s. Holmgren writes that there are 12 basic design principles in permaculture:

1. **Observe and interact:** By taking time to engage with nature we can design solutions that suit our particular situation.
2. **Catch and store energy:** By developing systems that collect resources at peak abundance, we can use them in times of need.
3. **Obtain a yield:** Ensure that you are getting truly useful rewards as part of the work that you are doing.
4. **Apply self-regulation and accept feedback:** We need to discourage inappropriate activity to ensure that systems can continue to function well.
5. **Use and value renewable resources and services:** Make the best use of nature's abundance to reduce our consumptive behavior and dependence on non-renewable resources.
6. **Produce no waste:** By valuing and making use of all the resources that are available to us, nothing goes to waste.
7. **Design from patterns to details:** By stepping back, we can observe patterns in nature and society. These can form the backbone of our designs, with the details filled in as we go.
8. **Integrate rather than segregate:** By putting the right things in the right place, relationships develop between those things and they work together to support each other.
9. **Use small and slow solutions:** Small and slow systems are easier to maintain than big ones, making better use of local resources and producing more sustainable outcomes.
10. **Use and value diversity:** Diversity reduces vulnerability to a variety of threats and takes advantage of the unique nature of the environment in which it resides.
11. **Use edges and value the marginal:** The interface between things is where the most interesting events take place. These are often the most valuable, diverse, and productive elements in the system.
12. **Creatively use and respond to change:** We can have a positive impact on inevitable change by carefully observing, and then intervening at the right time.

Source: David Holmgren. 2011. Permaculture: Principle and Pathways Beyond Sustainability. Hampshire, UK: Hyden House.

production, especially in affluent, consumer societies, these costs will continue to grow.

Disease was the first and most obvious cost of a high-consumption society. Cheap and abundant food combined with less rigorous labor in the urban environment created some of the most notorious diseases of modernity—cancer, diabetes, heart disease, and obesity. All are strongly connected to poor diets, especially those high in refined carbohydrates, fats, and artificial additives. And all are staples of the modern industrial food supply.

What is significant is that these health problems—especially obesity—are really environmental problems. They are essentially energy- and resource-allocation problems. People now have the luxury of consuming far more energy (calories) than they can burn through physical activity. The food crisis of traditional agrarian societies is under-consumption, while that of modern industrial societies is over-consumption.[12]

The resources required to sustain the consumer lifestyle are considerable. Food choice in a consumer society is made possible by processed, fast, refrigerated, and frozen foods, all of which require considerable energy inputs and packaging. Refrigerated and frozen foods score the worst in this regard. They are heavily packaged and require refrigeration throughout their entire product cycle—in transit, at the place of sale (grocery store), and in the home. No modern home is without a refrigerator, which consumes more energy than any other household appliance.[13]

But the greatest irony of industrial agriculture is that, despite the great breakthroughs in food production, transportation, and storage, it is tremendously wasteful. One reason is that the size and scale of the enterprise simply creates inefficiency. Another is that food is cheap, reducing incentives to save. And the United States is the worst offender. About half of all food grown in the United States is squandered as it moves through the food chain. The average food wasted in America is 200 pounds per person per year.[14]

Another environmental cost of the consumer society is embedded in choice itself. Wealthy consumers prefer high-calorie diets, which means more protein (meat), fat, and sugar. All of these luxury goods require more land, water, and energy inputs than does the production of fruits, grains, and vegetables.[15] As societies become richer the world over, these high input foods are in greater demand, and this requires more resources.

Intensification of production of these commodities has occurred, with some success. But it has also created new ethical and environmental problems. This is especially the case with the industrial (factory) production of milk and meat (especially pork and poultry), which has spread rapidly in the last 20 years. Production is intense. Animals are kept in small enclosures and fed a diet heavy in protein, growth hormones, and antibiotics to ensure rapid growth. Because of the intense feeding regimen, animals can be brought to market in short period of time.

This makes factory meat production a good financial investment, but a poor social and environmental one. There are now many health concerns over the amount of antibiotics and growth hormones passed on into the human diet. Animal rights activists criticize the poor living conditions of the animals, and environmentalists are concerned about the enormous waste produced by so many animals confined to small areas. Waste is stored in large ponds. But heavy rains can flood and even destroy the dams, leading to massive spillage and subsequent pollution of streams and rivers.[16]

Despite these obvious problems, factory meat production continues. And it is driven by the consumer demand for inexpensive meat (fast food chains receive almost their entire meat inventory in this way). In response, environmentalists and social activists have pursued production alternatives that create better living conditions for animals (e.g., free range) and provide healthier products. Livestock production is a latecomer to the organic revolution. But because of the ethical and environmental aspects, it may be the most important in developing alternatives to industrial production—one clearly driven by the ethical concerns of consumers.

AGRICULTURE AND ENVIRONMENTAL CHALLENGES IN THE 21ST CENTURY

Feeding a growing world population while protecting the environment will be one of the greatest environmental struggles of the 21st century. And this struggle will be most acute in the Global South. The first problem is extensive agriculture by poor subsistence farmers, who are destroying fragile habitats (deserts and drylands) and those high in biodiversity (tropical rainforest) at an alarming rate. Much of this land has low productive value, forcing farmers to convert even more wilderness.

This problem is worsened when governments lack the resources, policies, or political will to make changes. This is especially true with respect to food security policy. This is an intrinsically political issue. It involves not only investment in education, training, infrastructure, and technology, but also changing market conditions. Most importantly, it involves reforming land tenure. A small population owns most of the land in most developing countries. And most of this land is used for cash—not

Box 8.2 Urban Agriculture

Many permaculture principles are especially suited for production in an urban setting. Yet urban agriculture has become a movement and method in its own right, with a distinctive focus on production and distribution of agricultural goods in densely populated modern cities. Urban agriculture is expanding in developed and developing societies alike.

One of its main goals is enhancement of food security. All cities in the world are almost completely reliant on outside sources for food and other resources. This reliance and economic vulnerability can be reduced by producing secure and stable food supplies within the city. The energy used to transport food to cities can also be greatly reduced. Another benefit, especially in the developing world, is job creation.

Healthier food is another benefit. Many urban gardens are organic and focus on vegetable, herb, and fruit production. These are foods that many poor people do not eat in adequate quantities. In the United States, urban agricultural groups are targeting the problem of obesity, especially in the inner cities. Employing the poor and providing them with quality food is a social goal, one that is already gaining political support, as a healthier and happier population is less prone to social ills.

Advocates also argue that urban agriculture provides many intangibles benefits, like enhanced aesthetics and building stronger community ties. As such, urban agriculture has become an important component of urban planning, in which it is becoming a focal point of housing development. And urban agriculture is conducive to almost any urban setting. It can use any available space, like rooftops, terraces, patios, vacant lots, alleys, and even walls (vertical farming) to increase production. Added green spaces also reduce pollution and noise.

Source: U.S. Department of Agriculture, Alternative Farming Systems Information Center, http://afsic.nal.usda.gov/farms-and-community/urban-agriculture.

food—production. Changing tenure relations is fraught with difficulty, but it would greatly benefit food production and the environment.

The neglect of food production (for whatever reason) leads to environmental neglect, which leads to political insecurity, which leads to conflict, which again undermines food production. Few conventional political and economic analysts understand this vicious cycle. But a growing number of political ecologists do, arguing that many cases of political insecurity, especially in the Middle East, North Africa, and the African Sahel, can be traced to the breakdown of agro-ecological systems.

So in many cases, an already volatile demographic problem is compounded by political problems. When governments cannot create viable development programs for poor farmers, then it is these poor people and the environment that must be sacrificed. Many wilderness areas the world over could be conserved if better and more efficient agricultural systems were in place. Only better governance can bring this about.

Wealthy countries of the Global North also pursue policies that have detrimental social and environmental impacts. The United States and the European Union subsidize agriculture. The result is overproduction and lower prices. When these goods are then dumped on global markets, small farmers are driven off of the land. Any incentive to conserve land and intensify yields is removed. Cheap grain also promotes more factory meat farming (see Case Study One).

There are countries that are pursuing more successful food security policies, especially the densely populated countries of Asia. They focus on intensification. While land use is more efficient and productivity has increased, these programs all follow the industrial model. As such, they have all the same problems of increased energy and chemical use to increase yields. The first phase of this intensification was dubbed the "green revolution."

This agricultural revolution occurred after World War II, and was promoted by the United States and American agribusiness. It was a form of industrial agriculture that focused mainly on increased grain (rice and corn). Yields increased dramatically, but also required many more inputs. In the end the green revolution benefitted rich farmers, who could afford these added inputs. The poor were often forced to leave the land, moving to already crowded cities.[17]

The situation has been further complicated in the last few decades with the introduction of genetically modified (GM), sometimes called genetically engineered (GE), crops. These are genetically modified to increase yields, reduce water usage, and resist insects and disease. All involve genetic changes that would normally not occur in nature. As such, they are different from genetic selection (selecting good seeds and plants), which farmers have done for millennia. GM crops are created in laboratories and the seeds are patented and controlled by large agribusinesses.

The use of GM crops has set off furious debates between its proponents and environmentalists and healthy food advocates (see Case Study Two). Proponents argue that hardier, more productive GM crops will help preserve more habitat from further cultivation. Opponents argue the environmental and health risks are unknown and could spread rapidly with the equally rapid spread of these crops.

GM crops have spread rapidly in the last 15 years. America produces most GM crops, and half of all corn and over 90 percent of soybeans grown in America are GM. They are also widespread in China and India, and are spreading in other developing nations. GM crops are least planted in Europe, where popular sentiment is most opposed to them.[18]

Agricultural production methods remain hotly debated. Some environmental and social analysts believe all industrial methods must eventually be changed. Others are more pragmatic, arguing that—at least in the short run—every agricultural production method must be employed to deal with the dual problem of feeding a growing world population and conserving habitat and resources. In time, adjustments can be made. But for now, time is of the essence and production must be increased quickly.

Another important part of the agricultural–environmental debate is transportation and storage. Here vast inefficiencies exist the world over and lead to tremendous food waste. Better delivery and storage systems are needed. This is especially true in developing countries, where food production is often adequate, but food spoils before it reaches the market because of lack of transport and storage facilities. This is another example of poor food security.

A final change in agriculture that could have environmental benefits is diet. This is especially the case in affluent societies, where people are heavily reliant on foods that require high resource inputs. The goal is to consume foods that require fewer resource inputs. This could conserve more land, energy, and other resources. And it is an area where individual choice can have a real environmental impact.

There is enough food in the world to feed all of its people, and this can be done while protecting precious habitat and resources. But to achieve this will require the concerted effort of citizens, consumers, activists, scientists, inventors, and investors. It will especially require political will and resolve—something often in short supply.

CASE STUDY 8.1

The WTO, Poverty and Environmental Degradation

The World Trade Organization (WTO) is the main IO that promotes global free trade. The goal of free trade is to reduce trade barriers (subsidies, tariffs, et cetera) to facilitate the international movement of goods, services, and labor. This, in turn, increases wealth in developed and developing countries alike. However, when applied to agriculture, critics charge that these policies have had the opposite effect. Poverty and environmental destruction have increased.

Agriculture is a unique economy. It is inherently volatile, due to diseases, climate, and other natural forces. Because of this, governments throughout the world support farmers and crop prices with policies like crop insurance, price supports, and credit. But the WTO has pushed government to reduce or eliminate these supports. The idea is that lower prices will increase demand and facilitate trade. Cheaper food prices will also help consumers, especially the poor.

But WTO policy has had several unintended consequences. First, lower prices have forced farmers to increase production to maintain profits. This often means converting more wilderness to cultivation—hence the environmental cost of free trade. Second, this situation benefits wealthy farmers who can afford expansion. Poor farmers are penalized by lower prices. First, they consume much of what they produce, so they do not get trade benefits from lower prices. They also cannot afford production expansion. The end result is many go bankrupt and move to already overcrowded cities.

Wealthy farmers, especially in the United States and European Union, also benefit because their governments provide subsidies (payments) to offset lower farm incomes due to low commodity prices. This not only counters WTO policy (the United States and European Union use sophisticated accounting methods to avoid censure), it allows these farmers to continue overproduction, which maintains low prices. These large farms, many of which are corporate agribusinesses, also rely heavily on industrial production and harvesting methods, which means more chemical additives, machinery, and fuel, all of which have negative environmental consequences.

Perhaps the greatest beneficiaries of the WTO free trade system are agribusinesses like Archer Daniels Midland, Cargill, and Continental grain that purchase, process and trade agricultural commodities worldwide. They benefit from low commodity prices and, because of their size and scale, have a virtual monopoly on global agricultural commodity trade. These groups also have enormous political clout with the WTO and governments throughout the world, which helps maintain and expand the WTO system.

Environmental NGOs, farm, and community groups argue that here is an alternative to the WTO free trade system. A central principle of such an alternative is multifunctionality. According to this concept, agriculture is not just concerned with commodity production for the market. Rather, it has many functions for society. Good farming protects rural families and communities. It protects their culture and way of life. And it protects the environment. In the end, good farming is more sustainable than the WTO alternative.

The WTO and its supporters counter that the global free trade system is still in its infancy. It will require better policies and technological changes to alleviate current problems. Critics remain skeptical. Either way, what the WTO case shows is the centrality of farming to the lives of most of the world's peoples and to the environment as a whole. As such, this case will remain pivotal to the debate over the relationship between poverty and the environment for years to come.

Source: Peter M. Rosset. 2006. *Food Is Different: Why We Must Get the WTO Out of Agriculture*. London: Zed.

CASE STUDY 8.2

The GM Agriculture Debate

Genetically modified (GM) crops are one of the most hotly debated topics in modern agriculture. These crops (most are plants) are developed by taking genetic material from another plant, even an animal, to produce a new one with higher yields, drought and disease resistance, or other traits. Proponents argue these crops will feed the world's growing populations while also reducing land and resource use. Opponents believe there are hidden health and environmental costs that will create new and worse problems.

From a critical standpoint, the first problem is that all GM crops are produced by large agribusinesses. Here scientists create new plant and animal varieties by transferring genetic materials from one organism to another. Specific traits can be targeted to produce a desired result. For example, genes from drought-tolerant desert plants can be added to corn genes to produce a new drought-tolerant corn plant. This process cannot be accomplished in nature.

So power and control is one of the first concerns. Only large agribusinesses like the Monsanto Corporation (one of the GM leaders) create and market these new crops. The crops are patented and the seeds are sterile so they cannot be collected and planted again (something poor farmers often must do to survive). So rich farmers, who can afford GM crops, and rich corporations are the main beneficiaries.

Another concern is the overall effect of these new plans and animal varieties on the gene pool. Will traits like disease and drought tolerance spread (through pollen) to other plants, especially undesirables like weeds or pests? And what are the health effects on people and livestock who consume GM crops? Will new toxins and allergens emerge in a GM-saturated ecosystem? These questions have not been fully answered, in part because the spread of GM crops has been so rapid, the evidence has yet to be amassed.

GM defenders argue that the evidence has not proven to be as negative as critics charge. Moreover, while negative effects can be expected from GM crops, the overall benefits far outweigh the costs. And if GM technology is not used, what is the alternative? Will it be more extensive farming methods, which destroy habitat? GM technology is the only viable alternative for densely populated countries with limited farmland. And it may give these countries some relief from foreign aid or costly food imports.

One neutral group, the Union of Concerned Scientists, sees benefits in GMO technologies. But it is critical of the political aspects of the industry. First, the production and distribution of GM crops is poorly regulated. Furthermore, independent scientific research is inadequate. Existing patent laws protect the genetic secrets of GM producers, making access, testing, and evaluation impossible. Food-labeling laws are equally inadequate. Most people do not even know they are eating GM foods, and many have never heard of them.

More trenchant critiques see GM foods as more insidious. They are another, far more powerful, expansion of industrial agriculture. These critics advocate organic alternatives, especially better plant breeding (through natural selection rather than genetic engineering), plus a focus on ecosystems to produce crops best suited to specific conditions (agroecology). They also criticize governments for not creating better agricultural polices, which could greatly increase productivity in many ways. But the greatest fear is whether genetic engineering, once perfected with plants and animals, will be applied to people.

Sources: http://www.ucsusa.org/food_and_agriculture and http://www.isaaa.org/resources/publications/pocketk.

ENDNOTES

1. Clive Ponting, *A New Green History of the World* (New York: Penguin, 2007), 42–52.
2. For a history of the plantation, see Philip Curtin, *The Rise and Fall of the Plantation Complex: Essays in Atlantic History* (Cambridge: Cambridge University Press, 1990).
3. Ibid., 145–147.
4. For a brief overview of these changes, see Ponting, *A New Green History of the World*, 239–43.
5. Ponting, *A New Green History of the World*, 236–37.
6. Many farmers, especially organic producers, now use no-till methods, which retain organic matter and topsoil.
7. Ponting, *A New Green History of the World*, 240.
8. Rachel Carson, *Silent Spring* (Boston: Houghton Mifflin, 1962).
9. Jennifer Chalt, "6 Largest Organic Retailers in North America 2011." Available at http://organic.about.com/od/marketingpromotion/tp/6-Largest-Organic-Retailers-In-North-America-2011.htm.
10. Jayson Beckman, Allison Borchers, and Carol A. Jones, *Agriculture's Supply and Demand for Energy and Energy Products*, Economic Research Report 112 (Washington DC: U.S. Department of Agriculture, 2013). Available at http://www.ers.usda.gov/media/1104145/eib112.pdf. Patrick Canning, Ainsley Charles, Sonya Huang, Karen R. Polenske, and Arnold Waters, *Energy Use in the U.S. Food System*, Economic Research Report Number 94 (Washington DC: U.S. Department of Agriculture, 2010). Available at http://www.ers.usda.gov/media/136418/err94_1_.pdf.
11. Jonathan Bloom, *American Wasteland: How America Throws Away Nearly Half of Its Food (and What We Can Do About It)* (Cambridge, MA: Da Capo Press, 2010), 4.
12. Bloom, *American Wasteland*; Tristram Stuart, *Waste: Uncovering the Global Food Scandal* (New York: W.W. Norton and CO., 2010).
13. Refrigerators are more efficient than in the past. But the U.S. Energy Department still ranks them second after air conditioners in household energy use. See http://www.eia.gov.
14. Bloom, *American Wasteland*, xii.
15. Canning et al., *Energy Use in the U.S. Food System.*
16. For critiques of factory farming, see Daniel Imhoff, *The CAFO Reader: The Tragedy of Industrial Animal Factories* (San Francisco: Foundation for Deep Ecology, 2010); and David Kirby, *Animal Factory: The Looming Threat of Industrial Pig, Dairy, and Poultry Farms to Humans and the Environment* (New York: St. Martins, 2011).
17. For critiques of the green revolution, see Bernhard Glaeser, *The Green Revolution Revisited: Critiques and Alternatives* (New York: Routledge, 2013); and Gordon R. Conway and Edward B. Barbier, *After the Green Revolution: Sustainable Development for Agriculture* (London: Earthscan, 1990).

18. For an overview of the GMO debate, see David Ruse, *Genetically Modified Foods: Debating Biotechnology* (Buffalo, NY: Prometheus, 2012); and Peter Pringle, *Food, Inc.: Mendel to Monsanto—The Promises and Perils of the Biotech Harvest* (New York: Simon and Schuster, 2003).

RECOMMENDED READINGS/SOURCES

Baram, Michael. 2011. *Governing Risk in GM Agriculture.* Cambridge: Cambridge University Press.

Blaxter, Kenneth, and Noel Robertson. 1995. *From Dearth to Plenty: The Modern Revolution in Food Production.* Cambridge: Cambridge University Press.

Bloom, Jonathan. 2010. *American Wasteland.* Cambridge, MA: Da Capo.

Conway, Gordon R., and Edward B. Barbier. 1990. *After the Green Revolution: Sustainable Agriculture for Development.* London: Earthscan.

Gabriel, Doreen. "Food Production and Biodiversity: Comparing Organic and Conventional Agriculture." *Journal of Applied Ecology* 50, no. 2 (2013): 355–64.

Grigg, David. 1990. *The Transformation of Agriculture in the West.* Oxford: Basil Blackwell.

Holmgren, David. 2011. *Permaculture: Principle and Pathways Beyond Sustainability.* Hampshire, UK: Hyden House.

Kirby, David. 2011. *Animal Factory: The Looming Threat of Industrial Pig, Dairy, and Poultry Farms to Humans and the Environment.* New York: St. Martins.

Leathers, Howard D. 1998. *The World Food Problem: Tackling the Causes of Undernutrition in the Third World.* Boulder, CO: Lynne Rienner.

Pringle, Peter. 2003. *Food, Inc.: Mendel to Monsanto—The Promises and Perils of the Biotech Harvest.* New York: Simon and Schuster.

Roberts, Jack. 2012. *Organic Agriculture: Protecting our Food Supply or Chasing Imaginary Risks?* Minneapolis, MN: 21st Century.

Ruse, David. 2012. *Genetically Modified Foods: Debating Biotechnology.* Buffalo, NY: Prometheus.

Smil, Vaclav. 2000. *Feeding the World: A Challenge for the Twenty-First Century.* Cambridge, MA: MIT Press.

Southgate, Douglas, Douglas H. Graham, and Luther Tweeten. 2007. *The World Food Economy.* Oxford: Blackwell.

Vijoen, Andre, Katrin Bohn and Joe Howe. 2005. *Continuous Productive Urban Landscapes.* Burlington, MA: Architectural.

Population and Urbanization

by **TOBIAS LANZ**

CHAPTER NINE

INTRODUCTION

The dramatic increase in human population over the last 200 years is one of the greatest changes in world history. From 1800 to 2000 the human population increased six-fold, from 1 to 6 billion. And it is still growing. It will probably reach 10 billion people by the mid-21st century, and may then begin to slowly stabilize.[1] This large human population means greater demand on land, timber, energy, and other natural resources, which also places ever-greater demands on the world's ecosystems.

The rapid rise and size of the human population raises several important environmental questions:

1. What is the carrying capacity of the Earth (the number of people it can support)?
2. What standards of living will or should these populations have?
3. Will or should biodiversity be sacrificed to provide for these populations?

Box 9.1 Key Terms in Population Studies

Demography: The study of population and population trends

Population growth rate: Percentage increase of a given population per year

Fertility rate: Number of children born per woman per year in a given population

Birth (natality) rate: Number of children born in a given population (per thousand people) per year

Death (mortality) rate: Number of people who die in a given population (per thousand people) per year

Zero population growth: A condition in a given population where birth and death rates are equal

Morbidity rate: Disease rate of a given population (per thousand people)

Average life expectancy: The average life span per person in a given population

POPULATION GROWTH: ITS CAUSES AND CONSEQUENCES

The causes and consequences of human population growth, especially the surge of the last 200 years, are not completely clear. It is commonly believed that all population increases are due simply to high fertility rates (women having many children). But large families have been the norm throughout history. And human populations remained low throughout most of history. Other factors were involved.

One was the increase in the quality and quantity of food (see Case Study 9.1). The increase in agricultural production, plus the increase in food trade, especially overseas trade, introduced the world's peoples to many new and nutritious foods. The global spread of New World crops like corn, potatoes, and cassava, which could be grown in many different soils and climates, had the most dramatic impact on increasing productivity and nutrition. As a result of this food revolution (see Chapter 8), malnutrition and famine became less common. Naturally, populations grew worldwide.

A second factor was improved health and hygiene. Improvements in medicine and sanitation drastically reduced disease and death rates, especially among children. One of the most important sanitation developments was the purification and distribution of clean (potable) water. This occurred after science discovered unclean water was a major health hazard, after which time providing clean water became an important policy issue. Yet, even today unsanitary water, especially in the Global South, remains a serious health concern and is the cause of more human misery than any other health problem.

Medical developments were equally significant in increasing population. One of the most important was the discovery and mass production of penicillin in the 20th century. This led to dramatic reductions in infectious diseases. Another was the development of vaccines and inoculations to prevent life-threatening diseases. Rapid advances in medical technology, especially surgical procedures, also helped save more human lives and increase longevity.

The great catalyst to all these transformations was the spread of scientific knowledge and the application of scientific methods to social problems. This was accomplished through the Industrial Revolution, the growth of government, and the attendant spread of markets. (This development also created many new problems for society and the environment.) While the Industrial Revolution is usually associated with the development of machines and technologies, its first and most dramatic impact was on food and sanitation. But this revolution, especially on human life and longevity, is rarely recognized. As renowned scientist and policy analyst Vaclav Smil writes,

> Our "postmodern" civilization would do quite well without Microsoft and Oracle, without ATMs and the WWW—but it would disintegrate in a matter of years without synthetic nitrogen fertilizers, and it would collapse in a matter of months without thriving bacteria.[2]

The global human population surge caused by these revolutionary changes first occurred in Europe, whose population increased from 200 to 400 million in the 19th century. The Asian population, which had already reached 600 million by 1800, did not experience a dramatic increase until the 20th century, when it increased from 950 million to 3.6 billion. The other inhabited continents of the world—North America, South America, and Africa—all increased their populations in the 20th century. Africa currently has the highest growth rate of any continent.[3]

The populations of Europe and Asia were either stable or declining by the late 20th century. They are experiencing what demographers call demographic transition. According to demographic transition theory, a population will eventually transition from high to low birth rates as wealth and security increase. It is one of the consequences of industrialization. Most industrial societies have experienced this transition.

Population in pre-industrial societies is actually relatively stable, with high birth and death rates that are roughly even. Industrialization, which increased food production and improved sanitation and medicine, created higher birth rates and declining death rates. This led to rapid population increases. As industrialization produced greater wealth and security, birth rates began to fall and once again equaled death rates. As a result, population again stabilized.

Demographic transition theory was based on the European experience in the 19th century, and remained the dominant population model beginning in the 1930s. Yet by the 1970s critics emerged with ample data that contradicted it.[4] There were many factors that determined both demographic increase and decline. It was found that wealth or perceived wealth could actually prompt people to have more children. Conversely, the prospect of future poverty actually reduced birth rates, especially among the poorest people.

Many demographers believe the problem of large populations and rapid population growth rates must be addressed through a combination of government policy, cultural practices, and individual initiative. Some countries, like China, have enacted strict population controls, as witnessed in the one child policy (see Case Study One). In other societies, the focus has been on individual initiatives and behavior to reduce birth rates.

In Europe and Asia, the reduction of birth rates has taken about 150 years. It is underway or partially underway in other continents. Yet, a stable or declining population does not necessarily mean lower environmental impacts. All of these industrial societies, with their lower fertility rates and smaller families, also have far higher per capita consumption rates than poor agrarian societies, despite their higher birth rates and larger families.

Paradoxically, as population growth rates have fallen, consumption rates have increased. Currently all industrial societies (the Global North) have 25 percent of the world population, but consume about 75 per cent of all resources. The United States, with only 5 percent of the world population, consumes 25 percent of all resources. There would not be enough natural resources in the world—at current technological and institutional capacities—to sustain the world's peoples if all achieved the industrial lifestyle.[5]

One population trend in industrial societies is individualization, one feature of which is that an increasing number of adults live alone. This is sometimes seen as a resource-reducing trend, as most individuals live in smaller dwellings, delay marriage and childbirth, or avoid it altogether. But individual living can actually lead to higher per capita resource use rates. For example, the number of appliances, automobiles, electronic devices, and energy required per person is generally greater than a family or communal living arrangement in which those resources are shared.

The dramatic growth in aggregate and per capita resource consumption by industrial nations has shifted the focus of population studies away from simply examining population size and growth rates. It has also shifted emphasis away from food production and land requirements for food. Other resource pressures must be considered. Measures such as the carbon or ecological footprint, which calculates resource use per person, institution, nation or the entire planet, take into account many resources.

The carbon footprint refers specifically to the amount of carbon emissions (CO_2 and CH_4) produced from various types of energy use—coal, petroleum, electricity, nuclear, and so on. This measure is often used to discern the impact that energy use has on global warming and climate change. The ecological footprint is a broader measure that represents the amount of land and sea area needed to support human populations and assimilate waste.

Both measures have been critiqued because they are too abstract and do not take into account local factors and other contingencies. This also makes them difficult to operationalize for policy purposes. Advocates argue these measures are developed to address one key dimension of human behavior—the extent to which the Earth's ecosystems have the capacity to accommodate human resource demands. Proponents argue that the main idea of the carbon and ecological footprint is to better understand the overall relationship between human demand and the Earth's resources.[6]

POPULATION DEBATES

Debates over the effects of human population growth are found throughout history. Confucius (551–478 BC), Plato (427–347 BC), and Aristotle (384–322 BC) all expressed concern over the negative impact of rapid population growth on social stability and food supply. Conversely, the Romans, medieval Christians, and some early modern thinkers believed large human populations enhanced political power, social stability, and wealth creation, respectively.[7]

These debates became more intense and sophisticated in the modern era (post-1500). Population growth, the spread of wealth and commerce, increased resource use, and urbanization had now become more consistent and observable social phenomena. This led to the emergence of population studies in which questions about the relationship between these factors and potential social and environmental consequences became more salient.[8] The debate between those who saw population trends as negative (pessimists) versus those who saw them as positive (optimists) was also established.

The most famous pessimistic view on the relationship between population growth and resource use was by Thomas Malthus (1766–1834). Malthus, a cleric and political economist, wrote *An Essay on the Principle of Population as it Affects the Future Improvement of Society*. In it, he argued against the utopians of his day (like Godwin and Condorcet) who believed human society would see constant improvement. Malthus argued that human population growth would quickly overcome food production capabilities, leading to starvation and social chaos.

Malthus' reasoning was that human population growth increased geometrically (1, 2, 4, 16, 32, et cetera), whereas food production increased arithmetically (1, 2, 3, 4, 5, et cetera). This disparity would eventually lead to crisis. He did believe that human societies could slow population growth through a variety of measures, like birth control and delayed marriage. But he also believed that poverty could never fully be eradicated, and that disease and famine were part of human existence.

Europe and North America were able to increase standards of living and life expectancy in the 19th century through a number of political, economic, and technical changes. But the Malthusian prognosis still remains, especially as it pertains to populations in the Global South. Moreover, to be a Malthusian is still a widely used term, referring to someone who is skeptical of the human condition and the ability of the planet to sustain growing human populations.

The Malthusian theme reemerged in the late 20th century as population rates, especially in the Global South, surged. The term "population explosion" was coined after Paul Ehrlich published *Population Bomb* in 1968. He warned that the 1970s and 1980s would see massive famine and social upheaval in developing countries if population growth rates were not quickly curbed. Although this scenario never occurred, Ehrlich and his generation saw population growth as a more general environmental problem that went beyond food scarcity. It placed great demands on all the world's resources.

Ehrlich's book was followed by an NGO—the Club of Rome—and its report *Limits to Growth* (1972). It focused even more explicitly on natural resources, especially energy, which it held could not sustain a constantly growing world population.

The report's predictions seemed to be accurate after the first oil shock in 1973, which for the first time since World War II created widespread energy shortages in the industrial world. Although energy prices have fluctuated since, the oil shock and the Club of Rome report made energy efficiency and potential energy shortages a permanent public policy issue.

Lester Brown, of the Worldwatch Institute in Washington, DC, is another analyst who predicts future environmental catastrophe if world population growth is not brought under control. He has, since the 1970s, argued that global food scarcity and famine will become widespread.[9] His analysis has a strong ecological focus, examining problems like soil degradation, deforestation, and species loss as other consequences of rapid population growth besides food shortages.

Optimists quickly countered these claims, arguing that this research was either based on faulty data or poor research models.[10] Moreover, evidence has contradicted all the dire scenarios predicted by the pessimists. Human technology and institutions have actually increased agricultural yields and the quality of human life and longevity since the 1970s. Many optimists went even further to argue that the Earth could sustain many more people than pessimists claim—15, 18, even 20 billion people or more.

German demographer Fritz Baade (1893–1974) held that the Earth, with maximum food production, could sustain 65 billion people. To him the limiting factor was living space, not arable land.[11] Cesare Marchetti believed even higher numbers were possible. He argued that debating the Earth's carrying capacity was absurd because, given the right technology (he saw solar energy as the ideal), an "absurdly large number of people" could be sustained on Earth.[12]

One of the most famous optimists was economist Julian Simon (1932–1998). He and Paul Ehrlich vigorously debated the population bomb thesis, and famously made a bet on the future of resources and resource prices, which Simon won. Simon believed that the number of people the Earth could support was essentially unlimited, given human propensity to innovate and adapt. He believed population was not a problem but a solution, because humans would make the necessary changes to overcome resource shortages.

The population debate continues and there are extreme positions on both sides.[13] However, both sides also present important arguments and facts. Pessimists correctly note that ever-growing human populations place ever-greater demands on the environment. Pollution, biodiversity loss, soil erosion, climate change, and a host of other environmental ills have only increased in the era of rapid human population growth.

The weakness of this position is it assumes this level of degradation will only increase. Moreover, there is the belief that oblivion is somehow unavoidable. Critics counter that humans have recognized many of these environmental problems and have developed solutions. Much of the resource-use problem is not due simply to greater demand on limited resources, but to waste and inefficient allocation. These are problems that can be readily remedied to at least stabilize the situation.

Pessimists also argue that stringent population control measures must be enacted worldwide to prevent further environmental damage. This might include political coercion, as in China. Critics counter that other factors will naturally lead to a slowing of world population. Rather than use political capital to stop population growth, governments and other institutions must focus on developing incentives and social conditions that will lower birth rates. There are many ways in which societies can and have controlled populations (see Box 9.2).

In contrast, optimists believe humans are infinitely inventive and can overcome any obstacle with better institutions, technologies, and policies. They argue these factors have prevented the dire scenarios predicted by the pessimists, especially massive food shortages and famine. But pessimists charge that optimists also exaggerate human abilities. Even when solutions exist, they are often applied too late, if at all. And many governments, especially in the Global South, lack the capacity to enact proper solutions, even when they are available. Also, the increase in food supply, indeed the entire global food economy, is still based on fossil fuel use. Critics ask whether the world can still be fed if this most vital resource ever diminished.

Pessimists also assert that the optimistic positon is very anthropocentric. It examines the world and its resources only in terms of human use—how many people can the Earth's land, energy, and other resources sustain. The impact on the Earth's biodiversity remains unexamined. Pessimists ask how much species-rich rainforest, wetland, grassland, and so on must be sacrificed to accomodate human populations. People may survive, but in an an ecologically impoverished world. And this world may also be inhabited by large numbers of impoverished people.

URBANIZATION

The growth of cities (urbanization) is another feature of modern world population growth. In 1800 less than 5 percent of the world's population lived in cities. Today it is over 50 percent. Moreover, the world's urban population has increased 100-fold in those 200 years.[14] And like population, the city has become an important area of environmental analysis and debate.

Box 9.2 How Societies Control Population

All societies throughout history have controlled population in some way. Some methods are relatively benign; others involve violation or death, and have thus evoked criticism and condemnation. These various methods include the following.

Birth control potions and pills: These prevent pregnancy. Historically this was achieved by imbibing potions of different kinds. Modern societies use a range of industrially produced pills and other products.

Abortion: This is the removal of the fetus to prevent birth. Historically, this has been accomplished by imbibing poisons and potions, internal probes, blows to the stomach, and violent exercise. Modern societies use surgical procedures.

Monitoring menstrual cycles: Women throughout history and in different societies have monitored their menstrual cycles to regulate sexual activity and control pregnancy.

Delayed childbirth and child spacing: Delaying the birth of the first child and spacing the years between births lowers fertility rates of women.

Celibacy and chastity: This involves short-term or lifetime commitments to sexual abstinence. This cultural practice is often an important part of religious vows and devotions.

Infanticide and geronticide: This is the killing infants or elderly members of society, respectively. They are deemed unfit, unhealthy, or a burden to society.

Sterilization: This is the removal of reproductive organs to prevent pregnancy. Historically, it was mostly confined to men (eunuchs) who performed certain social roles or tasks. Modern industrial societies use surgical procedures on both men and women.

Emigration: People have moved voluntarily or by force from over-populated to less-populated countries or regions.

The city is the most artificial environment. It replaces natural biomes with an almost completely human-made environment, one composed largely of concrete, asphalt, steel, and glass. It is also the most parasitic, relying almost exclusively on food, energy, and other resources from outside sources.

The vast majority of people lived in villages and towns for most of the last 10,000 years. But small cities did begin to develop during this period, and were closely associated with the rise of agriculture (the Neolithic Revolution) and the wealth and population growth it fostered. All of the large agrarian civilizations—the cradles of civilization—had one or more large cities with populations numbering in the thousands.

These pre-industrial cities were located where wealth was produced—fertile agricultural areas, or along coastlines and rivers where they benefitted from trade. Some were also located in strategic locations for defensive purposes. And in almost all cases, these cities were densely built and surrounded by high walls for protection. Cities were also centers of political, economic, and religious power. But the majority of the urban population comprised servants, slaves, and scores of poor beggars who came to escape even more difficult rural conditions.

The coexistence of the very rich and poor was already a defining feature of ancient cities, and would continue to be so into the present age. Disease and environmental problems were another defining feature—then and now. The dense living conditions, often shared with dogs, pigs, and other livestock, made it a breeding ground for disease. The accumulation of human and animal waste and other garbage was another chronic problem. It was burned, consumed by animals, or simply dumped into rivers, which also served as the main water supply.

Prior to 1500 all of the world's largest cities were in the Middle East or Asia, especially China. Europe did not begin to urbanize until after that time, much of it due to the demographic collapse caused by the 14th century Black Death (bubonic plague). But improved agriculture and wealth accumulated through colonial empires soon began to increase population and urban growth. This was most rapid in Great Britain and the Netherlands.

Industrialization in 19th-century Europe transformed the city even more. The creation of mass employment, the mass production of goods, and new technologies facilitated rapid urban growth. It also changed the character of the city. Industrialization allowed cities to grow upward. Industrial building materials and methods allowed for construction of far larger buildings with many stories. Moreover, new forms of energy—electricity, coal, and fossil fuels—could now heat and light these enormous structures.

Industrialization also allowed cities to grow outward. The modern city was laced with a grid of concrete and asphalt, facilitating more rapid and efficient transportation. These transportation grids soon spread out from the city center with the development of fossil fuel powered vehicles—cars, trucks, buses, trolleys, and trains. People could now afford to live further from urban congestion and work. These new "sub" urban areas extended for miles. These transportation networks also linked cities to other cities, facilitating trade, which fostered more economic development.

By 1900 most of the world's largest cities were in Europe or North America. But demographic trends changed again in the 20th century. It was now centered in the Global South, where population growth rates often exceeded 4 percent per year. By 2000, New York was the only European or North American city represented in the world's ten largest cities. All were now in the Global South, especially Latin America and Asia. The largest of these cities are dubbed mega-cities or super-cities—those with populations over 10 million people.[15]

There is one major difference between urbanization in Europe and North America and that of the Global South. When the former urbanized, it did so alongside industrialization. This allowed for the employment of many urban immigrants, and ultimately created a higher standard of living and a middle class in these cities. Industrialization has not occurred to the same degree in the Global South, creating greater unemployment and widespread poverty. Today some of the world's worst human poverty is in these cities.

Yet people keep migrating at the rate of 200,000 per day in the belief work and wealth can be found in the city. The numbers of destitute urban dwellers in Global South cities is around 1 billion people, and will likely double by 2030. This will represent one-fourth of the world's population.[16] Almost all of these people are homeless. They live on the streets or in makeshift shelters—in shantytowns or slums—that sprawl for miles around the periphery of major cities. These are the "suburbs" in the Global South.

Most of these dwellings are illegal; hence these people are referred to as squatters. Conditions are crowded and there is little access to clean water, toilet facilities, medicine, and reliable shelter. Crime is often rampant. One writer describes a common scene in a slum outside of Nairobi:

> Outside, a mound of garbage formed the border between Southland and the adjacent neighborhood of Langata. It was perhaps 8 feet tall, 40 feet long, and 10 feet wide, set in a wider watery ooze. As we passed, two boys were climbing the Mt. Kenya of trash. They couldn't have been more than

Box 9.3 The United Nations Human Settlements Programme (UN–Habitat)

This organization is the special UN agency for human settlements and sustainable urban development. It was established in 1978 in Vancouver, and its headquarters are Nairobi, Kenya.

The organization has actively focused on international urban issues, especially as they impact the poor. The mandate for UN–Habitat was established in 1996 at the UN Conference on Human Settlements in Istanbul, Turkey. The Habitat agenda was established at that time, which focuses on two main goals: 1. Provide adequate shelter for all the world's people, and 2. promote sustainable urban development.

UN–Habitat focuses on several social, economic, political, and environmental themes related to these goals:

1. **Climate change:** The goal is to reduce urban emissions, because cities produce some of the highest and most concentrated levels of greenhouse gases. Cities are also among the most vulnerable habitats to climate change.
2. **Water and sanitation:** The goal is to provide better water access, clean (potable) water, and overall improved sanitation in cities. Many of these problems exist because urban populations have grown faster than the city's capacity to deal with them.
3. **Land:** The goal is better land allocation and cleaning up land. Land is in short supply in many large and rapidly growing cities. Land is also polluted with chemical, trash, and other waste.
4. **Energy use:** The goal is to create more efficient and widespread access to energy. Electricity, coal, and fossil fuels are often unavailable to many city dwellers, especially the poor. Many energy delivery systems are also inefficient.
5. **Transportation:** The goal is to create better and more energy efficient transportation networks. The main concern is the spread of roads and the growth of gas-powered vehicles (cars, motorcycles, et cetera), which create pollution and traffic.

Source: http://www.unhabitat.org.

> 5 or 6 years old. They were barefoot, and with each step their toes sank into the muck, sending hundreds of angry flies scattering from the rancid pile. I thought they might be playing King of the Hill. But I was wrong. Once atop the pile, one boy lowered his shorts, squatted, and defecated. The flies buzzed angrily around his legs.[17]

In the past, governments tried to eliminate these shantytowns by physically destroying them or incarcerating the residents. Brazil's government even tried to create a new city—Brasilia—to help disperse the large populations of poor in Sao Paolo and Rio de Janeiro. But the squatters kept coming. Most governments now simply allow them to build their shantytowns. NGOs and IOs also work with and aid these communities, providing many needed services and resources (see Box 9.3).

URBAN PLANNING AND URBAN ECOLOGY

The growth of the city and urban problems led to the development of urban studies and urban development. One of the recent subfields in these areas of study is urban ecology, which is the conceptualization and study of cities as distinct ecosystems—ecosystems with unique social and ecological problems. Urban ecology is a synthesis of ecology, sociology, economics, and history. This discipline is becoming one of the most important in environmental studies, as urban areas continue to grow, and environmental and social problems caused by cities continue to multiply.

Redefining cities as ecosystems is an important shift in perspective, because it allows urban areas and their problems to be understood holistically and from a biophysical perspective. All urban areas, especially those undergoing rapid growth, seriously distort essential biological functions, like the hydrological (water), carbon, nitrogen, and phosphorus cycles. Cities also distort energy and resource flows—as they consume far more than they produce (see Box 9.4).

To alleviate these problems requires not only specific (reductionist) policies like improved housing, traffic control, and water treatment; more green spaces; forest and agricultural development; and extensive and more efficient transportation and energy systems. It also requires a holistic (ecological) approach to planning and management that emphasizes ecological principles like biodiversity, adaptiveness, interconnectedness, resilience, regenerative capacity, and symbiosis.[18]

The issue at the center of the urban planning debate is controlling growth or sprawl. One problem is the space it consumes—forest and farmland. The other is

Box 9.4 Urbanization Problems—Urban Heat Islands

Urban heat islands are urban areas that have higher average temperatures than surrounding rural areas. The main causes for heat islands are 1. urban construction—buildings, roads, parking lots, and other urban development store a considerable amount of heat (short-wave radiation); and 2. energy use. The use of electricity, fossil fuels, and coal releases heat into the surrounding atmosphere.

Heat islands continue to expand worldwide as urbanization intensifies. The average temperature of these islands can be several degrees warmer than the surrounding countryside. This heat buildup can impact the environment and human health in several ways.

1. **Increased energy consumption:** Higher temperatures increase electricity demand during warm months as the use of fans and air conditioners increases. Heat islands can greatly impact peak demand for energy, and lead to power outages.
2. **Increased air pollution and greenhouse gases:** Increased electricity demand also increases power plant activity. This results in increased coal and fossil fuel use. The burning of these fuels releases more air pollution and greenhouse gases into the environment.
3. **Human health problems:** Higher temperatures create general discomfort for people. They also exacerbate respiratory problems, heat cramps, heat stroke, and exhaustion. These can all be fatal.
4. **Impaired water quality:** Buildings, roads, parking lots, and other urban development collects rain water. When this water is heated and often mixed with oil and gas runoff, polluted water is the result. This eventually enters waterways and has a negative impact on people and wildlife.

There are several ways of mitigating the effects of urban heat islands.

1. Planting trees and vegetation: This involves widespread urban planting on road medians, parking lots, and domestic and commercial properties.

Environmental effects:

- Lowers temperature by providing shade
- Absorbs carbon and pollutants, improving air quality
- Reduces water runoff and filters water, improving water quality
- Provides aesthetic value that enhances the quality of life

2. Green roofs or rooftop gardens: This involves planting lawn, ground cover, or entire gardens on (usually) flat roofs.

Environmental effects:

- Lowers temperature by insulating buildings
- Absorbs carbon and pollutants, improving air quality
- Reduces water runoff and filters water, improving water quality
- Provides aesthetic value that enhances the quality of life

3. Cool roofs: They use materials that increase solar reflection, which deflects sunlight and heat from buildings.

Environmental effects:

- Reduces energy for cooling buildings
- Reduces heat, which increases human comfort and health
- Provides aesthetic value that enhances the quality of life

4. Cool pavements: They are made from special materials that reduce heat absorption and increase water percolation.

5. Environmental effects:

- Reduces water runoff and improves water quality
- Reduces automobile noise
- Provides aesthetic value that enhances the quality of life

Source: The Environmental Protection Agency, http://www.epa.gov/heatisland/impacts/index.htm and http://www.epa.gov/heatisland/mitigation/index.htm.

the high levels of energy and extensive transportation grids required to transport suburban dwellers to work, and to supply their resource needs. Even Global South megacities will require ever more roads and rails, filled with more fossil fuel–powered vehicles, to sustain their enormous and continually growing urban populations.

An emerging urban planning concept, directly influenced by an ecosystem approach, is that of "smart growth." This idea, which has been implemented in North America, Europe, and Asia, argues that urban growth should take into account the environment, the economy, and the community. Smart growth focuses on several key planning principles:[19]

1. Open space conversion
2. Boundaries limiting the outward extension of growth
3. Compact, mixed use developments amenable to walking and transit
4. Revitalization of older downtowns, inner-ring suburbs, and rundown commercial areas
5. Viable public transit to reduce automobile dependence and support alternative development patterns
6. Regional planning, coordination of transportation and land use
7. Equitable sharing of fiscal resources and financing burdens, including affordable housing across metropolitan areas

Critics charge that smart growth will entail higher costs, regulations, and taxes. This is true in many cases. But proponents argue that the current state of uncontrolled urban growth will impose even higher social and ecological costs in the long run. No matter what kind of urban policy is adopted, ecological factors can no longer be ignored. The city is becoming a planetary phenomenon that will be the dominant human habitat on Earth.

CASE STUDY 9.1

Population Trends and Policy in China

China had a population of 1.4 billion in 2015, making it the world's most populous country. The country has long been known for its large and dense populations (it has 3 of the world's 12 largest urban areas). And recently it has become equally famous for its one child policy, which is the most restrictive population control policy enacted by any modern nation. China's large population, coupled with its spectacular economic rise (making it a major resource consumer), makes it one of the most important cases for demographic studies.

China's high population growth and densities (concentrated in the east and south) is due first to geographic and climatic conditions. A mild climate, combined with rich alluvial soils that have long been irrigated by elaborate networks of canals, aqueducts, dams, and levies, has been able to feed large populations for centuries. Moreover, the main crop—rice—can produce high yields and several harvests over a growing season. This system can support large populations.

The country already had a population of 400 million people by 1840. It reached 500 million by the mid-20th century, growing at 2 percent per year (meaning the population grew by 11 to 12 million people per year). The population continued to grow after the Communist Revolution of 1949, in part because Chairman Mao Zedong promoted population growth, believing it would lead to development and the transformation of China into a world power.

Chairman Mao and many in the Communist party ridiculed ideas of population control, especially those of Thomas Malthus and his predictions about the negative relationship between population growth and food production. They believed this was Western propaganda. Famine was not due to overpopulation, but rather to private property (found in capitalist societies). As such, private property had to be abolished and large communist (collective) farms created to resolve any food problems.

China embarked on an ambitious national economic reform program in 1958—the Great Leap Forward, which sought to modernize the country's economy, especially agriculture. This was followed by the Cultural Revolution, a political program designed to spread and enforce communist ideas in every corner of the nation. Both programs were unable to deal with growing food shortages. Ironically, tens of millions of Chinese peasants perished due to famine during this period.

The population continued to grow despite the large number of deaths. It went from 580 million in 1954 to over 900 million by 1975. The 1970s was the first time government officials began to worry that population growth would threaten economic development. The government got involved. It pushed the slogan "later-longer-fewer," encouraging people to marry late, space births, and have fewer children. Two children were now seen as too many. One was ideal.

Pressure toward compliance was at first relatively mild. Government sought simply to encourage people to adopt these policies. By the late 1970s the party became worried, as population growth rates had not greatly diminished. The famous one child policy came into force in 1978. And the government would use force to ensure compliance. Families with one child would receive special economic benefits, while those with two would not. And couples who defied the government and had three children would be penalized with economic sanctions and sent to labor camps.

The government created an extensive bureaucracy to ensure compliance. Birth control pills, sterilization, and other procedures are widely available, as is abortion on demand. Economic development, especially (and ironically) through the pursuit of capitalism has greatly increased food production. As a result, famine has been avoided thus far, even though the nation must still import grain. Overall, the one child policy is considered a success by the Chinese government.

However, human rights and religious groups have strenuously critiqued it, as it is invasive and undermines human freedom. Many women are forced to become sterilized and undergo abortions. Feminists have added that most abortions are of females, as the Chinese people prefer male children. This has also led to serious imbalances between the sexes, with more men than women.

Debates over China's one child policy continue. Proponents believe it was necessary and timely. China has an enormous population that must be fed, and as it grows wealthier, will require ever more resources. An even larger population could not have been sustained. The one child policy was relaxed in 2015, allowing couples to have a second child, to support China's large and aging population.

Source: Neurath, Paul. 1994. *From Malthus to the Club of Rome and Back: Problems of Limits to Growth, Population Control, and Migrations*. Armonk, NY: M. E. Sharpe. See Chapter 8, "Chinese Population Policy from 1949 to 1984."

ENDNOTES

1. There are many debates and predictions about world population numbers. Some see future population substantially higher, whereas others believe some stability will occur as the population reaches 10 billion. See Vaclav Smil, "How Many People Can the Earth Feed?" *Population and Development Review* 20 (1994): 255–92; and Joel E. Cohen, *How Many People Can the Earth Support?* (New York, NY: W. W. Norton and Co., 1995).
2. Vaclav Smil, *Feeding the World: A Challenge for the Twenty-First Century* (Cambridge, MA: MIT Press, 2000), xvi.
3. Clive Ponting, *A New Green History of the World* (New York: Penguin Books, 2007), 232–35.
4. Virginia Abernathy, *Population Politics: The Choices That Shape Our Future* (New York: Insight Books, 1993), 33–41.
5. Worldwatch Institute, "The State of Consumption Today," http://www.worldwatch.org/node/810.
6. For information on the general idea of the ecological footprint, see http://www.footprintnetwork.org. For a detailed discussion of critiques, see http://www.footprintnetwork.org/en/index.php/GFN/page/responses_to_published_criticisms/.
7. Paul Neurath, *From Malthus to the Club of Rome and Back: Problems of Limits to Growth, Population Control, and Migrations* (Armonk, NY: M. E. Sharpe Inc., 1994), 1–9.
8. Some population pioneers during this period included John Gaunt, Edmund Halley, and Gregory King. Ibid., 12–20.
9. Some of Brown's early works include Lester R. Brown, "Global Food Insecurity," *The Futurist* 8, no. 2 (1974): 56; and Lester R. Brown, "World Population Growth, Soil Erosion, and Food Insecurity," *Science* 214 (1981): 995–1002.
10. The models used in *Limits to Growth* have been critiqued in particular. See Neurath, *From Malthus to the Club of Rome and Back*, 92–125.
11. Quoted in Neurath, *From Malthus to the Club of Rome and Back*, 49.
12. C. Marchetti, "On 10 to the 12th Power: A Check on Earth Carrying Capacity for Man," International Institute for Applied Systems Analysis, Wien-Laxenburg, Paper No. RR-78-7, May (1978).
13. See Smil, *Feeding the World: A Challenge for the Twenty-First Century* (Cambridge, MA: MIT Press, 2000), ix-xvi, for a good overview of these positions.
14. Ponting, *A New Green History of the World*, 294.
15. Cities are defined several ways—from the city proper, to urban areas comprising many cities and towns that cover an entire geographic region.
16. Robert Neuwirth, *Shadow Cities: A Billion Squatters, A New Urban World* (London: Routledge, 2005), 9.
17. Ibid., 5.

18. Peter Newman and Isabella Jennings, *Cities as Sustainable Ecosystems: Principles and Practices* (Washington DC: Island, 2008), 92.
19. Oliver Gillham, *The Limitless City: A Primer on the Urban Sprawl Debate* (Washington DC: Island, 2002), 158.

RECOMMENDED READINGS/SOURCES

Brenner, Neil. 2014. *Implosions/Explosions: Towards a Study of Planetary Urbanization*. Berlin: Jovis Verlag.

Cohen, Joel E. 1995. *How Many People Can the Earth Support?* New York: W. W. Norton and Co.

Ehrlich, Paul R. 1968. *The Population Bomb: Population Control or Race to Oblivion*. San Francisco, CA: Sierra Club/Ballantine.

Gillham, Oliver. 2002. *The Limitless City: A Primer on the Urban Sprawl Debate*. Washington DC: Island.

Glaeser, Edward. 2011. *Triumph of the City: How Our Greatest Invention Makes Us Richer, Smarter, Greener, Healthier, and Happier*. New York: Penguin.

Grimm, Nancy B., Stanley H. Faeth, Nancy E. Golubiewski, Charles L. Redman, Jianguo Wu, Xuemei Bai and John M. Briggs. *Global Change and Ecology of Cities*. *Science* 319, no. 5864 (2008): 756–60.

Kahn, Matthew E. 2006. *Green Cities: Urban Growth and the Environment*. Washington DC: Brookings Institute.

Malthus, Thomas. 1798. *An Essay on the Principle of Population as It Affects the Future Improvement of Society with Remarks on the Speculations of Mr. Godwin, M. Condorcet, and Other Writers*. London: J. Johnson.

Marzluff, John M. 2008. *Urban Ecology: An International Perspective on the Interaction Between Humans and Nature*. New York: Springer.

Meadows, Donella H., Dennis L. Meadows, Jorgen Randers, and William W. Behrens III. 1972. *The Limits to Growth*. New York: Signet.

Neurath, Paul. 1994. *From Malthus to the Club of Rome and Back: Problems of Limits to Growth, Population Control, and Migrations*. Armonk, NY: M. E. Sharpe.

Neuwirth, Robert. 2005. *Shadow Cities: A Billion Squatters, A New Urban World*. London: Routledge.

Newman, Peter, and Isabella Jennings. 2008. *Cities as Sustainable Ecosystems: Principles and Practices*. Washington DC: Island.

Riddell, Robert. 2004. *Sustainable Urban Planning*. Oxford: Blackwell.

United Nations Department of Economic and Social Affairs, Population Division, http://www.un.org/en/development/desa/population/.

Sustainable Development

by **EDWARD R. CARR** and **MICHAEL H. FINEWOOD**

CHAPTER TEN

INTRODUCTION

Sustainable development is popularly defined as development that meets the needs and aspirations of the present without compromising the well-being of future generations. This seemingly straightforward definition obscures the long, complex history of the concept. Sustainable development is a remarkably pliable term, as both sustainability and development can be construed in various ways, so that completely contrary initiatives and goals are conflated. Furthermore, the focus on intergenerational equity implicit in most sustainable development approaches overlooks significant intra-generational equity issues. Finally, the implementation of sustainable development has raised significant questions about how best to understand and operationalize this nebulous goal. All of these issues will require resolution if sustainable development is to become more than a slogan.

HISTORY

The contemporary use of the term sustainable development is usually traced to *Our Common Future*.[1] However, the Brundtland Report captured and organized ideas that had coalesced in the 1960s and 1970s, when concerns for human impacts on the environment emerged. For example, Carson's *Silent Spring*, while focused on the issue of toxic pesticides in the environment, both highlighted the human capacity to damage the environment and the impacts of such damage on human well-being.

Soon after, Hardin's "Tragedy of the Commons" and Ehrlich's *The Population Bomb* adopted some of Thomas Malthus' earlier concerns for the impact of population on the environment[2] into a neo-Malthusian concern for unsustainable natural resource use as an inevitable result of growing global population pressures.

The work of Carson, Ehrlich, Hardin, and others were principally focused on exploring the human impacts on the environment.[3] This work focused on industrializing countries, their related population growth, and the environmental impacts of growing primary and secondary industries. The impact of environmental degradation and overuse of resources on human populations, while considered in these works, was not their principal focus. This environment-first (ecocentric) focus is reflected in the first global institutional responses to the then-vague crisis of sustainability. For example, the *Convention on Wetlands of International Importance, Especially as Waterfowl Habitat* (the Ramsar Convention), signed in 1971, recognized the loss of wetlands as an environmental challenge, and the need to find ways to conserve and sustain their ecological benefits. The 1972 United Nations Conference on the Human Environment (UNCHE; the Stockholm Conference) was the UN's first major attempt to address global environmental issues. This conference led to the establishment of the United Nations Environment Programme (UNEP), which is mandated to draw attention to regional environmental issues and develop policies to address them. These efforts were principally focused on protecting the environment from degrading human activities. These efforts did not lack concern for human well-being, but in many cases, the human benefits of such actions were left implicit.

In 1987, the Brundtland Report published its now-famous definition of sustainable development: "development that meets the needs of the present without compromising the ability of future generations to meet their own needs."[4] This definition, and the larger report to which it belongs, shifted the nascent sustainability conversation from an environmental to a more anthropocentric focus. In linking previous concerns for environmental sustainability to conversations about development, the report made a direct and overt connection between sustainability and human well-being. The Brundtland Report, by recognizing sustainability as an outcome of the complex interplay between environment, economy, society, and culture, made the link between environmental quality and human well-being explicit.

This shifting focus captured a sea change in the understanding of the relationship between people and the environment taking place in the 1980s. The sources of these changes are many, but the aid community's experiences during the pan-African famines of this period illustrated this trend. Until these famines, food security and famine were largely seen as outcomes determined by food supplies to the area. Links between the environment and human well-being were relatively straightforward: drought, flooding, new pathogens or pests, or overuse of land, could all compromise food supplies. Efforts to manage famine therefore focused on addressing issues of food supply through trade adjustments, new technology development, or bringing food aid to particular places.

The pan-African famines, like those of 1984–85, upended this understanding of the connection between the environment and human well-being. Empirical experience demonstrated that food supply alone was not a key determinant of famine outcomes. Rather, it was influenced by access and production, which related to social roles and status. The empirical evidence that accumulated from these studies challenged previous assumptions about the causal links between food shortages and food security, suggesting that society, markets, perception, and knowledge had more important roles in food outcomes than was previously thought. In light of these developments, famine came to be understood as a complex outcome of the locally specific interplay of environment, economy, and society.

Therefore, the Brundtland Report was not a groundbreaking work. Rather, it crystallized the shifting understanding of sustainability as it related to development and human well-being. Because of the high visibility of the report, by the early 1990s, work in the social sciences that had long argued for the importance of political economy in understanding of the connection between the environment and society (and implicitly in the understanding of sustainability),[5] had gained traction in academic and policy circles. Further, this new understanding of sustainable development directly contributed to the framing of the 1992 UN Conference on Environment and Development (UNCED)—the Earth Summit.

UNCED marked an institutional change in understanding sustainability. Where UNCHE primarily focused on understanding human impacts on the environment, and left the importance of such impacts for human well-being implicit and therefore underdeveloped, UNCED approached sustainability through the lens of development, and the more complex concerns laid out in the Brundtland Report. This meeting generated efforts to define and create sustainable development through policy and application, such as Agenda 21. Agenda 21, which focused on the importance of local participatory action in creating sustainability, developed a global action plan to address the linked challenges of development and environmental change and degradation through local initiatives and community participation.[6] The United Nations Commission on Sustainable Development was established to ensure appropriate actions were taken to address Agenda 21 items.

Principle 4 of the *Rio Declaration on Environment and Development* is an important moment in the history of sustainable development, for it marks the beginning of the mainstreaming of the environment in development policy and practice. Principle 4 argued that "to achieve sustainable development, environmental protection shall constitute an integral part of the development process and cannot be considered in isolation from it."[7] Subsequently, this viewpoint evolved into official policy. Agencies like the United Nations Development Programme now observe that "environmental mainstreaming [places] the environment at par with economic and social aspects of decision-making," forcing decision makers to find "a strategic nexus and compatibility between development priorities and environmental management objectives where trade-offs can be addressed pragmatically and capitalize on potential opportunities that benefit both environmental resources and functions and development priorities."[8]

While the complex environment-and-development understanding of sustainable development dominates contemporary understandings of this concept, neither the Brundtland Report nor UNCED represented a clean break from sustainability's "environment-first" past. For example, one of the key outcomes of UNCED was the development of environmental conventions such as the *Convention on Biological Diversity* (CBD). In many ways the CBD looks similar to the Ramsar Convention, which was adopted in the era of environment-first sustainability. The CBD's objectives are clear: "the conservation of biological diversity, the sustainable use of its components and the fair and equitable sharing of the benefits arising out of the utilization of genetic resources."[9] The CBD is clearly focused on the problem of diminishing biodiversity, and takes a science-first approach to its mandate, arguing that "the fundamental requirement for the conservation of biological diversity is the in-situ conservation of ecosystems and natural habitats and the maintenance and recovery of viable populations of species in their natural surroundings."[10] Though developed in the post-Brundtland era, most of the environmental concerns of the CBD have been linked, post-hoc, to issues of human well-being to suit the shifting institutional goals of UNEP and other organizations.

At the other end of the spectrum is the *United Nations Convention to Combat Desertification in Countries Experiencing Serious Drought and/or Desertification, Particularly in Africa* (UNCCD). The UNCCD, in contrast to the CBD's environment-first approach, sees sustainable development as a complex interaction between the environment, society, economy, culture, and politics. Its prologue states that "desertification is caused by complex interactions among physical, biological, political, social, cultural and economic factors," calls for a consideration of "the impact of trade and relevant aspects of international economic relations on the ability of affected countries to combat desertification adequately," and notes that "desertification and drought affect sustainable development through their interrelationships with important social problems such as poverty, poor health and nutrition, lack of food security, and those arising from migration, displacement of persons and demographic dynamics."[11] By the end of the 20th century, sustainable development was a complex, confusing, and contradictory mix of environment-first versus environment-and-development framings.

SUSTAINABLE DEVELOPMENT: DEBATES IN THE NEW MILLENNIUM

The new millennium affirmed the conception of sustainable development promoted by the Brundtland Report and Agenda 21, but with no greater conceptual clarity. Point 6 of the United Nations Millennium Declaration states:

> Prudence must be shown in the management of all living species and natural resources, in accordance with the precepts of sustainable development. Only in this way can the immeasurable riches provided to us by nature be preserved and passed on to our descendants. The current unsustainable patterns of production and consumption must be changed in the interest of our future welfare and that of our descendants.[12]

While this continues to mainstream environmental concerns in development policy, the Declaration provides no clear definition of sustainable development, or how to identify and define the "riches" of nature that should be preserved and passed on.

The Johannesburg Declaration on Sustainable Development, a product of the 2002 World Summit on Sustainable Development (also called Rio +10) is an affirmation of Agenda 21, though this document more fully embraces the importance of political economy first hinted at in the Brundtland Report. It notes that "the rapid integration of markets, mobility of capital and significant increases in investment flows around the world have opened new challenges and opportunities for the pursuit of sustainable development."[13] In a policy sense, this represents an evolution of the sustainable development idea. However, these concepts are nearly 30 years old.

Efforts to reaffirm and mainstream Brundtland's sustainable development visions have led to a greater convergence of environment and development agendas at the policy level. UNEP's 2007 Fourth Global Environment Outlook (also known as GEO-4) is titled *Environment for Development*, marking the current apotheosis of this convergence.[14] However, while mainstreaming environmental concerns is now commonplace in development practice, the meaning of this mainstreaming remains contentious. The potential for achieving sustainable development ranges from optimistic to highly pessimistic and skeptical.

The Brundtland Report, with its environment and development focus, is optimistic about our ability to achieve sustainable development, based on the precursor to what is today called a soft sustainability or weak sustainability approach. Under this approach, natural capital (the natural resource stocks from which environmental goods and services are produced) is assumed to be substitutable by human-made forms of capital. As long as the total amount of capital, natural and otherwise, remains the same or increases, one can argue that economic and population growth is beneficial and consumption is sustainable. Such an approach does not ignore the environment, but sees it as one of several means of maintaining human well-being. For example, advances in chemistry, biology, and genetics have allowed parts of agricultural ecosystems to be modified and replaced with human engineered organisms, thus synthetically generating food crops that can grow in places and under conditions that other crops cannot, and can provide yields greater than their natural counterparts. For some, this sort of substitution shifts the focus from environmental conservation to that of technology and innovation, creating a future where continued innovations allow us to replace environmental resources with new organisms (such as GM crops) and resources (harvesting methane from landfills) of our own making, as we deplete their natural antecedents. The concern is not the maintenance of any particular species, but the flow of goods and services from agricultural ecosystems, regardless of how that flow is maintained.

Then there are those who argue that the environment must be prioritized above human well-being,[15] for example by sacrificing our current standard of living to ensure human survival into the future. This reflects a strong sustainability stance. This group also argues that not all forms of natural capital are substitutable for human-made capital. Because they do not see all forms of natural capital as substitutable, proponents of strong sustainability focus on the conservation of key environmental processes and goods to ensure continued access to needed goods and services. For example, from this perspective one might argue that converting a wetland into another use cannot be completely offset by human-made products. For example, niche habitats for endangered species found in a given wetland cannot always be reconstructed in other areas. So some species loss will be inevitably associated with the conversion of wetlands into other uses. This loss of biodiversity will precipitate rising extinction rates that contribute to the likelihood of nonlinear environmental events, which can accelerate environmental degradation and create unforeseeable costs.

These are not necessarily contradictory stances. If strong sustainability supporters are correct in their assessment that damage done to the environment through human development cannot be undone by human-made goods and services, and will fatally compromise the human existence in the long term, then the only way for us to meet the needs of the present without compromising the ability of future generations to meet their own needs is to revise our contemporary assessment of our needs, and cut our consumption and production of goods and energy. Until such time as technologies and policies create a world in which non-polluting energy is effectively free, this may be the only way of achieving soft sustainability. The idea of reducing human consumption and production, however, forces policymakers to address the questions of whose needs should be revised, how much revision is necessary, and who enforces the new standards of living. These issues are difficult to resolve in a just manner through regularly negotiated democratic processes.

A key, if controversial, idea that could bridge strong and soft sustainability is market environmentalism. Here, sustainable development aims to meet the needs and aspirations of the current generation, and those of future generations, by sustaining capitalism, or at least key aspects of this economic system, to ensure sufficient economic growth to provide opportunity for future generations. From this perspective, one can argue that the path to sustainability, which relies on the extension of current growth rates into the future, lies in an ever more streamlined market that privatizes and commodifies resources and is not constrained by regulation, including environmental regulation.

A market environmentalism approach to sustainable development rejects the mainstreaming of the environment into policies that govern markets, because mainstreaming creates an economic environment that cannot sustain current rates of growth. Instead, it assumes the costs of environmental degradation will filter into markets and correct behaviors that might push us past environmental or economic tipping points (e.g., ecosystem collapse resulting from over-exploitation), and that increased technology and innovation (funded through the increased wealth created by economic expansion) will address any issues resulting from the delayed reaction of markets to these issues. This assumption, in turn, rests on the idea that the value of the various services we receive is calculable and can be measured across scales of action.

The current calculation of value for these services raises the question of who determines the value, and under what terms. Using the wetland example, ecosystem analysis can produce specific values for ecosystem services, and thus normalize wetland characteristics, rendering them useful for wetland banking. For example, several governmental agencies may use differing hydroperiod criteria to define a wetland. This can have profound consequences. For example, there are amphibian species that breed primarily in temporary wetlands with hydroperiods of a month or so per year. But if such wetlands do not meet a particular agency's definition of wetland, and do not qualify for protection, these animals are threatened. In this way, market environmentalism brings to the fore the pressures natural scientists feel to define sustainability.[16] Lélé and Norgaard highlight this:

> On the one hand, measurable, objective, value-neutral criteria seem necessary for effective action. Environmental, resource, and development agencies at all levels of government seek such criteria so they can do their work without constantly being held up by the politics of value choices. On the other hand, world views and values seem to be integral to the concept of sustainability.[17]

In the end, the identification of ecosystem attributes and their valuation are not simply efforts to assign economic value to environmental resources in an objective, value-neutral setting. Such identifications and valuations are political in that they are shaped by policy decisions and subject to the analysis of particular scientists and their field efforts. Whether the politics of valuation undermines the productive application of market principles to conservation remains to be seen.

In summary, while environmental conservation is closely linked to sustainable development, it is principally a means of maintaining human well-being in the present and future. Strong or soft sustainability determines how seriously conservation is taken within a particular sustainable development initiative. Market-led approaches seek to speak to both sustainability approaches, by creating financial disincentives to degrade specific environmental resources (strong sustainability), or by driving interest and financing for alternative technologies that can substitute for lost natural capital (soft sustainability). At this time we lack the technology to achieve a true soft sustainability, as not all goods and services received from the environment can be recreated through human processes. Therefore, preliminary efforts at market environmentalism have yet to produce a definitive, effective path for sustainable development.

EQUITY AND ETHICS IN SUSTAINABLE DEVELOPMENT

The most common framing of sustainable development, as development that meets the needs and aspirations of the present without compromising the ambitions and well-being of future generations, implicitly engages the idea of intergenerational equity. Nearly all arguments for sustainable development (perhaps excluding those that predict calamity within the lifetimes of the current generation) inherently rest on a sense of responsibility to future generations. Sometimes this is the clear goal of sustainable development. For example, point 6 of the Millennium Declaration, argues that "current unsustainable patterns of production and consumption must be changed in the interest of our future welfare and that of our descendants."[18] In other cases, this sense of responsibility is subordinate to other, overt agendas. The CBD preamble contains 23 points, all noting the importance of biological diversity to present standards of living and raise issues surrounding biological diversity in the present. However, the final point notes that the convention signatories are "determined to conserve and sustainably use biological diversity for the benefit of present and future generations,"[19] thus putting forth the idea that these benefits are not merely for the present generation, but also those of the future.

Sustainable development also engages ideas of intra-generational equity. But here the literature is remarkably thin. Various ecological footprint studies illustrate that current consumption levels in the Global North are not only unsustainable, but viable in the present only because the vast majority of people on Earth have a much lower standard of living and use far fewer resources.[20] Such studies suggest that it would take approximately three Earths worth of resources to allow everyone on the planet to enjoy the standards of living experienced of the United States. The state of global capture fisheries illustrates this point. Twenty-five percent of capture fisheries are already overharvested, primarily by commercial fishing boats from the Global North.[21] These enterprises supply a market containing less than 18 percent of the global population. It is therefore clear that levels of fish consumption cannot rise to this level throughout the world without the complete collapse of all capture fisheries. These facts present a fundamental challenge to the idea of sustainable development, as they make it clear that we cannot raise the standard of living for the global population to that of those living in the Global North (often the assumed or unstated long-term goal of development) and use environmental resources in a sustainable manner simultaneously.

If sustainable development is not a viable intra-generational goal, then the current goal of intergenerational equity implicitly relies on future distributions of wealth and consumption that are largely unchanged from those seen today. To assume otherwise, one must believe either that those living in the Global North will reduce resource consumption dramatically, or that energy and other technological discoveries will enable greater equity in resource consumption. Current trends do not suggest the Global North is changing its consumption patterns, and technologies that might create clean, cheap energy and products are not currently in widespread use. Under these conditions, some have argued that sustainable development is nothing more than a vehicle for neocolonialism, a new means of keeping the developing world in its place.[22] These authors argue that by promoting sustainable development, countries in the Global North are justifying the slowing of economic growth in the Global South in the pursuit of an unachievable goal, thus indefinitely preserving the quality of life for their own populations by ensuring that existing inequalities remain largely unchanged. Further, they argue, the demand that the Global South develop sustainably ignores the unsustainable environmental practices pursued by the Global North through its economic growth and rise to wealth. Finally, the Global North's efforts to protect its own resources do not address unsustainable practices, as much as it displaces resource degradation to the Global South. For example, developed countries are often able to support green production and development practices internally because they benefit from the consumption of inexpensive commodities that are produced unsustainably in the Global South. These issues of intra-generational equity are real challenges that must be addressed through policy and technological innovation if sustainable development is to be realized. Further, they are significant political issues that create rifts between the Global North and Global South, preventing cooperation on these and other issues.

Environmental mainstreaming, as it is currently practiced, may perpetuate the challenges of intra-generational equity. While mainstreaming tries to maintain environmental quality and preserve environmental resources for human well-being, the frameworks used to assess the causes and consequences of environmental change may inadvertently maintain challenges to development that have, in the past, been barriers to the improvement of the circumstances of the world's poor. For example, two recent global environmental assessments, UNEP's GEO-4 and the Millennium Ecosystem Assessment (MA),[23] employ the Driver-Pressure-State-Impact-Response (DPSIR) framework to describe and analyze environmental changes, the causes of those changes, and human responses to the impacts of these changes. DPSIR was developed by the European Environment Agency as an environmental reporting framework.[24] GEO-4 and the MA both extend this reporting framework to the evaluation of sustainable development initiatives, in so doing mainstreaming environmental assessment into development conversations.

Carr et al. argue that the use of this framework inadvertently disempowers local communities, and downplays the importance of local knowledge in development.[25] DPSIR breaks down linked environment/development challenges into a series of causes, ranging from large-scale ultimate causes, like population and economic growth, through proximate causes, such as increased sewage output into the environment, to ecosystem-specific changes that impact human well-being. Responses to these impacts are generally conceived to address these challenges at each of these levels. However, within the DPSIR framework, the responses of local actors are generally constrained to the local ecosystem level, while governments and development agencies are privileged in their ability to address ultimate and proximate causes of environmental changes. In short, in its understanding of responses to global environmental change, DPSIR reproduces contemporary power relations in development, including the privileges of those living in the Global North. This outcome suggests that DPSIR, and environmental mainstreaming more generally, does not inherently address the ideas or needs of the poor unless those ideas and needs fit into and support the ideas, values, and careers of those working for development agencies.

Thus, sustainable development is not a clear-cut ethical issue. Ethical issues call the very goals of sustainable development into question. Further, efforts to assess the causes of unsustainable behaviors, and to identify appropriate development responses, may actually work against intra-generational equity, perpetuating the dominance of those in the Global North over the rest of the world.

ACHIEVING SUSTAINABLE DEVELOPMENT

The discussion above highlights two broad problems that stand in the way of the achievement of sustainable development: equity and valuation. Here we examine sustainable livelihoods, ecosystem services, and sustainability science that attempt to address these challenges to sustainable development.

Sustainable Livelihoods

The sustainable livelihoods approach to sustainable development emerged from the mid-1980s critique of development and food aid practices that ignored how local contexts shaped actual human well-being outcomes. Building on the ideas of access and entitlements, this approaches livelihoods as "the capabilities, assets (stores, resources, claims, and access) and activities required for a means of living."[26] This definition includes much more than income, focusing on the many ways a person might make a living.

In practice, this approach examines the sustainability of livelihoods through a focus on the assets individuals and communities use to make a living. These assets are grouped under five types of capital: natural, physical, human, financial, and social. Natural capital is "the natural resource stocks from which resource flows and services (e.g. nutrient cycling, erosion protection) useful for livelihoods are derived." Physical capital "comprises the basic infrastructure and producer goods needed to support livelihoods." Human capital "represents the skills, knowledge, ability to labour and good health that together enable people to pursue different livelihood strategies and achieve their livelihood objectives." Financial capital is "the financial resources that people use to achieve their livelihood objectives." Social capital is "the social resources upon which people draw in pursuit of their livelihood objectives."[27]

Assessing the sustainability of a particular livelihood starts with the vulnerability context of a community or individual. This includes various economic, environmental, social, and political trends that might affect local livelihoods, the shocks that might occur in each of these realms, and the seasonality of the local environment and economy. For example, the vulnerability context of rain-fed agriculturalists in southern Ghana includes declining precipitation, timing of seasonal rains, and a recent history of currency instability. The analysis proceeds to the impact of the vulnerability context on the various forms of capital that compose a community's livelihoods assets. In the Ghanaian example, we might find shifting rainfall patterns are depleting the natural capital (via soil degradation) of these farmers, forcing them back onto their savings (drawing down financial capital), or onto relatives and friends who can lend them money or get them access to more arable land (drawing down social capital). The analysis then examines how members of these communities interact with each other and the larger society, such as policies, institutions, and even power relations. This is the point at which individuals and communities access their various forms of livelihoods capital, and the context in which decisions are made about how to use these forms of capital. We might examine the land tenure system of the Ghanaian farmers to understand their possible points of access to new land, and even household relations of power that determine who grows what crop and for what purpose. This results in particular livelihoods strategies, which result in particular livelihoods outcomes—such as adequate food and income to support the household for the year. The sustainability of these strategies is assessed through a consideration of how their outcomes feed back to impact the livelihood assets (capital). If a livelihoods strategy manages to support the household only through the continuous extensification of the family farm into land accessed through one's extended family, thus drawing down both natural and social capital, it is not a sustainable livelihood.

The sustainable livelihoods approach avoids some of the conceptual issues with sustainability raised earlier. Under sustainable livelihoods, it is clear that livelihoods are being sustained, and, by association, the well-being of individuals, households, and communities. The environment is a resource through which livelihoods and well-being are conserved. However, the sustainable livelihoods approach does not ignore environmental degradation. If natural capital is drawn down too quickly, for example through farming practices that rob the soil of fertility faster than it is replaced by natural nutrient cycles, the end result will eventually be compromised livelihoods and declining human well-being. However, there is some ambiguity as to the place of environmental sustainability in sustainable livelihoods. For example, if an individual or community degrades the environment, but they can replace these components of natural capital with other forms of capital without negatively impacting their livelihoods, is this a sustainable livelihood? We argue that such behavior will result in changes in livelihood that, while preserving human well-being, do not preserve the livelihood itself. Thus, the livelihood itself is not sustainable. However, as the end goal of a sustainable livelihoods approach is the maintenance of human well-being, any livelihood that can accomplish this, even if it degrades one or more of the capitals that make up that livelihood, might be considered sustainable.

The sustainable livelihoods approach also takes a somewhat different approach to sustainable development because of its scale of analysis. The typical scale is a household or community. At this scale, the impacts of environmentally degrading behavior on larger biophysical cycles that might eventually negatively impact the vulnerability context of those under investigation are difficult to measure. For example, the carbon footprint of a rural community in the Global South is rather small, and its contribution to overall human greenhouse gas emissions negligible. As a result, it is possible to make the argument laid out above—that behavior that degrades the environment, but can be compensated for by other forms of capital, can be called a sustainable livelihood. While the impacts of a single community might have little effect on the large-scale components of the vulnerability context of that community, thousands of communities exhibiting the same behavior might have a measurable impact. The general inability of these small-scale studies to examine the impact of these behaviors on the vulnerability context is a key shortcoming to sustainable livelihoods analysis, as such analysis can justify otherwise problematic behaviors as sustaining human well-being, even as they are making very small, but important in aggregate, contributions to problematic changes to the vulnerability context. Thus, this approach might serve as a useful means of assessing the short-term viability of a particular strategy in a particular place, but it cannot assess the long-term viability of the strategy until it is able to measure and understand the impact of degrading behaviors on the vulnerability context.

Ecosystem Services

Another path to sustainable development is ecosystem services and trading, which has received particular attention from the field of market environmentalism[28] and the discipline of environmental economics.[29] Ecosystem services are the goods and services that nature produces on which humans rely to sustain their existence.[30] The Millennium Ecosystem Assessment recognizes four categories of services: provisioning services, which are obtained from ecosystems (i.e., food and energy); regulating services, which are the benefits from managing ecosystems (i.e., air and water quality); cultural services, which are the nonmaterial benefits people obtain from ecosystems (i.e., recreation and enjoyment); and supporting services, which are the functions required to produce ecosystems and are often characterized as having indirect benefits to humans (i.e., seed dispersal).[31]

Ecosystem services are a useful means of measuring environmental change in the context of sustainable development because they attempt to quantify, in terms of economic value, human gains and losses related to changes in ecosystems. By reducing all ecosystem services to this common measure, it becomes possible to evaluate the net impact of a variety of simultaneous changes in an ecosystem. For example, by logging a stand of forest, people exploit the provisioning service of that ecosystem. As these trees can be sold, it is easy to capture the economic value of this service. However, when these trees are cut, the ecosystem may lose supporting services for soil replenishment, as the canopy no longer shelters the soil from rainfall, and plant matter no longer falls to the forest floor, where it decomposes. Animals may lose habitat and disappear if these trees are cut. This could result in lost regulating functions (pests could rapidly multiply if their natural predators are eliminated), lost provisioning functions (if the species in question was a food item), or lost cultural services (if the lost species held local significance beyond food). Loss of supporting, regulating, and cultural services are much harder to quantify. What is the value of lost forest regeneration? Perhaps this can be measured in terms of the carbon that remains free in the atmosphere instead of in these trees, using current market prices for carbon. Soil productivity can be examined to estimate the lost production over time created by soil degradation related to tree cutting. We could identify the new costs of pesticides needed to control unchecked pest outbreaks, or the meat that now has to be purchased because it cannot be hunted. By adding these costs together, we can see that the loss of these often-overlooked ecosystem services will at least partially offset the economic gains generated by cutting down trees in the short term, and over the long term almost certainly outweigh the value of the timber (even if that value is invested in other activities and generates a profit). In short, through an ecosystem services approach, we gain a better sense of the true cost of harvesting environmental resources.

Measurement of ecosystem services generally follows the trend of assessment, valuation, and management. First, a region's ecosystem must be assessed to determine the range of services provided. This is complicated, as services often involve many actors and processes. Second, once services are determined, someone must estimate their economic value based not only on the services themselves, but also who wants or needs them. Finally, a management or policy scheme must be created to appropriate the services sustainably.

As with sustainable development in general, defining and measuring ecosystem services is problematic. Ecosystems are complex, and their products hard to catalogue and value. Further, the cataloging and valuing of ecosystem services is political, especially as these efforts generally support endeavors to manage and distribute ecosystem services through economic markets.

To understand the challenges inherent in the ecosystem services approach, we must examine the economic theory underlying it. The market orientation of ecosystem services comes from a neoclassical economic reading of market efficiency: getting out of ecosystems the service they perform most efficiently, and maximizing their value in global markets. Applications of neoliberal approaches to sustainable development generally suggest that market forces can produce the best outcomes for all aspects of social (or human) life. Therefore, regulations and bureaucracies that inhibit market forces should be eliminated. Neoliberal theorists make no exceptions for environmental regulations. From a neoliberal viewpoint, it is through privatization and commodification that natural resources are valued and ultimately put to use. This suggests that people, as rational actors, will purchase and put to use (make productive) natural resources as determined by supply and demand. Thus markets can determine appropriate outcomes for natural resources that might otherwise be viewed as free public goods, as demand for things like clean water and air will need to be met. Within this economic worldview, which assumes that markets transmit rational, apolitical information about societal needs and values through valuation and exchange, it is assumed that market-driven environmental protection will respond more directly to environmental changes that require our attention, focusing our efforts and resources on truly important issues.

Once natural resources (and their associated ecosystem services) are appropriated into private hands, these owners can assess their true value by placing them on markets. Proponents of this approach to sustainability argue that, under an ecosystem services approach, key services will become highly valuable, and their transfer to other actors via market exchange will generate the necessary wealth to either replace lost services through human products and inventions, or protect the remaining sources of irreplaceable services. In terms of environmental protection (or the protection of ecosystem services), this suggests that the more rapidly a place develops economically, the more capital comes to that place, benefiting everyone. ("A rising tide lifts all boats.") In this theoretical context, places can utilize their particular comparative advantage in resources, and that wealth will lead to the protection of the environment through private resources, as well as fixing any degradation that resulted from development with techno-scientific solutions. This can be observed in efforts surrounding the privatization of water provisioning, wetland banking, the privatization of the public trust, and even efforts to privatize wildlife.

These approaches have gained currency when state regulatory institutions fail to manage ecosystem protections. This trend is further bolstered because the framers of sustainable development programs are often economists (see the Millennium Declaration and Johannesburg Declarations). Finally, the ecosystem services concept has emerged as governance strategies have shifted from a centralized, Keynesian political–economic management of nation-states towards a neoliberal approach to managing the global economy (beginning in the 1980s). Neoliberal conventional wisdom regarding the efficient and objective nature of markets creates a plausible way to move away from the bureaucracy of corrupt and inefficient governments, as well as creating efficient outcomes in societies that value private property. In short, in this view markets will generate sustainable development.

The assumptions underpinning the ecosystem services approach are debated. For example, the case of market failure is a significant contradiction in ecosystem services thinking. Market failure is a common event in natural resource extraction and use. However, in the ecosystem services approach, such failures are managed through the same market mechanisms that were supposed to drive demand for protection of socially important environmental resources in the first place. In short, if the market for a particular resource fails, leading to the degradation of that resource, there is nothing to regulate the processes leading to degradation. Also, while overpopulation (particularly in the developing world) continues to be the specter of unsustainable development, it is consumption in the Global North that generates the largest ecological footprint. Contrary to neoliberal predictions, although wealth has reached unprecedented levels in the Global North, wealth has not accumulated evenly, and increasing economic growth has not fixed problems of resource degradation or consumption. One could suggest that the market orientation of ecosystem services continues the neoliberal global agenda that renders people and places as commodities in ever-reaching global markets, sustaining capitalism rather than producing equity or protected environmental resources.

Sustainability Science

The emergent field of sustainability science is another attempt to address some of the key issues raised with sustainable development. Calls for the development of sustainability science argue for a place-based approach to sustainability. This is not the same sort of localization found in the sustainable livelihoods approach. Instead, sustainability science, while incorporating the concerns of the sustainable livelihoods approach, attempts to overcome the scalar limitations of sustainable livelihoods analysis by explicitly linking local practices to both local and broader-scale processes. Thus, sustainability science seeks to integrate the findings of a sustainable livelihoods approach with biophysical evidence for the impacts of these local livelihoods with larger processes, and at the same time considers technological means of both augmenting these livelihoods and maintaining environmental quality.

Specifically, sustainability science highlights the essential interconnections between natural and human systems, making the parsing of sustainability into either the maintenance of human well-being or environmental quality impossible. In these coupled human and natural systems, vulnerability and sustainability are predicated on synergy between the human and biophysical subsystems, which, in turn, are affected by various spatiotemporal processes.

How sustainability science will achieve sustainable development remains to be seen. Much of the scholarship suggests that the regional scale will be a key site at which to engage the interaction of local particularity (i.e., sustainable livelihoods) and general biophysical processes (i.e., climate change driven by greenhouse gas emissions). However, there are few projects conducting this complex integration of qualitative and quantitative data across a variety of scales. One of the best-developed is called "syndromes of global change."[32] Syndromes of global change are "unfavorable and characteristic constellations of natural and civilizational trends and their respective interactions, and can be identified in many regions of the world."[33] While certain factors (like population growth) might be key components of multiple syndromes, it is assumed that connections between different syndromes are weaker than connections between processes and events within a syndrome, allowing "comprehensively isolated analyses of each single pattern."[34]

The syndromes approach to global change offers several opportunities.[35] First, syndromes organize the complex, locally specific interplay of nature and society into a finite set of general patterns of interaction. Such organization enables broad understandings of the causes and impacts of particular human activities and environmental changes, helps to understand the vulnerability of particular places to particular syndromes, and allows policymakers to develop efforts that might prevent the onset or intensification of a particular syndrome. Second, by considering causes, mechanisms, and effects as parts of a single system, the syndromes approach promotes the development of knowledge that might contribute to curing particular syndromes where they are already found. Finally, a syndromes approach identifies "non-sustainable domains" that can be "demarcated from permissible [read: sustainable] action space,"[36] operationalizing sustainable development.

While promising, the syndromes approach has not yet gained wide acceptance. This, in part, is because the approach does not lay out a clear definition of sustainable development. For example, the 1996 German Advisory Council on Global Change (WBGU) report describes sustainable development as "an acceptable coevolution of the ecosphere and the anthroposphere."[37] This is a remarkably vague definition that encompasses soft/weak sustainability, strong sustainability, and market environmentalism, despite the contradictions among them. According to the report, this vague definition is the result, in part, of the fact that "no consensus has been reached, either in Germany or in the EU, and especially not at global level, on how to operationalize [sustainable development]."[38] Instead of accepting a single approach to sustainable development as a working definition subject to later revision, the authors of the report instead cast the syndromes approach as a means of adjudicating between these competing visions of sustainability. It is difficult to see, however, how a single approach might not only identify the causes of and solutions for particular unsustainable situations, but also simultaneously work toward a definition of sustainable development. How will a particular constellation of human activities and environmental impacts be defined as a syndrome if these activities cannot be defined as sustainable or unsustainable from the outset?

Paths to Sustainable Development?

While each of the sustainable development foci described above contributes useful perspectives and information to conversations about sustainable development, none resolves all of the issues associated with defining and implementing sustainable development. The sustainable livelihoods approach operates from a clear definition of sustainability. However, because of its very narrow scale of analysis, it cannot, at this time, help to understand or address the broader issues of global environmental change affected by local activities that might feed back to the local vulnerability context, contributing to the sustainability or unsustainability of a particular livelihood. The ecosystem services approach relies upon a form of market fundamentalism to explain human behavior, but cannot provide all of the information to markets that is necessary for such economic assumptions to hold. The sustainability science approach promises to link global and local processes in a search for sustainable development, but the actual approaches taking shape under this heading have yet to settle on a clear definition of sustainable development. Whether any or all of these foci will develop into a truly functional tool for the achievement of sustainable development remains to be seen.

CONCLUSION

After more than two centuries of thought on the relationship between human and biophysical systems, the character of this relationship remains a subject of debate. As a result, at present there is no clear path to sustainable development. Each of the three dominant contemporary approaches to sustainable development—soft/weak sustainability, strong sustainability, and market environmentalism—bring particular challenges and needs if their visions of sustainable development are to be realized. The realization of any of these visions begins with explicitly addressing the ethical stance underlying the particular interpretation of their chosen approach to sustainability. Those who currently adopt a strong sustainability approach might be forced to sacrifice intra-generational equity in the name of intergenerational equity, perhaps by working to limit further environmental destruction in the Global South, even if such conservation limits economic growth and development in such countries. On the other hand, those whose primary focus is on intra-generational justice and equity might find the goal of meeting the needs and aspirations of the future impossible without significant changes to contemporary regimes of consumption or energy generation. The achievement of sustainable development, however it is to be defined, and who wins or loses, will require practitioners, researchers, and policymakers to make difficult choices. Without such choices, sustainable development will remain a vague, impossible goal to achieve.

ENDNOTES

1. World Commission on Environment and Development, *Our Common Future* (Oxford: Oxford University, 1987).
2. Rachel Carson, *Silent Spring* (New York: Houghton Mifflin, 1962), Garrett Hardin, "The Tragedy of the Commons," *Science* 162, no. 3859 (1968): 1243–48, Paul Ehrlich, *The Population Bomb* (New York: Ballantine, 1971), Thomas Malthus, *An Essay on the Principle of Population as it Affects the Future Improvement of Society with Remarks on the Speculations of Mr. Godwin, M. Condorcet, and Other Writers*. (London: J. Johnson, 1798).
3. Donella H. Meadows, Dennis L. Meadows, Jorgen Randers, and William W. Behrens III, *The Limits to Growth* (New York, NY: Signet, 1972).
4. World Commission on Environment and Development, *Our Common Future*, 43.
5. See Michael Watts, *Silent Violence: Food, Famine, and Peasantry in Northern Nigeria* (Berkeley: University of California, 1983); and Piers Blaikie and H. Brookfield, *Land Degradation and Society* (London: Methuen, 1987).
6. P. Selman, "Local Agenda 21: Substance or Spin," *Journal of Environmental Planning and Management* 45, no. 5 (1998): 553.
7. General Assembly of the United Nations, *Report of the United Nations Conference on Environment and Development: Annex I: Rio Declaration on Environment and Development* (New York: United Nations, 1992).
8. L. Ghanime, J. Opio-Odongo, and A. Comolet, *UNDP Environmental Mainstreaming Strategy* (New York: United Nations Development Programme, 2004): 9.
9. United Nations, *Convention on Biological Diversity (with Annexes)* (New York: United Nations, 1992): 146.
10. Ibid., 144.
11. United Nations, *Convention to Combat Desertification, Elaboration of an International Convention to Combat Desertification in Countries Experiencing Serious Drought and/or Desertification, Particularly in Africa* (New York: United Nations General Assembly, 2000), 2.
12. United Nations General Assembly, *United Nations Millennium Declaration* (New York: United Nations, 2000): 2.

13. United Nations, World Summit on Sustainable Development, *The Johannesburg Declaration on Sustainable Development* (New York: United Nations, 2002).
14. United Nations Environment Programme (UNEP), *Fourth Global Environmental Outlook (2007)* (New York: UNEP, 2007).
15. Derrick Jensen, *Endgame, Vol. 1: The Problem of Civilization* (New York: Seven Stories, 2006).
16. H.G. De Souza, *Inaugural Address*, International Conference on the Definition and Measurement of Sustainability: the Biophysical Foundations (Washington, DC: World Bank, 1992).
17. S. Lélé and R.B. Norgaard, "Sustainability and the Scientist's Burden," *Conservation Biology* 10, no. 2 (1996): 355.
18. United Nations General Assembly, *United Nations Millennium Declaration*, 2.
19. United Nations, *Convention on Biological Diversity*, 145.
20. W.E. Rees and M. Wackernagel, *Our Ecological Footprint*: *Reducing Human Impact on the Earth* (Gabriola Island, British Columbia: New Society, 1995).
21. D. Pauly, J. Alder, A. Bakun, S. Heileman, K. H. Kock, P. Mace and W. Perrin. "Marine Fisheries Systems," in *Ecosystems and Human Well-Being: Current State and Trends, Volume 1*, eds. H. Rashid, R. Scholes, and N. Ash (Washington DC: Island Press, 1999): 477–512.
22. G. Esteva and M.S. Prakash, "Grassroots Resistance to Sustainable Development," *The Ecologist* 22, no. 2 (1992): 45–51.
23. Millennium Ecosystem Assessment Conceptual Framework Working Group, *Ecosystems and Human Well-Being: A Framework for Assessment* (Gabriola Island, British Columbia: New Society, 2003).
24. European Environmental Agency (EEA), *Environmental Indicators: Typology and Overview*, Technical Report No. 25 (Copenhagen, Denmark: European Environmental Agency, 1999).
25. Edward R. Carr, Philip M. Wingard, Sara C. Yorty, Mary C. Thompson, Natalie K. Jensen, and Justin Roberson, "Applying DPSIR to Sustainable Development," *International Journal of Sustainable Development & Wildlife Ecology* 14, no. 6 (2007): 543–55.
26. R. Chambers and G. Conway, *Sustainable Rural Livelihoods: Practical Concepts for the 21st Century*, IDS Discussion Paper (Brighton, UK: Institute of Development Studies, 1992): 7; I. Scoones, *Sustainable Rural Livelihoods: A Framework for Analysis*, IDS Working Paper 72 (Brighton, UK: Institute of Development Studies, 1998).
27. Department for International Development, *Sustainable Development Guidance Sheets* (London: Department for International Development, 2001).
28. T.L. Anderson and D. Leal, *Free Market Environmentalism Today*, revised ed. (New York: Palgrave, 2001): 241.
29. D. Pearce, "An Intellectual History of Environmental Economics," *Annual Review of Energy and the Environment* 27 (2002): 57–81.

30. G. Daily, *Nature's Services: Societal Dependence on Natural Ecosystems* (Washington DC: Island, 1997): 392.
31. Millennium Ecosystem Assessment, *Ecosystems and Human Well-Being: A Framework for Assessment*, 56–60.
32. G. Petschel-Held, A. Block, M. Cassel-Gintz, J. Kropp. M. K. B. Ludecke, O. Moldenhauer, F. Reusswig and H. J. Schelnhuber. "Syndromes of Global Change: A Qualitative Modeling Approach to Assist Global Environmental Management," *Environmental Modeling and Assessment* 4 (1999): 295–314.
33. German Advisory Council on Global Change (WBGU), World in Transition: The Research Challenge. 1996 Report (Berlin: Springer, 1997).
34. Petschel-Held et al., "Syndromes of Global Change," 296.
35. WBGU, 114.
36. WBGU, 115.
37. WBGU, 114.
38. WBGU, 147.

RECOMMENDED READINGS/SOURCES

Blaikie, Piers, and H. Brookfield. 1987. *Land Degradation and Society*. London: Methuen.

Carr, Edward R., Philip M. Wingard, Sara C. Yorty, Mary C. Thompson, Natalie K. Jensen, and Justin Roberson. 2007. "Applying DPSIR to Sustainable Development." *International Journal of Sustainable Development & Wildlife Ecology* 14 (6): 543–55.

Esteva, G., and M.S. Prakash. 1992. "Grassroots Resistance to Sustainable Development." *The Ecologist* 22 (2): 45–51.

Hardin, Garrett. 1968. "The Tragedy of the Commons." *Science* 162 (3859): 1243–48.

Lélé, S., and R.B. Norgaard. 1996. "Sustainability and the Scientist's Burden." *Conservation Biology* 10 (2): 355.

Pearce, David. 2002. "An Intellectual History of Environmental Economics." *Annual Review of Energy and the Environment* 27: 57–81.

Petschel-Held, G., Block, A., Cassel-Gintz, M., Kropp, J., Ludeke, M.K.B., Moldenhauer, O., Reusswig, F., and Schellnhuber, H.J. 1999. "Syndromes of Global Change: A Qualitative Modeling Approach to Assist Global Environmental Management." *Environmental Modeling and Assessment* 4: 295–314.

Rees, W. E., and M. Wackernagel. 1995. *Our Ecological Footprint: Reducing Human Impact on the Earth*. Gabriola Island, British Columbia: New Society.

United Nations. 1992. *Convention on Biological Diversity (with Annexes)*. New York: United Nations.

United Nations. 1992. *Report of the United Nations Conference on Environment and Development: Annex I: Rio Declaration on Environment and Development*. New York: United Nations.

United Nations. 2000. *Convention to Combat Desertification, Elaboration of an International Convention to Combat Desertification in Countries Experiencing Serious Drought and/or Desertification, Particularly in Africa*. New York: United Nations General Assembly.

United Nations, World Summit on Sustainable Development. 2002. *The Johannesburg Declaration on Sustainable Development*. New York: United Nations.

Watts, Michael. 1983. *Silent Violence: Food, Famine, and Peasantry in Northern Nigeria*. Berkeley: University of California Press.

World Commission on Environment and Development. 1987. *Our Common Future*. Oxford: Oxford University Press.

CPSIA information can be obtained
at www.ICGtesting.com
Printed in the USA
LVHW03s1915250718
584915LV00001B/4/P

9 781631 890604